SMITHSONIAN INSTITUTIO
UNITED STATES NATIONAL MU

Bulletin 201

A REVIEW OF THE MYSIDACEA
OF THE UNITED STATES
NATIONAL MUSEUM

BY

WALTER M. TATTERSALL

UNITED STATES

GOVERNMENT PRINTING OFFICE

WASHINGTON : 1951

For sale by the Superintendent of Documents, U. S. Government Printing Office
Washington 25, D. C. - Price $1.00 (Paper)

ADVERTISEMENT

The scientific publications of the National Museum include two series known, respectively, as *Proceedings* and *Bulletin*.

The *Proceedings* series, begun in 1878, is intended primarily as a medium for the publication of original papers, based on the collections of the National Museum, that set forth newly acquired facts in biology, anthropology, and geology, with descriptions of new forms and revisions of limited groups. Copies of each paper, in pamphlet form, are distributed as published to libraries and scientific organizations and to specialists and others interested in the different subjects. The dates at which these separate papers are published are recorded in the table of contents of each of the volumes.

The series of *Bulletins*, the first of which was issued in 1875, contains separate publications comprising monographs of large zoological groups and other general systematic treatises (occasionally in several volumes), faunal works, reports of expeditions, catalogs of type specimens, special collections, and other material of similar nature. The majority of the volumes are octavo in size, but a quarto size has been adopted in a few instances in which large plates were regarded as indispensable. In the *Bulletin* series appear volumes under the heading *Contributions from the United States National Herbarium*, in octavo form, published by the National Museum since 1902, which contain papers relating to the botanical collections of the Museum.

The present work forms No. 201 of the *Bulletin* series.

REMINGTON KELLOGG,
Director, United States National Museum.

II

CONTENTS

	Page
Introduction	1
Systematic distribution	3
Geographical distribution	3
History of American Mysidacea	8
Systematic discussion	11
Class Crustacea	11
Subclass Malacostraca	11
Division Peracarida	11
Order Mysidacea	12
Suborder Lophogastrida	12
Family Lophogastridae G. O. Sars	12
Genus *Chalaraspidum* Willemoes-Suhm	13
Chalaraspidum alatum (Willemoes-Suhm) (A)[1]	14
Genus *Lophogaster* M. Sars	15
Key to the species of *Lophogaster*	16
Lophogaster typicus M. Sars	17
Lophogaster hawaiensis Fage	17
Lophogaster americanus Tattersall (A)	17
Lophogaster japonicus Tattersall	19
Lophogaster intermedius Hansen ?	20
Lophogaster sp. ?	20
Lophogaster spinosus Ortmann (A)	21
Lophogaster longirostris Faxon (A)	21
Genus *Paralophogaster* Hansen	22
Paralophogaster glaber Hansen (P)[1]	22
Paralophogaster atlanticus Tattersall (A)	24
Genus *Gnathophausia* Willemoes-Suhm	25
Gnathophausia ingens (Dohrn) (A) (P)	25
Gnathophausia gigas Willemoes-Suhm (A)	26
Gnathophausia gracilis Willemoes-Suhm (A) (P)	28
Gnathophausia longispina G. O. Sars (P)	28
Gnathophausia zoea Willemoes-Suhm (A) (P)	29
Gnathophausia zoea var. *scapularis* Ortmann (A)	31
Gnathophausia elegans G. O. Sars (P)	31
Family Eucopiidae Dana	32
Genus *Eucopia* Dana	32
Eucopia sculpticauda Faxon (A)	32
Eucopia australis Dana (A)	33
Eucopia major Hansen (A)	33
Eucopia unguiculata (Willemoes-Suhm) (A) (P)	34

[1] "A" designates American species; "P," *Albatross* Philippine species.

Class Crustacea—Continued
  Subclass Malacostraca—Continued
    Division Peracarida—Continued
      Order Mysidacea—Continued   **Page**

	Page
Suborder Mysida	35
Family Petalophthalmidae Czerniavsky	35
Genus *Petalophthalmus* Willemoes-Suhm	35
Petalophthalmus armiger Willemoes-Suhm (A) [1]	35
Petalophthalmus oculatus Illig (A)	40
Genus *Hansenomysis* Stebbing	43
Hansenomysis fyllae (Hansen) (A)	43
Genus *Scolophthalmus* Faxon	43
Scolophthalmus lucifugus Faxon (A)	43
Genus *Ceratomysis* Faxon	43
Ceratomysis spinosa Faxon (A)	43
Family Mysidae Dana	45
Subfamily Boreomysinae	45
Genus *Boreomysis* G. O. Sars	45
Boreomysis inermis (Willemoes-Suhm) (A)	46
Boreomysis nobilis G. O. Sars (A)	47
Boreomysis tridens G. O. Sars (A)	48
Boreomysis arctica (Krøyer) (A)	49
Boreomysis sibogae Hansen	51
Boreomysis californica Ortmann (A)	52
Boreomysis fragilis Hansen (A)	55
Boreomysis obtusata G. O. Sars	55
Boreomysis microps G. O. Sars (A)	55
Boreomysis rostrata Illig ? (A)	56
Subfamily Siriellinae	60
Genus *Siriella* Dana	60
Siriella thompsonii (H. Milne-Edwards) (A) (P) [1]	60
Siriella gracilis Dana (A) (P)	62
Siriella vulgaris Hansen (P)	62
Siriella vulgaris var. *rostrata* Tattersall (P)	63
Siriella affinis Hansen (P)	64
Siriella inornata Hansen (P)	65
Siriella media Hansen (P)	65
Siriella chierchiae Coifmann (A)	66
Siriella pacifica Holmes (A)	70
Siriella roosevelti Tattersall (A)	72
Siriella panamensis Tattersall (A)	76
Siriella aequiremis Hansen (A) (P)	78
Siriella anomala Hansen (P)	79
Siriella distinguenda Hansen (P)	79
Siriella dubia Hansen (P)	79
Genus *Hemisiriella* Hansen	80
Hemisiriella parva Hansen (P)	80
Hemisiriella abbreviata Hansen	80
Subfamily Gastrosaccinae	80
Genus *Archaeomysis* Czerniavsky	81
Archaeomysis grebnitzkii Czerniavsky (A)	81
Archaeomysis maculata (Holmes) (A)	86

---

[1] "A" designates American species; "P," *Albatross* Philippine species.

Class Crustacea—Continued
  Subclass Malacostraca—Continued
    Division Peracarida—Continued
      Order Mysidacea—Continued
        Suborder Mysida—Continued
          Family Mysidae Dana—Continued

	Page
Subfamily Gastrosaccinae—Continued	
Genus *Gastrosaccus* Norman	89
Gastrosaccus spinifer (Goës)	90
Gastrosaccus sanctus (van Beneden)	90
Gastrosaccus pacificus Hansen (P) [1]	90
Gastrosaccus sp.?	90
Gastrosaccus indicus Hansen (P)	90
Gastrosaccus philippinensis Tattersall (P)	90
Gastrosaccus johnsoni Tattersall (A)	93
Gastrosaccus dissimilis Coifmann (A)	97
Gastrosaccus mexicanus Tattersall (A) [1]	98
Genus *Anchialina* Norman and Scott	100
Anchialina typica (Krøyer) (A) (P)	100
Anchialina grossa Hansen (P)	102
Anchialina obtusifrons Hansen (P)	102
Anchialina penicillata Zimmer (P)	103
Anchialina zimmeri Tattersall (P)	103
Anchialina agilis (G. O. Sars)	105
Subfamily Mysinae	105
Tribe Erythropini	105
Genus *Holmesiella* Ortmann	106
Holmesiella anomala Ortmann (A)	106
Genus *Erythrops* G. O. Sars	110
Erythrops erythrophthalma (Goës) (A)	110
Erythrops microps G. O. Sars (A)	111
Erythrops abyssorum G. O. Sars (A)	111
Erythrops yongei Tattersall (P)	111
Genus *Euchaetomera* G. O. Sars	112
Euchaetomera typica Tattersall (A)	112
Euchaetomera tenuis G. O. Sars (A)	112
Euchaetomera plebeja Hansen (A)	112
Genus *Meterythrops* S. I. Smith	113
Meterythrops picta Holt and Tattersall (A)	113
Meterythrops robusta S. I. Smith (A)	113
Meterythrops microphthalma Tattersall	113
Genus *Metamblyops* Tattersall	116
Metamblyops macrops Tattersall (A)	116
Genus *Katerythrops* Holt and Tattersall	118
Katerythrops oceanae Tattersall (A)	118
Genus *Hypererythrops* Holt and Tattersall	118
Hypererythrops caribbaea Tattersall (A)	118
Genus *Longithorax* Illig	120
Longithorax capensis Zimmer (A)	120
Genus *Gibberythrops* Illig	122
Gibberythrops acanthura (Illig) (P)	122
Gibberythrops philippinensis Tattersall (P)	122
Genus *Synerythrops* Hansen	124
Synerythrops cruciata Tattersall (A)	124

[1] "A" designates American species ; "P," *Albatross* Philippine species.

Class Crustacea—Continued
 Subclass Malacostraca—Continued
  Division Peracarida—Continued
   Order Mysidacea—Continued
    Suborder Mysida—Continued
     Family Mysidae Dana—Continued
      Subfamily Mysinae—Continued   Page
       Tribe Erythropini—Continued
        Genus *Dactylerythrops* Holt and Tattersall____   126
         Dactylerythrops bidigitata Tattersall (A)___   126
        Genus *Dactylamblyops* Holt and Tattersall____   126
         Dactylamblyops sp. ? (A)_____   126
        Genus *Amblyops* G. O. Sars_____   128
         Amblyops abbreviata (G. O. Sars) (A)_____   128
         Amblyops sp. ? (A)_____   130
         Amblyops sp. ? (A)_____   130
         Amblyops ohlinii Tattersall (A)_____   130
        Genus *Paramblyops* Holt and Tattersall_____   132
         Paramblyops rostrata Holt and Tattersall
          (A)_____   132
        Genus *Pseudomma* G. O. Sars_____   132
         Pseudomma affine G. O. Sars (A)_____   132
         Pseudomma roseum G. O. Sars (A)_____   132
         Pseudomma truncatum S. I. Smith (A)____   134
         Pseudomma berkeleyi Tattersall (A)_____   135
         Pseudomma sp. ? (A)_____   135
         Pseudomma oculospinum Tattersall (A)___   135
        Genus *Caesaromysides* Colosi_____   137
         Caesaromysides liguriae Colosi (A)_____   137
        Genus *Michthyops* Tattersall_____   137
         Michthyops parva (Vanhöffen) (A)_____   137
       Tribe Leptomysini_____   138
        Genus *Leptomysis* G. O. Sars_____   138
         Leptomysis gracilis G. O. Sars_____   138
         Leptomysis mediterranea G. O. Sars_____   138
        Genus *Mysidopsis* G. O. Sars_____   138
         Key to the American species of *Mysidopsis*_   138
         Mysidopsis angusta G. O. Sars_____   139
         Mysidopsis gibbosa G. O. Sars_____   139
         Mysidopsis acuta Hansen (A)_____   139
         Mysidopsis bigelowi Tattersall (A)_____   139
         Mysidopsis inermis Coifmann (A)_____   142
         Mysidopsis californica Tattersall (A)_____   142
         Mysidopsis mortenseni Tattersall (A)_____   145
        Genus *Metamysidopsis* Tattersall_____   146
         Metamysidopsis munda (Zimmer) (A)____   147
         Metamysidopsis elongata (Holmes) (A)____   149
         Metamysidopsis pacifica (Zimmer) (A)____   151
        Genus *Promysis* Dana_____   151
         Promysis orientalis Dana (P)_____   151
         Promysis atlantica Tattersall (A)_____   152
        Genus *Doxomysis* Hansen_____   152
         Doxomysis quadrispinosa (Illig) (A) (P)__   152
         Doxomysis microps Colosi (A)_____   153

[1] "A" designates American species ; "P," *Albatross* Philippine species.

Class Crustacea—Continued
  Subclass Malacostraca—Continued
    Division Peracarida—Continued
      Order Mysidacea—Continued
        Suborder Mysida—Continued
          Family Mysidae Dana—Continued
            Subfamily Mysinae—Continued

	Page
Tribe Leptomysini—Continued	
Genus *Bathymysis* Tattersall	153
Bathymysis renoculata Tattersall (A) [1]	153
Genus *Pseudomysis* G. O. Sars	157
Pseudomysis dactylops Tattersall	157
Genus *Mysidetes* Holt and Tattersall	159
Mysidetes crassa Hansen (A)	159
Tribe Mysini	159
Genus *Inusitatomysis* Ii	159
Inusitatomysis serrata Tattersall	160
Genus *Antarctomysis* Coutière	163
Antarctomysis maxima (Hansen)	163
Genus *Arthromysis* Colosi	163
Arthromysis magellanica (Cunningham)(A)	163
Genus *Hemimysis* G. O. Sars	163
Hemimysis lamornae (Couch)	163
Genus *Mysis* Latreille	163
Mysis oculata (Fabricius) (A)	165
Mysis relicta Lovén (A)	167
Mysis mixta Lilljeborg (A)	168
Mysis stenolepis S. I. Smith (A)	170
Genus *Paramysis* Czerniavsky	174
Paramysis ornata (G. O. Sars)	174
Paramysis spiritus (Norman)	174
Paramysis parkeri (Norman)	175
Genus *Praunus* Leach	175
Praunus flexuosus (O. F. Müller)	175
Praunus inermis (Rathke)	175
Genus *Mesopodopsis* Czerniavsky	175
Mesopodopsis slabberi (van Beneden)	175
Genus *Stilomysis* Norman	175
Stilomysis grandis (Goës) (A)	175
Stilomysis major Tattersall	177
Genus *Neomysis* Czerniavsky	179
Key to the species of *Neomysis*	180
Neomysis rayii (Murdoch) (A)	181
Neomysis integer (Leach)	186
Neomysis mercedis Holmes (A)	187
Neomysis intermedia (Czerniavsky) (A)	188
Neomysis awatschensis (Brandt)	190
Neomysis kadiakensis Ortmann (A)	192
Neomysis japonica Nakazawa	194
Neomysis americana (S. I. Smith) (A)	195
Neomysis mirabilis (Czerniavsky) (A)	198
Neomysis czerniawskii Dershavin (A)	200
Neomysis patagona Zimmer (A)	202

---

[1] "A" designates American species; "P," *Albatross* Philippine species.

Class Crustacea—Continued
  Subclass Malacostraca—Continued
    Division Peracarida—Continued
      Order Mysidacea—Continued
        Suborder Mysida—Continued
          Family Mysidae Dana—Continued
            Subfamily Mysinae—Continued
              Tribe Mysini—Continued

	Page
Genus *Neomysis* Czerniavsky—Continued	
Neomysis meridionalis Colosi (A) [1]	203
Neomysis monticelli Colosi (A)	203
Genus *Acanthomysis* Czerniavsky	203
Key to the American species of *Acanthomysis*	203
Acanthomysis columbiae (Tattersall) (A)	204
Acanthomysis sculpta (Tattersall) (A)	206
Acanthomysis costata (Holmes) (A)	206
Acanthomysis stelleri (Dershavin) (A)	210
Acanthomysis dybowskii (Dershavin) (A)	213
Acanthomysis macropsis (Tattersall) (A)	215
Acanthomysis pseudomacropsis (Tattersall) (A)	217
Acanthomysis longicornis (Milne-Edwards)	218
Acanthomysis sp. ? (A)	218
Genus *Proneomysis* Tattersall	219
Proneomysis wailesi Tattersall (A)	220
Genus *Paracanthomysis* Ii	220
Paracanthomysis kurilensis Ii (A)	221
Genus *Mysidium* Dana	222
Key to the species of *Mysidium*	223
Mysidium columbiae (Zimmer) (A)	223
Mysidium gracile (Dana) (A)	223
Mysidium integrum Tattersall (A)	223
Genus *Diamysis* Czerniavsky	226
Diamysis americana Tattersall (A)	226
Genus *Antromysis* Creaser	229
Antromysis anophelinae Tattersall (A)	230
Antromysis cenotensis Creaser (A)	234
Tribe Heteromysini	234
Genus *Heteromysis* S. I. Smith	235
Key to the species of *Heteromysis*	235
Heteromysis formosa S. I. Smith (A)	235
Heteromysis bermudensis G. O. Sars (A)	237
Heteromysis antillensis Verrill (A)	238
Heteromysis odontops Walker (A)	239
Species not represented in the collections of the United States National Museum	242
New genera, species, and varieties described herein	250
Albatross dredging stations from which collections are reported (table 9)	251
Albatross hydrographic stations from which collections are reported (table 10)	260
Literature cited	263
Index	285

---

[1] "A" designates American species ; "P," *Albatross* Philippine species.

ILLUSTRATIONS

Figure		Page
1.	Antennal scales of various species of *Lophogaster*	18
2.	*Lophogaster japonicus* Tattersall and *Paralophogaster atlanticus* Tattersall	24
3, 4.	*Petalophthalmus armiger* Willemoes-Suhm	36, 38
5.	*Petalophthalmus oculatus* Illig	41
6.	*Boreomysis nobilis* G. O. Sars	47
7.	*Boreomysis tridens* G. O. Sars	48
8.	*Boreomysis arctica* (Krøyer)	50
9, 10.	*Boreomysis californica* Ortmann	52, 53
11–13.	*Boreomysis rostrata* Illig?	57–59
14.	*Siriella vulgaris* var. *rostrata* Tattersall	64
15, 16.	*Siriella chierchiae* Coifmann	67, 68
17.	*Siriella pacifica* Holmes	71
18, 19.	*Siriella roosevelti* Tattersall	73, 74
20.	*Siriella panamensis* Tattersall	77
21, 22.	*Archaeomysis grebnitzkii* Czerniavsky	82, 84
23, 24.	*Archaeomysis maculata* (Holmes)	86, 87
25.	*Gastrosaccus philippinensis* Tattersall	91
26–28.	*Gastrosaccus johnsoni* Tattersall	94–96
29.	*Gastrosaccus dissimilis* Coifmann	97
30.	*Gastrosaccus mexicanus* Tattersall	98
31.	*Anchialina zimmeri* Tattersall	104
32–33.	*Holmesiella anomala* Ortmann	107, 108
34.	*Erythrops erythrophthalma* (Goës)	110
35.	*Meterythrops robusta* S. I. Smith	114
36.	*Meterythrops microphthalma* Tattersall	115
37, 38.	*Metamblyops macrops* Tattersall	117, 118
39.	*Hypererythrops caribbaea* Tattersall	119
40.	*Longithorax capensis* Zimmer	120
41.	*Gibberythrops philippinensis* Tattersall	123
42.	*Synerythrops cruciata* Tattersall	125
43.	*Dactylerythrops bidigitata* Tattersall	127
44.	*Amblyops abbreviata* (G. O. Sars)	129
45.	*Amblyops ohlinii* Tattersall	131
46.	*Pseudomma roseum* G. O. Sars	133
47.	*Pseudomma truncatum* S. I. Smith	134
48.	*Pseudomma berkeleyi* Tattersall	135
49.	*Pseudomma oculospinum* Tattersall	136
50.	*Mysidopsis bigelowi* Tattersall	140
51, 52.	*Mysidopsis californica* Tattersall	143, 144
53.	*Mysidopsis mortenseni* Tattersall	145
54.	*Metamysidopsis munda* (Zimmer)	148
55.	*Metamysidopsis elongata* (Holmes)	150
56.	*Promysis atlantica* Tattersall	152
57, 58.	*Bathymysis renoculata* Tattersall	154, 155
59.	*Pseudomysis dactylops* Tattersall	158
60.	*Inusitatomysis serrata* Tattersall	161

Figure   Page
61. *Mysis oculata* (Fabricius) _____ 166
62. *Mysis relicta* Lovén _____ 168
63. *Mysis mixta* Lilljeborg _____ 169
64, 65. *Mysis stenolepis* S. I. Smith _____ 171, 173
66. *Stilomysis grandis* (Goës) _____ 176
67. *Stilomysis major* Tattersall _____ 178
68–71. *Neomysis rayii* (Murdoch) _____ 182, 184–186
72. *Neomysis mercedis* Holmes _____ 188
73. *Neomysis intermedia* (Czerniavsky) _____ 189
74. *Neomysis awatschensis* (Brandt) _____ 191
75. *Neomysis kadiakensis* Ortmann _____ 193
76. *Neomysis japonica* Nakazawa _____ 194
77. *Neomysis americana* (Smith) _____ 196
78. *Neomysis mirabilis* (Czerniavsky) _____ 199
79. *Neomysis czerniawskii* Dershavin _____ 201
80–82. *Acanthomysis columbiae* (Tattersall) _____ 204–206
83–85. *Acanthomysis sculpta* (Tattersall) _____ 207–209
86, 87. *Acanthomysis costata* (Holmes) _____ 210, 211
88. *Acanthomysis stelleri* (Dershavin) _____ 212
89. *Acanthomysis dybowskii* (Dershavin) _____ 214
90. *Acanthomysis macropsis* (Tattersall) _____ 216
91, 92. *Acanthomysis pseudomacropsis* (Tattersall) _____ 218
93, 94. *Proneomysis wailesi* Tattersall _____ 220, 221
95. *Paracanthomysis kurilensis* Ii _____ 222
96. *Mysidium integrum* _____ 224
97. *Diamysis americana* Tattersall _____ 226
98, 99. *Antromysis anophelinae* Tattersall _____ 231, 233
100, 101. *Heteromysis formosa* S. I. Smith _____ 236, 238
102, 103. *Heteromysis odontops* Walker _____ 239, 241

A REVIEW OF THE MYSIDACEA OF THE UNITED STATES NATIONAL MUSEUM

By Walter M. Tattersall [2]

INTRODUCTION

The Mysidacea included in this report form the largest individual collection of these crustaceans that has passed through the hands of a single worker. Included are 120 species, of which 19 species and one variety are described as new. There are included many interesting and rare species that have provided opportunity for the elucidation of obscure points in mysidacean morphology and classification. The greater part of the collection is of American origin, and it adds enormously to existing knowledge of the Mysidacea of the American Continent, both in shallow and deep water. It is particularly rich in the littoral species of *Neomysis* and *Acanthomysis* from the coasts of the North Pacific, both American and Asiatic, and I have been able to clear up the relationships of many obscure species from that area. The work of the United States Fish Commission, through its research vessels, especially the *Albatross*, resulted in considerable additions being made to our knowledge of the deep-water and oceanic species on both sides of the continent. This knowledge is particularly valuable in the Pacific, from which relatively scanty material has hitherto been available.

The principal expeditions of which the Mysidacea are here discussed include the various explorations of the *Albatross* in the Atlantic and Pacific waters of America and the Philippine Islands in 1907–1910 and the biological survey of San Francisco Bay in 1912 and 1913 [3]; the

[2] Dr. Walter M. Tattersall, professor of zoology and comparative anatomy, University College, Cardiff, Wales, died on October 1, 1943. For an obituary notice see "Professor W. M. Tattersall," by Stanley Kemp, Nature, vol. 152, p. 592, November 20, 1943.—Ed.

[3] I reported on this material in University of California Publications in Zoology, vol. 37, pp. 315–347, 1932. However, as complete lists of stations at which the various species were taken were not included in that paper, they have been given herein with the number of specimens taken at each station. In some instances the counts are approximations, as much of the material dried out while in storage at the university. The data for the San Francisco Bay stations are given in University of California Publications in Zoology, vol. 14, pp. 1–198, 1914.

As it may be of some interest a complete list of the species collected by the United States Fisheries steamer *Albatross* expedition to the Philippine Islands, 1907–1910, has been made a part of the Contents, such species being followed by the letter "P." All these species are represented in the collections of the United States National Museum.

Fish Hawk and *Bache* investigations along the Atlantic coast of the United States, the Gulf Stream, and Puerto Rican waters; and the Johnson-Smithsonian Deep-Sea Expedition to the Puerto Rican Deep of 1933 and the waters en route.

This paper is designated to fulfill four purposes:

1. To describe and record the species in the collections of the United States National Museum submitted to me. This is, of course, the primary purpose of the report, and I have included all the material that I have received from any part of the world.[4]

2. To provide as complete a guide as possible to the species of Mysidacea in the collections of the United States National Museum, of which the *Albatross* Philippine collections of 1907–1910 form a not inconsiderable part.[5] To that end I have included all the named material in the National Museum, and in those cases where I have not personally examined the material I have given the authority for the identification wherever that information is available. Such collecting records are indicated by an asterisk.

3. To provide an introduction to the mysidacean fauna of the American continents, including Canada, the United States, Central America, South America, and the American islands, both in the Atlantic and Pacific. For this purpose I have included all the species ever recorded from the American faunal area whether or not they are represented in the Museum collections. Species of which no specimens are included in the United States National Museum collections are grouped beginning on page 242. Under each species, I have given references to the literature, and I hope this information may form a useful basis for future work on the American Mysidacea.[6]

4. To provide as complete a list as possible of all the papers dealing with American species in any way whatever. I have tried to make this list complete, and, though it is too much to hope that no paper has been omitted, I believe it forms a full guide to the American literature.[7]

I am indebted to the authorities of the United States National Museum, especially to the late Dr. Mary J. Rathbun and to Dr. Waldo L. Schmitt, for their cooperation.[8]

[4] A list of new genera and species will be found on page 250.

[5] *Albatross* Philippine species are indicated in the Contents by a "P."

[6] Species indicated in the Contents by an "A" are American.

[7] Those papers included in the Literature Cited, p. 263, that deal with American species are annotated.

[8] The acknowledgments made by the author should be extended to include Dr. Fenner A. Chace, Jr., and Paul L. Illg, of the Division of Marine Invertebrates. U. S. National Museum, for clearing up a few technical points, and especially to Miss Gladys O. Visel, of the Editorial Division, Smithsonian Institution, for her invaluable services in preparing the manuscript for the printer.—Ed.

SYSTEMATIC DISTRIBUTION

The National Museum collection includes 120 species distributed among the families and subfamilies of the order as follows:

```
Family Lophogastridae_____ 15 species
       Eucopiidae_____ 3
       Petalophthalmidae_____ 4
       Mysidae:
Subfamily Boreomysinae_____ 7
          Siriellinae _____ 14
          Gastrosaccinae_____ 12
          Mysinae:
          Tribe Erythropini_____ 27
                Leptomysini _____ 8
                Mysini _____ 27
                Heteromysini_____ 3
```

The list of American species of Mysidacea includes 118 species, of which 113 are named and 5 cannot be identified or described because of the defective nature of the specimens or because of the paucity of the material available for study. The species are distributed among the families of the group as follows:

```
Family Lophogastridae_____ 10 species
       Eucopiidae_____ 2
       Petalophthalmidae_____ 5
       Mysidae:
Subfamily Boreomysinae_____ 7
          Siriellinae _____ 5
          Gastrosaccinae_____ 6
          Mysinae:
          Tribe Erythropini_____ 29
                Leptomysini_____ 12
                Mysini_____ 33
                Heteromysini_____ 4
```

GEOGRAPHICAL DISTRIBUTION

The mysidacean fauna of American waters is thoroughly representative of the order as a whole, only the two subfamilies Rhopalophthalminae and Mysidellinae, of the family Mysidae, being unrepresented. Speaking quite broadly the families Lophogastridae, Eucopiidae, and Petalophthalmidae, the subfamily Boreomysinae, and the tribe Erythropini, of the subfamily Mysinae, comprise the deepwater forms, while the shallow-water fauna includes the subfamilies Siriellinae and Gastrosaccinae and the tribes Leptomysini, Mysini, and Heteromysini, of the subfamily Mysinae. The American fauna is made up of approximately half deep-water and half shallow-water or littoral species.

If we analyze the mysidacean fauna of America still further the following facts emerge:

Fresh-water species.—Four species of fresh-water mysids are known from America. Of these *Mysis relicta*, found in the Great Lakes of North America, is also found in the relict lakes of Europe, in Ireland, England, Scandinavia, and northern Germany. It has probably been derived from the very abundant and widely distributed Arctic marine species *Mysis oculata*, following isolation as the result of glacial action.

The two species of *Antromysis*, *A. cenotensis* and *A. anophelinae*, found respectively in fresh-water caves in Yucatán and crab holes in Costa Rica, are peculiar to these places and the genus is unknown outside America.

Diamysis americana, found in ditches in the Botanic Gardens at Paramaribo, Dutch Guiana, is the American representative of a Mediterranean genus where its species occupy similar brackish and fresh-water habitats. I have suggested that it is a survival of the old Tethys Sea fauna, when the genus was probably widely distributed in that area, and retired to the Mediterranean and to the fresh waters of America when the Atlantic Ocean took on its present form. The genus *Antromysis* is more nearly related to *Diamysis* than to any other genus and may conceivably have been derived from members of that genus that took to the more specialized habitats of underground waters and crab holes.

Littoral and coastal species.—On the Atlantic coast of America from Labrador to the Straits of Magellan, 22 species of littoral mysids are known, and on the Pacific coast from Alaska to the Straits of Magellan the number of recorded species is 30. Only one species is common to the two coasts, *Gastrosaccus mexicanus* having been taken on both sides of the Isthmus of Panama. The genera found on both coasts are very similar and even identical, and the two coastal faunas are very parallel when viewed from the standpoint of the genera represented.

If we compare the genera of east-coast American mysids with those of the European coasts a certain similarity between the two faunas can be discerned, but the parallel is not so close as that between the east and west coasts of America. Table 1 sets forth not only the genera with number of species represented off the east and west coasts of America, but it furnishes a comparison between the east coast of America and the Atlantic coast of Europe:

TABLE 1.—*Forms of Mysidacea occurring off the coasts of America and the Atlantic coasts of Europe*

Genus	American species		Atlantic coasts of Europe species
	West coast	East coast	
Siriella	3	1	6
Gastrosaccus	1	3	3
Archaeomysis	2	0	0
Anchialina	0	1	1
Erythrops	0	0	1
Mysidopsis	2	3	2
Metamysidopsis	2	1	0
Promysis	0	1	0
Leptomysis	0	0	3
Mysidetes	0	1	0
Arthromysis	0	1	0
Mysis	1	3	2
Hemimysis	0	0	1
Paramysis	0	0	6
Praunus	0	0	3
Mesopodopsis	0	0	1
Neomysis	9	1	1
Acanthomysis	7	0	1
Mysidium	0	3	0
Proneomysis	1	0	0
Paracanthomysis	1	0	0
Heteromysis	1	3	1
Total	30	22	32

It will be observed that no fewer than 7 out of a total of 16 American genera are common to the two coasts, with 12 genera known from the east coast and 11 from the west coast. This close parallel between the two faunas is very striking. The most outstanding feature of the west coast fauna is the predominance of the genera *Neomysis* and *Acanthomysis*, represented by 9 and 7 species, respectively, out of a total of 30. On the east coast, in contrast, only one species of *Neomysis* and none of *Acanthomysis* is known.

Mysis oculata, of all the littoral species, alone represents the Arctic shallow-water fauna on the American coasts. It extends southward along the east coast to Labrador, where Arctic conditions give way to Boreal. It is the only species of coastal mysid known from the Arctic shores of North America, and it extends right around those coasts to Alaska, of which it just reaches the Pacific coast.

If a comparison is made between the littoral species of the east coast of America and those of the European coasts some interesting points emerge. Three species only are common to the two areas—*Mysis oculata, Mysis mixta,* and *Heteromysis formosa. Mysis oculata,* as stated above, is an Arctic littoral species and in Europe it reaches the northern coasts of Norway, Sweden, and Russia, where Arctic conditions prevail. *Mysis mixta* represents the Arctic-Boreal shallow-water fauna. It penetrates southward on the Atlantic coasts of America as far as the shores of New England, and on the European side to the Skagerrack and the Baltic. The American and European areas of distribution are connected by way of Greenland, Iceland, and other Boreal areas where a shallow-water fauna is to be found. *Heteromysis formosa* is known from Great Britain and the coast of Norway.

Out of a total of 22 genera represented in the combined areas, 7 are common to both sides of the Atlantic, out of 12 known from the east coast of American and 14 from the Atlantic coast of Europe. The American fauna lacks entirely such characteristic European genera as *Hemimysis*, *Paramysis*, *Praunus*, *Mesopodopsis*, and *Leptomysis*.

Deep-water bottom-living species of the continental shelf.—Turning now to the deeper water of the continental shelf, from roughly 100 to 1,000 fathoms, we find that 22 bottom-living species have been recorded from the East American area. Of these, no fewer than 15 are known also from the continental slope of Europe, off Norway and the west of Ireland. These 15 species are:

Hansenomysis fyllae	*Amblyops abbreviata*
Boreomysis tridens	*Dactylerythrops bidigitata*
Boreomysis arctica	*Meterythrops robusta*
Paramblyops rostrata	*Erythrops erythrophthalma*
Michthyops parva	*Erythrops microps*
Pseudomma affine	*Erythrops abyssorum*
Pseudomma roseum	*Stilomysis grandis*
Pseudomma truncatum	

Of these 15 species, 5 are known also from the Pacific continental slope off the west coast of North America, namely:

Boreomysis arctica	*Meterythrops robusta*
Pseudomma truncatum	*Stilomysis grandis*
Amblyops abbreviata	

In his account of the *Ingolf* Mysidacea Hansen (1908a) carefully distinguishes between the species of the warm and cold areas of the Arctic Ocean, the isotherm of 0° C. as a bottom temperature serving to separate the two areas. From the warm area he notes 17 species of bottom-living mysids, and of these 17 no fewer than 13 are included in the above list, and all of them are known from the continental slope of western Europe. It would appear, therefore, that there is a warm-area fauna in the deep water of the Arctic which is more or less circumpolar in distribution and which penetrates deeply into the Atlantic on both sides, and to a lesser extent into the Pacific. The striking similarity between the fauna of the continental slope on both sides of the Atlantic is thus explained. The species found on the American slope and not on the corresponding European shelf are:

Lophogaster americanus	Metamblyops macrops
Lophogaster spinosus	Synerythrops cruciata
Lophogaster longirostris	Bathymysis renoculata
Hypererythrops caribbaea	

All these species, with the exception of *Synerythrops cruciata*, are represented on the European continental slope by allied species of the same genera. There is, therefore, a much closer relationship between the deeper water faunas of eastern America and Europe than between the littoral and coastal faunas.

From the cold-water area of the Arctic Ocean Hansen records 8 species of bottom-living mysids, and of these two approach the American coast: *Boreomysis nobilis*, which has been recorded from deep water off the eastern coast of Labrador, and *Amblyops ohlinii*, from 1,060 to 1,081 fathoms off the northeastern coast of the United States. They are the only representatives of the cold-water fauna of the Arctic that reach American waters.

The deeper-water fauna of the continental shelf of the Pacific slope includes, besides the five species already mentioned above as found on the Atlantic slope as well, the following species:

Holmesiella anomala	Amblyops hispida
Pseudomma berkeleyi	Inusitatomysis serrata
Pseudomma oculospinum	Dactylamblyops sp.?

The last five of these species are known only from one or two localities, but *Holmesiella anomala* is an abundant species peculiar to the Pacific coast, which has a wide distribution at suitable depths.

Pelagic species.—There is only one upper-water, epiplanktonic, often surface species of mysid that may be included in the American fauna—*Siriella thompsonii*. Unlike the majority of species of this genus, which are coastal in habit, *S. thompsonii* is definitely oceanic and is usually caught at the surface, especially at night. It is widely distributed in both the Atlantic and Pacific Oceans in the tropical and subtropical zones.

The other pelagic mysids of the American fauna are deep-water, bathypelagic, mesoplanktonic forms, living usually at moderately great depths and widely distributed in the great depths of the oceans of the world. Twenty-four such species have been recorded from American waters. Of these, eight have been recorded from both the Atlantic and Pacific waters of America:

Gnathophausia ingens	Eucopia unguiculata
Gnathophausia gigas	Petalophthalmus armiger
Gnathophausia zoea	Euchaetomera typica
Eucopia sculpticauda	Euchaetomera tenuis

Those recorded only from the Atlantic waters are:

Paralophogaster atlanticus	*Meterythrops picta*
Petalophthalmus oculatus	*Longithorax capensis*
Boreomysis microps	*Katerythrops oceanae*

Those known only from the Pacific side are:

Chalaraspidum alatum	*Boreomysis inermis*
Gnathophausia gracilis	*Boreomysis californica*
Gnathophausia zoea var. *scapularis*	*Boreomysis rostrata*
Scolophthalmus lucifugus	*Caesaromysides liguriae*
Ceratomysis spinosa	*Doxomysis microps*

It should perhaps be mentioned that *Euchaetomera typica*, *E. tenuis*, and *Doxomysis microps* are not strictly bathypelagic but may and do occur at lesser depths, even sometimes at the surface.

Surveying the mysidacean fauna of America as a whole, we may suggest that the east coast of North America, from New England to the Gulf of Mexico and the west coast from Alaska to California are respectively two continuous and homogeneous faunal areas, in both the littoral and the deep-water fauna. The evidence is not very conclusive, for intensive investigation of the littoral fauna of the east coast south of New England has still to be carried out. This may reveal a number of species not found in the already well-known area off the New England coast. On the west coast the areas around San Francisco, British Columbia, and Alaska have been more closely worked and the distribution of the species of littoral mysids indicates a continuous faunal area extending from Alaska to San Francisco as shown in table 2.

TABLE 2.—*Distribution of littoral species of Mysidacea from Alaska to California and from British Columbia to California*

Alaska to California	British Columbia to California
Archaeomysis grebnitzkii. *Neomysis rayii.* *Neomysis kadiakensis.*	*Neomysis mercedis.* *Acanthomysis columbiae.* *Acanthomysis macropsis.* *Heteromysis odontops.*[1]

[1] Or even farther south.

HISTORY OF AMERICAN MYSIDACÈA

The growth of our knowledge of the Mysidacea of America has been a slow and gradual process extending over just a century. The first record was published in 1841, when Gould recorded *Mysis spinulosus* from the shores of Massachusetts. This was followed in 1844 by the record of the same species from New York State by De Kay. Both these records in all probability refer to the species now known as

Mysis stenolepis. Between 1850 and 1870 there was much activity in Arctic exploration, and this led to numerous records of *Mysis oculata* from the Arctic shores of North America down to Labrador. In the years 1871–74 the investigation of the fresh-water lakes of North America resulted in the discovery of *Mysis relicta* in the Great Lakes of Canada. The real basis of our knowledge of American Mysidacea was laid when the United States Fish Commission started work in 1871. Its dredging and trawling operations yielded a rich harvest of zoological material from the northeast coasts of the United States, and papers by Smith and Verrill, detailing the results of their examination of the Crustacea, gave the first description of the Mysidacea of this area. The most important of these papers, by S. I. Smith (1879), brought together all that was known of the American species at that date and included the rich material of the United States Fish Commission. This work was supplemented by similar investigations undertaken by the Canadian Fisheries Department (Whiteaves, 1874b). Thus was revealed the rich mysidacean fauna in the deeper waters of the Atlantic slope of this part of the American coast. As the work of the Fish Commission developed, the need for a larger research vessel made itself felt and resulted in the building and equipment of the *Albatross*. With the advent of this vessel the operations of the Commission were enormously extended. Not only was the deeper water of the Atlantic explored, but cruises were made in the Pacific and resulted in the important papers of Faxon (1893, 1895, 1896) and Ortmann (1894), in which a number of very important and interesting species were described from the west coast of Central America. The *Albatross* subsequently made many cruises in the North Pacific and accumulated a vast amount of valuable material, most of which is dealt with in this paper. In 1894 Holmes commenced his studies of the Pacific coast Crustacea, and between that date and 1900 he published three papers in which species of Mysidacea from that area were described (Holmes, 1894, 1896, 1900). In 1906 Ortmann commenced work on the collections of Mysidacea in the United States National Museum and published two valuable papers, one, in 1906, which dealt with the Lophogastridae and Eucopiidae, and the other, in 1908, on material from Alaska. It is greatly to be regretted that Ortmann was unable to complete the work so splendidly begun. Deep-sea expeditions from European countries have contributed their quota to our knowledge of the American fauna, mainly as the result of incidental collections made in American waters as the expeditions were passing through, so to speak. The *Challenger* expedition (1873–1876) called at Valparaiso, and collected *Siriella thompsonii* and *Euchaetomera tenuis* off the coast of Chile, then worked southward along the coasts of South America, through the Straits of Magellan into the Atlantic. In her operations in the Atlantic the *Challenger* also collected *Eucopia unguiculata*, *Boreomysis microps*, and *Siriella thompsonii* in the deeper waters off the Atlantic slope of eastern America, and *Heteromysis bermudensis* at Bermuda. The *Vettor Pisani* (1882–1885), an Italian expedition, made collections at several points near the American coasts. The Mysidacea were described by Colosi (1924) and Coifmann (1937), and several new species were recorded, mainly from the coasts of South America and from the Caribbean Sea. The German plankton expedition, 1889, touched at the northern coasts of Brazil, and Ortmann (1893) described *Chlamydopleon aculeatum* from those waters. The Swedish Antarctic expedition, 1901–1903, made several dredgings in the neighborhood of the Falkland Islands, and Hansen (1913a) described *Mysidopsis acuta* and *Mysidetes crassa* from that area. The Italian naval cruiser *Liguria* collected material in the Caribbean Sea and off the coasts of South America, and from these collections Colosi (1916, 1919, 1920) recorded *Anchialina typica*, *Siriella thompsonii*, *Euchaetomera tenuis*, *Doxomysis tattersallii*, *Doxomysis microps*, and *Caesaromysides liguriae*, the last an aberrant bathypelagic species of great interest. The *Terra Nova* expedition, 1910, collected *Promysis atlantica* off Rio de Janeiro (Tattersall, 1923). In recent years American-equipped deep-sea expeditions have added their quota of species to the American fauna. The most important of these are Dr. Bigelow's explorations off the coasts of Maine (Tattersall, 1926), Mr. Vanderbilt's various cruises (Boone, 1930), Dr. Beebe's expeditions in the western Atlantic (Tattersall, 1936a), the Johnson-Smithsonian Expedition to the Puerto Rican Deep, 1933 (Tattersall, 1937), and the Presidential Cruise, 1938 (Tattersall, 1941). The cumulative work of a century has resulted in a fairly complete knowledge of the mysidacean fauna of the American Continent. It now includes 112 species, a complete list of which is herein part of the table of contents. Much work, however, remains to be done. The littoral fauna of the eastern coasts of North America south of Virginia, the whole coast of South America, and much of the west coast of the United States require systematic investigation, while the results of deep-sea exploration give promise that many species still await discovery in the deeper waters off the continent of America.

Reference to the Contents (p. III) of this volume will indicate which of the species contained herein are American. Such species are marked with an "A" after the specific name.

SYSTEMATIC DISCUSSION

Class CRUSTACEA

Subclass MALACOSTRACA

Division PERACARIDA

Carapace, when present, leaving at least four of the thoracic somites distinct; first thoracic somite always fused with the head; protopodite of the antenna typically of three segments; mandible with lacinia mobilis (except in parasitic and other modified forms), and a spine row between the incisor and molar parts; maxillule with lobes usually from the first and always from the third joints; maxilla usually with exopod attached to the third joint; thoracic limbs flexed between the merus and carpus as in the Syncarida and Eucarida; oöstegites attached to some or all of the coxal joints of the thoracic limbs in the female, forming a brood pouch; no appendix interna on the pleopods; hepatic caeca few and simple; heart generally elongated, extending through the greater part of the thoracic region, or displaced into the abdomen; spermatozoa generally filiform; development taking place in the brood pouch; young set free at a late stage.

Hansen (1925) has demonstrated quite conclusively that the flexure in the endopod of the thoracic limbs (knee) in the Peracarida occurs between the merus and carpus as in the Syncarida and Eucarida. It was formerly supposed that the knee joint occurred between the carpus and propodus, and that this constituted a character in which the Peracarida differed from the other two divisions (Calman, 1904). Hansen is also of the opinion that in the endopod of the thoracic limbs of the Peracarida there is a joint, called by him the prae-ischium, interpolated between the basis and ischium.

A further point of great morphological interest is raised in Hansen's survey of the thoracic limbs of the Crustacea, namely, the demonstration of a procoxal joint in some of the thoracic limbs of some of the Peracarida. This discovery means that in the thoracic appendages, at any rate, there is a 3-jointed protopodite, composed of precoxa, coxa, and basis. Hansen did not attempt to extend this interpretation of the protopodite to the head appendages but it seems to me that if this were done it is possible to unify the morphological conception of all the appendages to a common scheme, based on a 3-jointed protopodite. For instance, Hansen states that in the maxilla of the Peracarida the exopod is attached to the third joint, to which also the endopod is attached. If we interpret the maxilla as composed of a 3-jointed protopodite on which an endopod and exopod are borne on the third joint or basis the appendage is brought into morphological line with the thoracic appendages. Similarly the maxillule can be interpreted as representing only the protopodite of the limb with well-marked lobes on the precoxal and basal joints. A 3-jointed protopodite to the antenna is generally accepted.

Order MYSIDACEA

Pericarida which retain more or less completely the primitive caridoid facies; the carapace extends over the greater part of the thoracic region but does not coalesce dorsally with more than three of the thoracic somites; the eyes, when present, are movably pedunculate; the antennules are biramous; the antennae usually have a large scalelike exopodite; the thoracic limbs (except sometimes the first, second, and eighth pairs) have natatory exopodites; the first and sometimes also the second pair are modified as maxillipeds; a lamellar epipodite is present on the first pair; ramified branchiae may be attached close to the bases of the thoracic limbs; the pleopods are often reduced; the uropods are lamellar forming a tail fan; the young leave the brood pouch provided with all the appendages of the adult.

Hansen (1925) regards the branchiae of the Lophogastrida as borne on the precoxal joint, therefore prae-epipodial in nature. This interpretation of the branchiae means that they are podobranchs and not arthrobranchs, as was supposed by Sars.

Suborder LOPHOGASTRIDA

Segments of the thorax all well defined dorsally; first pair of thoracic limbs developed as maxillipeds, robust; exopodite imperfectly developed or absent; epipodite very large, projecting within the branchial chamber; well-developed ramified branchiae present on the second to the seventh thoracic limbs, rudimentary or absent on the eighth pair; seven pairs of oöstegites in the female; pleopods well developed, biramous, natatory in both sexes, none modified in the male; no statocyst on the inner uropod.

Family LOPHOGASTRIDAE G. O. Sars

Carapace large, more or less calcareous; second pair of thoracic limbs developed as gnathopods; third to eighth pairs of thoracic limbs developed as normal pereiopods, not chelate.

There are five genera in this family, *Lophogaster*, *Paralophogaster*, *Ceratolepis*, *Chalaraspidum*, and *Gnathophausia*. All but *Ceratolepis* are represented in the National Museum collection.

Genus CHALARASPIDUM Willemoes-Suhm

Chalaraspis (pars) WILLEMOES-SUHM, 1876b, p. 592.
Chalaraspis G. O. SARS, 1885, p. 50.
Chalaraspidum WILLEMOES-SUHM, 1895, p. 521.
Eclytaspis FAXON, 1895, p. 219.

The genus *Chalaraspis* was founded by Willemoes-Suhm in 1875 to include the species *unguiculata*. In his *Challenger* Report Sars showed that the genus *Chalaraspis*, as defined by Willemoes-Suhm, was clearly the same as the genus *Eucopia* founded by Dana in 1852, so that the genus *Chalaraspis* became a straight synonym of *Eucopia*. In his letters from the *Challenger* expedition, which were collected and published in 1877 but which had appeared separately at intervals from 1873–1877, and also in other reports which he made on the *Challenger* expedition (1876a), Willemoes-Suhm used the generic name *Chalaraspis* for another species of mysidacean, *C. alata*, collected at station 158 of the *Challenger* expedition in the Southern Ocean near Kerguelen. Unfortunately the specimen was lost but notes and a drawing of it were found among the papers of Willemoes-Suhm after his death. Sars utilized these in his *Challenger* Report and published them under the name *Chalaraspis alata*. Sars recognized that this species was, in fact, related to the genus *Lophogaster* and not to *Eucopia*, but, on the grounds that *Chalaraspis unguiculata* was a synonym of *Eucopia australis*, he retained the generic name *Chalaraspis* for *C. alata*. This is clearly not in accordance with the accepted principles of zoological nomenclature, and Faxon (1895) on these grounds proposed the generic name *Eclytaspis*, with *C. alata* as the genotype. There is, however, another name that I think can be used for this species and ought to have priority. In the two volumes of the "Summary of the Scientific Results" of the *Challenger* expedition, published in 1895, under station 158 on page 521, appears the following passage: "and a specimen of *Chalaraspidum*, n. gen., characterized by shorter legs and a much longer carapace, which extends over the third abdominal segment and is extremely soft." It was at station 158 that the only specimen of *C. alata* captured by the *Challenger* expedition was taken, and the excerpt quoted above clearly refers to this specimen. The quoted passage is taken practically verbatim from one of Willemoes-Suhm's notebooks under date of March 7, 1874. It would appear that Willemoes-Suhm himself recognized that *C. alata* belonged to a different genus from *Chalaraspis unguiculata*, and, had he survived, would no doubt have published this fact. The volume of the "Summary" in which the quoted passage appears was received at the British Museum on March 20, 1895. Faxon's paper in which the name *Eclytaspis* was published has the date April 1895 on the wrapper. *Chalaraspidum*, therefore, antedates *Eclytaspis* by one month. It may be objected that no genotype is mentioned for *Chalaraspidum* and that, therefore, as a generic name it is void, but the passage quoted above refers beyond doubt to *C. alata*, and there need be no hesitation in quoting it as the genotype. The use of the generic name *Chalaraspidum* has the additional value of emphasizing Willemoes-Suhm's association with this remarkable crustacean, and, by its closely similar sound, reminding workers on this group of Crustacea of the affinities of the genus as they suggested themselves to its discoverer.

CHALARASPIDUM ALATUM (Willemoes-Suhm)

Chalaraspis alata WILLEMOES-SUHM, 1876b, p. 592.—G. O. SARS, 1885, p. 51, figs. 1, 2.—HANSEN, 1912, p. 182, pl. 1, fig. 1,*a–l.*—FAGE, 1939, p. 68, figs. 1–7.

Occurrence.—CALIFORNIA: *Albatross* station 4334, 1 specimen, 32 mm. JAPAN: *Albatross* station 4919, 1 specimen, 38 mm.; *Albatross* station 4960, 1 specimen, 37 mm. WEST COAST OF SOUTH AMERICA: *Albatross* stations 4672* and 4719*, identified by Hansen (1912).[9]

Distribution.—South of Australia (*Challenger*); west of Peru (Hansen, 1912); China Sea and near New Guinea (Fage, 1939); west of California and the Eastern Sea (present material). The species is therefore widely distributed in the deep water of the Pacific Ocean, and it is not yet known from elsewhere. Zimmer (1914) has recorded a specimen of the genus from the deep water of the Atlantic near the Azores, but the material was not apparently in a sufficiently good state of preservation to describe. The specimen appears to belong to a new species.

Remarks.—The specimen from station 4334 agrees very closely with the descriptions and figures given by Hansen (1912) and Fage (1939). The other two specimens differ in the following particulars: (1) The rostral plate has the outer anterolateral angles drawn out into conspicuous spines; the margin between these spines is lightly concave in the center and is microscopically serrulated; there are three or four spinules on the lateral margins of the rostral plate on each side and a prominent ocular spine on the carapace margin over the eye; there are also scattered microscopic spinules on the lateral area of the carapace below and behind the eyes. (2) The outer margin of the antennal scale has only three or four teeth in addition to the terminal tooth.

Both these specimens have seven spines on the lateral margins of the telson. One of them also still has the apical armature of the telson almost intact and shows this to consist of four rather stout and closely set spines, the inner pair nearly twice as long as the outer pair. This is the first time it has been possible to indicate the apical armature of the telson. In Hansen's specimen the tip of the telson is clearly broken. Fage says that the apex of the telson is provided with four short spines,

---

[9] Specimens from stations marked with an asterisk were not examined by me.

but, unless this represents a third character in which my specimens differ from those described by Hansen and Fage, I think that Fage's specimens too must have had the apex of the telson damaged.

The question now arises as to the interpretation to be placed on these differences. A glance at Willemoes-Suhm's drawings published in the *Challenger* Report will show that the *Challenger* specimen agreed with the specimens from stations 4919 and 4960 in the characters of the rostral plate and antennal scale. In the description published by Sars from Willemoes-Suhm's notes the rostral plate is described as follows: "Anteriorly, it [the carapace] projects as a short, but very broad, frontal plate, abruptly truncate at the extremity, the anterior margin being slightly emarginate and finely serrate, the lateral corners somewhat extended." This is precisely the condition in the two specimens from stations 4919 and 4960. The lateral view of the *Challenger* specimen shows three teeth on the outer margin of the antennal scale in addition to the terminal tooth, the dorsal view six.

The specimens from stations 4919 and 4960 clearly represent the true *C. alatum*, and if the specimen from station 4334 and those described by Hansen and Fage are to be regarded as a different species, it is to these specimens that a new name must be given.

However, another explanation may be given for the facts. The *Challenger* specimen was obviously a female, for the incubatory lamellae are shown in the figure. Both Hansen's and Fage's specimens were males, and I think the differences between them and the *Challenger* specimen can be explained as secondary sexual characters. It is in this light that I regard them. Unfortunately, I cannot confirm this conclusion from the present material, since in none of the specimens is there any trace of incubatory lamellae and the material is not sufficiently well preserved to show the position of the genital openings. In fact, I cannot with certainty give the sex of the specimens. The examination of better preserved material must be awaited to settle the entire question but the evidence available is sufficiently good to warrant the suggestion that all the material belongs to one species with well-marked secondary sexual characters. The geographic distribution of the species, as available from published literature, does not indicate that two separate species are involved.

Genus LOPHOGASTER M. Sars

Lophogaster M. SARS, 1857, p. 160.
Ctenomysis NORMAN, 1862, p. 151.

I have found myself in the same difficulty as Ortmann (1906) in determining the species of *Lophogaster* in this collection, at least those specimens that appear to be very closely allied to the type species, *L. typicus*, and yet cannot be referred to it with any confidence. Ortmann examined specimens from three separate geographical regions, east coast of North American and Japan (1906), and from Hawaii (1905). He referred all the specimens to *L. typicus* but made careful notes of the differences and variations met with. He paid special attention to three characters, the length of the rostrum, the number of teeth on the antennal scale, and the number of spines on the lateral margins of the telson, and he came to the conclusion that the variations met with in these characters was so wide as to render them of little specific value. There are, however, two other characters to which Ortmann, unfortunately, gave no attention, the tuberculation of the carapace and the shape of the antennal scale. In the typical form of *L. typicus* the carapace is coarsely tuberculose, particularly in the anterior central region, and the antennal scale is rotund, the breadth being about 0.7 to 0.75 of the total length. In *L. intermedius* (Hansen, 1910) the tubercles of the carapace are much finer and more numerous, and the antennal scale is longer and narrower, about twice as long as broad, with the terminal spiniform process straighter and longer than in *L. typicus*. In *L. rotundatus* (Illig, 1930) the carapace is practically smooth and the antennal scale has the shape and proportions of the type species.

Using these additional characters it has seemed to me desirable to separate the west Atlantic and Japanese forms as new species, and the following key will serve as a guide to the known species of the genus.

KEY TO THE SPECIES OF LOPHOGASTER

a^1. Posterolateral angle of carapace rounded (carapace smooth, antennal scale of "rotundate" type)_____**rotundatus** [10]
a^2. Posterolateral angle of carapace produced into a spine.
  b^1. Antennal scale of broad "rotundate" type.
    c^1. Carapace tuberculose_____**typicus** (p. 17)
    c^2. Carapace microscopically spinulose_____**americanus** (p. 17)
  b^2. Antennal scale of "elongate" type, about twice as long as broad, apical spine long and straight.
    c^1. Rostral spine longer than antennal peduncle.
      d^1. Rostral spine very long, far outreaching antennal scale.
                                                        spinosus (p. 21)
      d^2. Rostral spine shorter than antennal scale.
        e^1. Carapace smooth; 6 to 9 teeth on antennal scale excluding terminal spine; telson with 5 to 8 spines on lateral margins including long spines at apex_____**longirostris** (p. 21)
        e^2. Carapace finely tubercular; 2 or 3 teeth on antennal scale; telson with 4 spines on lateral margins, including terminal ones.
                                                    intermedius ? (p. 20)
    c^2. Rostral spine equal in length to antennular peduncle; carapace coarsely granular; antennal scale with 2 or 3 teeth excluding terminal spine; telson with 4 spines including terminal ones_____**japonicus** (p. 19)

_____
[10] Illig, 1930, pp. 405–407, figs. 7–10.

I cannot place *L. erythraeus* Colosi and *L. affinis* Colosi in this key. *L. erythraeus* is very closely allied to *L. typicus* but, according to Colosi, differs in the degree to which the rostral plate covers the antennular peduncle and in trivial differences in the spinulation of the telson. *L. affinis* is very similar to *L. intermedius* but differs in that the rostral plate covers a larger area of the eye and in the slightly different shape of the antennal scale.

On the basis of the key I can place all but one of the specimens in the collection. This odd specimen I have not named, preferring to await further material before deciding whether the characters noted are constant.

LOPHOGASTER TYPICUS M. Sars

Lophogaster typicus M. SARS, 1857, p. 160.

Occurrence.—Ireland; identified by A. M. Norman*.

LOPHOGASTER HAWAIENSIS Fage

Data for this species will be found on page 242.

LOPHOGASTER AMERICANUS, new species

FIGURE 1, a

Lophogaster typicus ORTMANN, 1906, p. 23 (west Atlantic specimens).—TATTERSALL, 1926, p. 6.
Lophogaster sp. SMITH, 1881, p. 445; 1884, p. 55.—VERRILL, 1885, pp. 556, 558.

Description.—Carapace not tuberculose but very minutely spinulose, particularly on the anterior dorsal region and on the rostral plate; rostral plate with the median process longer than the lateral and extending forward as far as the distal end of the antennular peduncle; posterolateral angle of the carapace produced into a short spine; antennal scale (fig. 1, *a*) of the "rotundate" type, the proportion of length to breadth 10 : 6; 6 to 7 teeth on the outer margin in addition to the terminal spine; telson with 6 spines on the lateral margins including the spines at the apex.

Type.—A male, U.S.N.M. No. 81252, from the east coast of the United States, *Fish Hawk* station 870, latitude 40°2′36″ N., longitude 70°22′58″ W.

Occurrence.—EAST COAST OF THE UNITED STATES: *Fish Hawk* stations 870, 1 male, damaged, but about 20 mm., type; 7282*, Gulf Stream off Key West, Fla., latitude 24°21′15″ N., longitude 81°52′15″ W., 109 fathoms, February 19, 1902; 7283*, Gulf Stream off Key West, Fla., latitude 24°17′30″ N., longitude 81°53′30″ W., 127 fathoms, February 19, 1902; 7286*, Gulf Stream off Key West, Fla., latitude 24°18′00″ N., longitude 81°47′45″ W., 133 fathoms, February 19,

1902; *Albatross* stations 2418, 1 female with young in brood pouch, 18 mm.; 2314*, 2399*, 2401*, 2403*, 2601, 2602*. Bahama Islands: *Bache* station 10209, March 22, 1914, north of Bahama Bank, latitude 27°57′ N., longitude 78°15′ W., 100–0 m., 1 immature specimen. All the material denoted by an asterisk was examined by Ortmann (1906) and referred to *L. typicus.* I believe it should all be considered this new species.

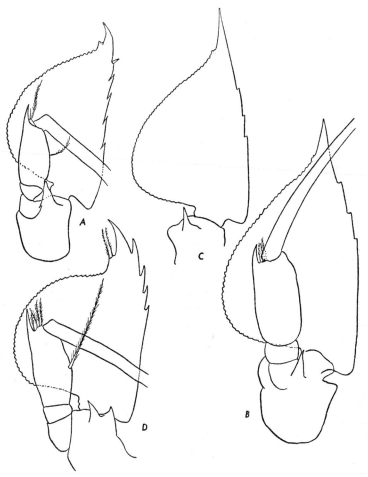

Figure 1.—Antennal scales of various species of *Lophogaster: a, Lophogaster americanus,* new species, type, × 22½; *b, L. japonicus,* new species, × 20; *c, L. intermedius* Hansen ?, × 22½; *d, Lophogaster* sp. ?, *Albatross* station 4891, × 22½. (*A* and *d,* "rotundate" type; *b* and *c,* "elongate" type.)

Distribution.—Off the east coast of North America from Massachusetts to the Gulf of Mexico.

Remarks.—This species may be distinguished from *L. typicus* by the absence of tubercles on the carapace and their replacement by a coating of microscopic spinules, and by the slightly narrower antennal scale. The specimens from the Carolinas, the Gulf of Mexico, and Key West, described by Ortmann (1906), agree very closely with the above description as regards the rostrum, the teeth on the antennal scale, and the spines on the telson, but Ortmann gives no indication of the nature of the ornamentation on the carapace. I believe they belong to this new species. Ortmann's notes on the variations met with in this species are valuable; in the two specimens I have examined the antennal scales are asymmetrical, having six teeth on one side and seven on the other.

The specimen from *Fish Hawk* station 870 is the one about which Smith (1881) wrote: "A species very distinct from *L. typicus*, Sars." The same specimen was also referred to by Verrill (1885, p. 558).

Both Smith (1884) and Verrill (1885) refer to *Lophogaster* sp. with a bathymetric range from 1,022 to 2,949 fathoms captured during the cruise of the *Albatross* in 1883. There are no specimens in this collection from the *Albatross* stations of 1883, and I do not know to what species Smith and Verrill refer unless it is to *eucopia*, which occurred at stations 2094 and 2099, with depths of 1,022 and 2,949 fathoms, respectively. The small specimen that I perhaps rather hastily called *L. typicus* and recorded from the western Atlantic in 1926 should in all probability be referred to this new species.

LOPHOGASTER JAPONICUS, new species

FIGURES 1, *b*; 2, *a*

Lophogaster typicus (pars) ORTMANN, 1906, p. 23 (Japanese specimens).

Description.—Carapace (fig. 2, *a*) coarsely tuberculate especially anteriorly in front of the cervical sulcus and at the sides, quite as tuberculate as *L. typicus;* rostral plate with the median process longer than the lateral and extending forward slightly beyond the distal end of the antennular peduncle but not to the extremity of the antennal scale; posterolateral angle of the carapace produced into a short spine; antennal scale (fig. 1, *b*) of the "elongate" type, about twice as long as broad, with the terminal spine long and straight, with 2 or 3 teeth on the outer margin in addition to the terminal spine; telson with 4 spines on the lateral margins including the spines at the apex and with 6 to 8 spinules between the long terminal spines.

Cotypes.—Two males, U.S.N.M. No. 81253; *Albatross* station 4815, Japan, latitude 38°16′ N., longitude 138°52′ E.

Occurrence.—JAPAN: *Albatross* stations 4815, 2 males, 28 mm., types; 4816, 1 male, 29 mm.; 4817, 1 female with young in the brood pouch, 25 mm.; 4903, 1 male, 30 mm. SEA OF OKHOSTSK: *Albatross* stations 3707*, 3714*, 3715*, 3717*, 3718*, 3740*. All the material from the Sea of Okhotsk was examined and identified as *L. typicus* by Ortmann (1906). I believe it should be referred here.

Distribution.—Seas around Japan, 48 to 139 fathoms.

Remarks.—This species may be distinguished by the combination of characters afforded by the coarse tuberculation of the carapace, the scale of the "elongate" type with few teeth on the outer margin, and the form of the rostral plate. I think it is almost certain that the specimens recorded by Ortmann from Japan should be referred to this new species. The characters of the rostrum, scale, and telson given by Ortmann agree exactly with the above definition. The species is closely allied to *L. intermedius* Hansen.

LOPHOGASTER INTERMEDIUS Hansen ?

FIGURE 1, c

Lophogaster intermedius HANSEN, 1910, p. 14, pl. 1, figs. 1, *a*–1, *e*.—TATTERSALL, 1922, p. 448.

Occurrence.—Japan: *Albatross* station 4944, 1 female with embryos in the brood pouch, 20 mm.

Distribution.—Waters of the Dutch East Indies, 75 to 141 meters; Mergui Archipelago, 62 fathoms.

Remarks.—This specimen differs from the specimens of *L. japonicus* in having the tubercles of the carapace altogether much finer and more regular in size, and in this respect it appears to agree with *L. intermedius*, in which the carapace is described as "finely granulated." The rostrum agrees exactly with that of *L. intermedius*. The antennal scale (fig. 1, *c*) is about twice as long as broad and thus is rather broader than in *L. intermedius*, and it has two teeth on the left side and three teeth on the right side, in addition to the long terminal spine. The telson has four spines on the lateral margins including the apical spines, and between the latter are six spinules. I refer this specimen with some doubt to *L. intermedius*. It may be merely a variety of *L. japonicus*.

LOPHOGASTER sp.?

FIGURE 1, d

Occurrence.—*Albatross* station 4891, 1 male, 20 mm.

Remarks.—I cannot fit this specimen into any known species of the genus. The carapace has no tubercles or granules, but these are replaced by rather scattered microscopic spinules. The rostral plate has the central spine equal in length to the lateral spines and extending only about halfway up the last joint of the antennular peduncle. The antennal scale (fig. 1, *d*) is of the "rotundate" type, about 1½ times as long as broad, with the terminal spine somewhat curved, with four teeth on the outer margin in addition to the terminal spine. The telson has six spines on the lateral margins including the apical spines, and between the latter are five spinules. In most of its characters this specimen agrees with *L. typicus* but lacks entirely the tubercles on the carapace so characteristic of that species. The form of the scale and the rostral plate are quite distinct from those of *L. japonicus* and *L. intermedius*. Further material must be had before it is given a specific name.

LOPHOGASTER SPINOSUS Ortmann

Lophogaster spinosus ORTMANN, 1906, p. 26, pl. 1, figs. 1*a*, 1*b*.—ZIMMER, 1914, p. 382.—TATTERSALL, 1926, p. 7; 1937, p. 1.

Occurrence.—BAHAMA ISLANDS: *Bache* station 10195, north of Bahamas, latitude 29° N., longitude 76°23′ W., 100–0 meters, February 28, 1914, 1 juvenile specimen. WEST INDIES: Johnson-Smithsonian expedition, 1933, station 86, series number 495, latitude 19°18′30″ N., longitude 65°16′ W., about 350 fathoms, February 27, 1933, 4 specimens, 16 to 20 mm. SOUTHEASTERN COAST OF THE UNITED STATES: *Albatross* station 2666*, type, identified by Ortmann (1906).

Distribution.—Deep water of the Atlantic Ocean from about latitude 30° N. to latitude 30° S.

Remarks.—I recorded these specimens in 1937 without comment, and I now add a few notes on them. The length of the specimens given above is measured from the eye to the telson. The rostral process is about one-fifth of this length and extends forward beyond the eye and well beyond the antennal scale. The posterolateral spines of the carapace extend backward for lengths varying from the end of the second abdominal somite in the smaller specimens to the end of the third abdominal somite in the larger specimens. The antennal scale has 9 to 12 teeth on the outer margin in addition to the terminal spine. In no specimen is the scale symmetrical in this respect on both sides of the same individual. The lateral margins of the telson have 5 or 6 spines including the apical spines, and between the latter are 6 spinules. The carapace is smooth. This species is a very distinct form characterized mainly by the very long rostral and posterolateral spines of the carapace and the long and somewhat narrower form of the antennal scale, with its large number of teeth on the outer margin.

LOPHOGASTER LONGIROSTRIS Faxon

Lophogaster longirostris FAXON, 1896, p. 164, pl. 2, figs. 8–10.—TATTERSALL, 1937, p. 1.

Occurence.—WEST INDIES: Johnson-Smithsonian expedition, 1933, station 23, series number 117, latitude 18°32′ N., longitude 66°21′15″ W., 260 fathoms, February 4, 1933, 1 speciman, 37 mm.; station 93, series number 542, latitude 18°37′15″ N., longitude 65°3′ W., 300 fathoms, March 3, 1933, 1 specimen, 19 mm.

Distribution.—Gulf of Mexico and Caribbean Sea, 119 to 300 fathoms.

Remarks.—These specimens were also recorded by me in 1937. They agree very closely with Faxon's description and figures. The carapace is smooth, without tubercles or spinules. The antennal scale has nine teeth on the outer margin in addition to the terminal spine, rather more than in Faxon's specimen where there were only six teeth. The telson has five to seven spines on the lateral margins including the apical spines, and between the latter are five to seven spinules. In both specimens the rostrum extends well beyond the antennular peduncle but is shorter than the scale.

Genus PARALOPHOGASTER Hansen

Paralophogaster HANSEN, 1910, p. 15.

PARALOPHOGASTER GLABER Hansen

Paralophogaster glaber HANSEN, 1910, p. 16, pl. 1, figs. 2a–2n.—TATTERSALL, 1923, p. 279.

Occurrence.—JAPAN: *Albatross* stations 4816, 1 specimen, 20 mm.; 4817, 1 specimen, 20 mm. PHILIPPINE ISLANDS: *Albatross* station 5121, 6 specimens up to 25 mm.; 5456, 4 young specimens, 6 mm.

Distribution.—East Indian seas, off New Zealand, western north Atlantic.

Remarks.—These specimens agree well with Hansen's description and figures except that the antennal scale is only 1½ times as long as the antennular peduncle. There is a prominent median dorsal blunt spine on the carapace at the base of the rostral plate. Two of the young specimens from station 5456 have no median rostral tooth and in all the young specimens there are only two or three spines between the two long spines near the apex of the telson.

In 1937, when describing *P. atlanticus*, I compiled a key to the known species of this genus. Since that paper a further species, *P. intermedius*, has been described by Coifmann (1936, p. 10). The paper in which this species was described reached me too late for inclusion in my paper. There are thus six described species of the genus.

One of the characters upon which I relied for the separation of the species was the relative length of the antennal scale. This was described as twice as long as the antennular peduncle in *P. glaber* and *P. macrops*, and only 1½ times as long in the other species. The examination of the present material shows that, as far as *P. glaber* is concerned, this character does not hold, for the antennal scale is only 1½ times as long as the antennular peduncle. Hansen's specimens were "very mutilated and badly preserved," and this condition may account for the discrepancy.

The four juvenile specimens in the collection show two interesting points. Two of them lack the median rostral spine and the other two have it, yet they are all comparable in size. Hansen figures the rostral plate of an immature specimen of *P. glaber*, 13 mm. in length, in which the median rostral tooth is missing and suggests that this is a juvenile character. One of the main characters upon which *P. macrops* was founded by Colosi is the absence of the median rostral tooth. The four known specimens of this species measure 9 to 13 mm. The interpretation of this character is as yet a matter of doubt. It may be, as Hansen suggests, a juvenile character; yet of the four young specimens in my material, all smaller than any of the recorded specimens, two possess the median tooth and two are without it. It may be a not infrequent variation which persists throughout life, or it may represent, as Colosi appears to think, a definite specific character.

The second interesting point shown by the young specimens is the armature of the telson. They have only two or three small spines between the two large spines near the apex of the telson, whereas in fully grown specimens of *P. glaber* there are six to seven such spines. I have interpreted this difference as due to difference in size and age and have supposed that the number of these spines increases with the growth of the individual. If the known species of the genus are arranged according to size it will be seen that they differ in respect to the number of small spines between the two large marginal spines at the posterior end of the lateral margin in precisely the same way as if they were stages in the growth of one species. *P. sanzoi* differs from the other species in the larger number of spines on the lateral margins of the telson proximal to the large pair of terminal spines, eight as against three or four in the other species. *P. microps* is separated on the much smaller size of the eye.

TABLE 3.—*Species of* Paralophogaster *arranged to show ratio of small spines to size of species*

Species	Length in mm.	Number of small spines
glaber	25	6–7
intermedius	15	5
sanzoi	13–18	3
macrops	9–13	4
microps	7–15	4
atlanticus	6–12	3

The point I wish to make is that a great deal more information is required as to the changes which accompany growth in this genus and also on the extent of individual variation in adults. The described species are all of them very closely allied, and I do not feel that they have all been separated on characters of sufficient importance, or which cannot be explained either as growth changes or variations. Future workers with more material at their command may well pay attention to the points I have raised. I think it is more than probable that the number of valid species will be reduced by more extensive investigation.

PARALOPHOGASTER ATLANTICUS Tattersall

FIGURES 2, b, c

Paralophogaster glaber TATTERSALL, 1926, p. 8.
Paralophogaster atlanticus TATTERSALL, 1937, p. 4, figs. 1, 2.

Occurrence.—WEST INDIES: Johnson-Smithsonian expedition, 1933: station 6, series number 27, latitude 18°30'45'' N., longitude 66°0'50''

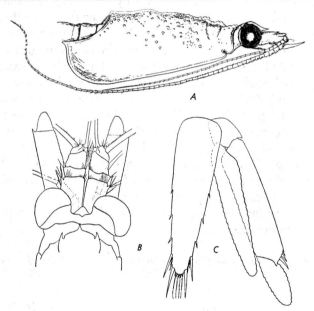

FIGURE 2.—*Lophogaster japonicus*, new species: *a*, Lateral view of carapace to show tuberculation; *b*, *Paralophogaster atlanticus* Tattersall, dorsal view of anterior end to show rostral plate, eyes, antennular peduncle, and antennal scale, × 25; *c*, *P. atlanticus* Tattersall, telson and uropods, × 25.

W., 100 fathoms, February 1, 1933, 1 specimen; station 29, series number 173, latitude 18°40'30'' N., longitude 66°21'15'' W., 260 fathoms, February 8, 1933, 1 specimen; station 30, series number 175, latitude 18°40'30'' N., longitude 66°36'15'' W., 1,200 fathoms, February 8,

1933, 3 specimens; station 60, series number 321, latitude 19°16′45″ N., longitude 69°4′45″ W., 500 fathoms, February 18, 1933, 1 specimen; station 74, series number 383, latitude 18°36′10″ N., longitude 65°48′30″ W., 360 fathoms, February 24, 1933, 2 specimens; station 82, series number 444, latitude 18°32′45″ N., longitude 65°23′45″ W., 300 fathoms, February 26, 1933, 1 specimen; station 86, series number 495, latitude 19°18′30″ N., longitude 65°16′ W., 350 fathoms, February 27, 1933, 4 specimens; station 98, series number 567, latitude 18°39′30″ N., longitude 64°56′ W., 300 fathoms, March 3, 1933, 3 specimens; station 99, series number 573, latitude 18°40′ N., longitude 64°51′ W., 200 fathoms, March 3, 1933, 2 specimens; station 106, series number 730, latitude 18°31′30″ N., longitude 66°18′20″ W., 150 to 195 fathoms, March 8, 1933, 1 specimen (type).

Distribution.—West Indies and the Bahamas.

Remarks.—The material is not in a very satisfactory condition and is composed mainly of small specimens 6 to 12 mm. in length. I have already recorded the material and discussed it in my earlier paper. In the light of what is written above under *P. glaber* I am not satisfied that the species is well founded. I reproduce my earlier figures illustrating this species (fig. 2, *b*, *c*).

Genus GNATHOPHAUSIA Willemoes-Suhm

Gnathophansia WILLEMOES-SUHM, *in* Thomson, 1873, p. 400.
Gnathophausia HUMBERT, 1874, p. 206.—WILLEMOES-SUHM, 1875, p. 28.
Gnathophausa SMITH, 1884, p. 55—VERRILL, 1885, p. 556.

GNATHOPHAUSIA INGENS (Dohrn)

Lophogaster ingens DOHRN, 1870, p. 610, pl. 30, figs. 12–14.
Gnathophausia calcarata ORTMANN, 1906, p. 30, pl. 1, figs. 2a–2f.

Occurence.—CALIFORNIA: *Albatross* stations: 2937, 1 male, 57 mm.; 2839*, 2919*, 2923*, 2929*, 2936*, 2980*, 2986*; specimens from the following *Albatross* stations were identified by Ortmann (1906): 3127*, 3348*, 3627*, 3670*, 4335*, 4337*, 4354*, 4528*; specimens from *Albatross* station 3681* were identified by Hansen (1912). PHILIPPINE ISLANDS: *Albatross* stations: 5638, 1 male, 71 mm.; 5650, 1 male, 76 mm. HAWAIIAN ISLANDS: *Albatross* stations: 4109*, 4142* identified by Ortmann (1905). GULF OF MEXICO: *Albatross* station 2384*.

Distribution.—Ortmann (1906) records a single specimen from the eastern waters of America, in the Gulf of Mexico in 940 fathoms. He gives a long list of records from the western American coast. The specimen from station 2937 is from the west coast of California and therefore supplements Ortmann's earlier records. The other two specimens are from the waters around the Philippine Islands, from which locality the species was recorded by the *Challenger.* The Hawaiian Islands are here added to the records.

Remarks.—The length of these specimens is in all cases measured from the level of the eye to the end of the telson. The antennal scale has four teeth on the lateral margin in addition to the terminal spine in the small specimen, and five and six teeth in the two larger specimens. The rostrum is broken in the two smaller specimens. In the largest specimen it measures 22 mm. from the level of the eye to the tip. The median posterior dorsal spine of the carapace does not extend backward as far as the posterior end of the first abdominal somite and the posterolateral spines of the carapace extend backward as far as the distal end of the second abdominal somite. Ortmann (1906) has given a series of figures illustrating the changes which take place in *G. ingens,* in the form of the epimera of the sixth abdominal somite, with growth. The small specimen has the epimera of the form shown in Ortmann's figure 2, *c,* and the other two specimens as in figure 2, *d.*

GNATHOPHAUSIA GIGAS Willemoes-Suhm

Gnathophansia gigas WILLIMOES-SUHM, *in* Thomson, 1873, p. 400, figs. 4, 5.
Gnathophausia gigas WILLEMOES-SUHM, 1874a, p. iii; 1875, p. 28, pl. 9, figs. 16, 17.
Gnathophausia drepanephora HOLT and TATTERSALL, 1905, p. 113, pl. 18.
Gnathophausa sp. (pars) SMITH, 1884, p. 55.—VERRILL, 1885, p. 556.
Gnathopausia gigas FOWLER, 1912, p. 539.—STEPHENSEN, 1933, p. 9.

Occurrence.—EAST COAST OF NORTH AMERICA: *Albatross* station 2083, 2 specimens, 58–60 mm. EAST COAST OF THE UNITED STATES: *Albatross* stations 2034*, identified by S. I. Smith (unpublished); 2099, 1 male, 60 mm.; 2101, 1 male, 80 mm., 1 young, 27 mm.; 2104, 1 specimen, 45 mm.; 2174, 1 male, 73 mm. (labeled *Gnathophausa* sp.); 2211, 1 specimen, 54 mm.; 2221, 1 specimen, 95 mm.; 2229, 1 specimen, 50 mm.; 2729, 1 specimen, 65 mm. (labeled A. E. V. *Gnathophausa*); 2741*; 2748, 1 male, 85 mm. (labeled *Gnathophausa*). BERING SEA: *Albatross* stations 3307, 1 specimen, 24 mm.; 3603, 1 specimen, 30 mm.; 3329* and 3340* identified by Ortmann (1906). NORTHWEST COAST OF NORTH AMERICA: Specimens from *Albatross* stations 2860*, identified by Ortmann (1906); 4267*, identified by Ortmann (1908); 4766, 1 specimen from 300 fathoms, 33 mm.; 4767, 1 specimen, 32 mm.; 4785, 2 specimens from 300 fathoms, 24 to 25 mm. JAPAN: *Albatross* station 4956, 1 specimen, 30 mm. HAWAIIAN ISLANDS: *Albatross* station 4144*, identified by Ortmann (1905).

Distribution.—This species has been recorded from the east coast of America by Ortmann (1906), in 852 fathoms, between Cape Charles and Long Island. Smith (1884) and Verrill (1885) both refer to two species of *Gnathophausa* (*lapsus calami*), one from 959 to 2,949 fathoms, and the other from 858 to 2,033 fathoms in 1883. I think the former must refer to those specimens of *G. gigas* from *Albatross* stations 2083 and 2099. Fowler's paper (1912) is merely a compilation of previous literature and I think his records of *G. gigas* must be based on Ortmann's paper. In error he gave Thomson as the authority for both *G. gigas* and *G. zoea*, and curiously enough he refers both species to the Stomatopoda.

On the west coast of America Ortmann recorded this species from four localities off the coast of Alaska and most of the specimens from the Pacific in the list of records came from localities in the North Pacific more or less in the same area as Ortmann's. This species penetrates into northern latitudes in the Pacific farther than any other species of the genus, and Stephensen (1933) has recorded it from near the coast of Greenland, in the North Atlantic Ocean.

Remarks.—In table 4 I have given measurements showing the total length of the specimens, measured from the eye to the end of the telson, the percentage of that length of the rostrum and the posterolateral spines, and also the number of teeth on the antennal scale excluding the terminal spine.

TABLE 4.—*Percentages of length of rostrum and posterolateral spines to total length of specimens, and the number of teeth on the antennal scale in* Gnathophausia gigas

Station No.	Total length in mm.	Rostrum		Posterolateral spines		Number of teeth on antennal scale
		Length in mm.	Percentage of total	Length in mm.	Percentage of total	
2291	95	22	23	2. 5	2. 6	4
2748	85	(¹)	--------	3. 0	3. 5	4
2101	80	15	19	2. 0	2. 5	4
2174	73	(¹)	--------	5. 0	6. 9	5
2729	65	20	31	6. 0	9. 3	5
2099	60	20	33	6. 0	10. 0	4
2083	60	17	28	6. 0	10. 0	4
2083	58	16. 5	29	4. 5	7. 7	4
2211	54	(¹)	--------	4. 5	8. 3	5
2229	50	(¹)	--------	6. 0	12. 0	4
2104	45	14. 5	32	4. 5	10. 0	5
4766	33	12. 5	38	3. 5	10. 0	4
4767	32	13. 5	41	4. 0	12. 0	3
3603	30	12	40	3. 0	10. 0	4. 3
4956	30	10	33	3. 0	10. 0	3
2101	27	13	48	4. 0	16. 0	4
4785	25	10	40	4. 0	16. 0	2
4785	24	10	42	4. 0	16. 6	2
3307	24	(¹)	--------	4. 0	16. 6	2

¹ Broken.

The specimens are arranged in order of length, and, though they are few, they cover a wide range of size, 24 to 95 mm. Allowing for the small numbers, individual variation, and the somewhat rough nature of the measurements, the table does indicate that the relative lengths of the rostrum and the posterolateral spines of the carapace do decrease with age and that the number of teeth on the antennal scale does increase with age. This is, of course, exactly what Ortmann contended in his paper (1906), but I have thought it worth while to give the above figures in support of his contention.

GNATHOPHAUSIA GRACILIS Willemoes-Suhm

Gnathophausia gracilis WILLEMOES-SUHM, 1875, p. 33, pl. 9, fig. 1.—ORTMANN, 1906, p. 39.
Gnathophausia dentata FAXON, 1893, p. 217.
Gnathophausia brevispinis FAXON, 1895, p. 216, pl. J.
Gnathophausia bidentata ILLIG, 1906b, p. 229, fig. 2.
Gnathophausia sp. CHUN, 1900, pp. 289, 516, 531; 1903, p. 551, pl. facing p. 536.

Occurrence.—PHILIPPINE ISLANDS: Albatross stations 5299, 1 male, 45 mm.; 5670, 1 female, 61 mm. WEST COAST OF AMERICA: Specimens from *Albatross* stations 3361*, 3400*, and 3411* were identified by Faxon (1895) as *G. brevispinis;* Ortmann (1906) identified specimens from *Albatross* station 3128*; and specimens from *Albatross* stations 4652* and 4656* were identified by Hansen (1912).

Distribution.—Faxon recorded this species from the west coast of Mexico, off Panama, 1,201 to 1,471 fathoms, and from off the Galápagos Islands in 551 to 1,322 fathoms. Ortmann's specimen came from the coast of California in 627 fathoms. These are the only records from near the American coast. All the specimens that I examined are from the waters around the Philippine Islands.

Remarks.—The two specimens that I examined agree with the description of this species given by Ortmann. In both specimens the gastric crest is very prominent and the lower of the two spines at the posterolateral angle of the carapace is obsolete. In the smaller specimen the rostrum is 27 percent of the length of the specimen from the eye to the end of the telson and in the larger specimen it is only 20 percent of this length. The latter is a female in which the incubatory lamellae are still very small and undeveloped.

GNATHOPHAUSIA LONGISPINA G. O. Sars

Gnathophausia longispina G. O. SARS, 1884, p. 8; 1885, p. 46, pl. 7, figs. 1–5; pl. 8.—ORTMANN, 1905, p. 969; 1906, p. 41.—HANSEN, 1910, p. 17.—SHIINO, 1937, p. 184, fig. 2.

Occurrence.—JAPAN: *Albatross* stations: 4905, 7 specimens; 4906, 2 females, 35 mm., and 1 male, 40 mm.; 4907, 2 males, 3 females, and 1 immature, 24 to 40 mm.; 4908, 1 male, 2 females, and 1 immature, 27 to 41 mm.; 4911, 1 male, 1 female, and 2 immature, 23 to 48 mm.;

4912, 6 specimens; 4913, 7 specimens; 4914, 2 males, 1 female, and 1 immature, 19 to 44 mm.; 4915, 1 male and 1 female, 37 to 39 mm. PHILIPPINE ISLANDS: *Albatross* stations 5238, 1 male, 38 mm.; 5364, 1 male, 44 mm.; 5438, 1 female, 49 mm.; 5618, 1 male, 45 mm., 1 female, 43 mm.; 5628, 1 female, 42 mm.; 5630, 1 female, 49 mm. HAWAIIAN ISLANDS: Ortmann (1906) identified material from the following *Albatross* stations: 3467*, 3473*, 3475*, 3824*, 3826*, 3907*, 3908*, 3909*, 3911*, 3925*, 4105*, 4106*, 4107*. The National Museum collection contains one specimen, a male, 35 mm., without locality.

Distribution.—This species is not known from the coasts of America. It has been recorded from the Philippine Islands, 255 fathoms (Sars), from several localities in the neighborhood of Hawaii, 222 to 498 fathoms (Ortmann), from the waters of the East Indian Archipelago, 521 to 694 fathoms (Hansen), and by Shiino (1937) from off Japan. The specimens in this collection are from two sets of localities, one in the waters southwest of Japan, 391 to 434 fathoms, and the other in the waters of the Philippine Islands. The species appears to be confined to the western part of the Pacific Ocean and to waters of comparatively shallow depth, not exceeding 500 fathoms. In these waters it is an abundant species.

Remarks.—I have nothing to add to the descriptions of Sars and Ortmann, with which these specimens are in complete agreement. None of the specimens that I have examined is as large as those recorded by Hansen.

GNATHOPHAUSIA ZOEA Willemoes-Suhm

Gnathophansia zoea WILLIMOES-SUHM, *in* Thomson, 1873, p. 401, fig. 6.
Gnathophausia zoea WILLEMOES-SUHM, 1875, p. 32, pl. 9, figs. 2–15.—FAXON, 1896, p. 164c.—ORTMANN, 1906, p. 42, pl. 2, figs. 2a, b.—HANSEN, 1910, p. 17.— FOWLER, 1912, p. 539.—STEPHENSEN, 1933, p. 8.
Gnathophausia willemoesii G. O. SARS, 1884, p. 6; 1885, p. 38, pl. 5, figs. 1–6.— FAXON, 1895, p. 215, pl. K, fig. 1.
Gnathophausia sarsi WOOD-MASON and ALCOCK, 1891a, p. 187.
Gnathophausia cristata ILLIG, 1906b, p. 319, fig. 1.
Gnathophausia willemoesia BOONE, 1930, p. 192.

Occurrence.—EAST COAST OF NORTH AMERICA: *Albatross* stations 2038, 1 female, 92 mm.; 2072, 1 male, 94 mm.; 2083, 1 specimen, 65 mm.; 2094, 1 female, 82 mm.; 2105, 1 male, 82 mm.; 2117 2 specimens, 25–40 mm.; 2182, 1 specimen, 40 mm.; 2192, 1 female, 90 mm.; 2351*, identified by Ortmann as *G. zoea sarsi* (1906); 2528, 1 specimen, 30 mm.; 2723*, identified by Ortmann (1906); 2734, 1 female, 94 mm. GULF OF MEXICO: *Albatross* station 2383*, identified by M. J. Rathbun (unpublished). WEST AMERICAN COAST: *Albatross* stations 3406*, 3420*, 3425*, identified by Faxon (1895); 4641*, identified by Hansen (1912). PHILIPPINE ISLANDS: *Albatross* stations 5219, 1 specimen, 28 mm.; 5498, 1 specimen; 5544, 1 specimen, 25 mm.; 5637, 1 female,

50 mm.; 5638, 1 female, 52 mm.; 5655, 1 female, 97 mm.; 5667, 1 specimen, 55 mm. CHINA SEA, VICINITY OF FORMOSA: *Albatross* station 5320, 1 male, 44 mm. HAWAIIAN ISLANDS: *Albatross* stations 3887* and 4038*, identified by Ortmann (1905) as *G. Willemoesi;* 4005* and 4166*, identified by Ortmann (1905) as *G. sarsi.*

Distribution.—The specimens here recorded as having been examined by me fall into two geographical regions, the waters of the east coast of North America and the waters around the Philippine Islands. The species has been recorded from the east coast of America by Ortmann, but the specimens referred to by Smith (1884) and Verrill (1885) as *Gnathophausia* sp., from 858 to 2,033 fathoms, must, I think, also refer to this species, and actually to the specimens from stations 2038 and 2072 recorded above. Fowler's record (1912) is merely a reference to Ortmann (1906). Off the west coast of the American Continent it has been recorded by Faxon (1895) from near the Galápagos Islands and in the Gulf of Panama, by Ortmann (1906) from off the coast of California, and by Boone (1930) in the Gulf of Panama. It is one of the commonest and most widely distributed species of the genus.

Remarks.—Included in table 5 are measurements of the specimens examined, comparable to table 4 for *G. gigas.* The length is, in all cases, the measurement from the eye to the end of the telson. The rostrum and posterolateral spines are given as percentages of the total length, and in the last column is given the extent to which the pos-

TABLE 5.—*Percentages of length of rostrum and posterolateral spines to total length of specimens in* Gnathophausia zoea

Station No.	Total length in mm.	Rostrum (percent of total length)	Posterolateral spines (percent to total length)	Extent to which posterolateral spines project backward
5655	97	20	11	End of segment 2
2072	94	20	10. 6	Halfway segment 2
2734	94	(1)	10. 6	End of segment 2
2038	92	24	10	End of segment 2
2192	90	23	11	End of segment 2
2094	82	br.	14	End of segment 3
2105	82	1 20	12. 5	End of segment 3
2083	65	36	15	End of segment 3
5667	55	47	18	Halfway segment 4
5638	52	46	13	End of segment 3
5637	50	(1)	17	End of segment 4
2182	40	(1)	27. 5	End of segment 5
2117	40	58	25	End of segment 5
2528	30	47	30	End of segment 5
5219	28	50	30	End of segment 6
2117	25	50	20	End of segment 5
5544	25	(1)	32	End of segment 6

1 Broken.

terolateral spines of the carapace project backward. The specimens are arranged in order of length commencing with the largest.

The table brings out quite clearly the fact that the rostral and posterolateral spines of the carapace gradually shorten, in relation to the total length, as the animal increases in size. I have nothing to add to the elaborate discussion given by Ortmann of age changes in this species, but I present the above table as evidence in support of his conclusions.

GNATHOPHAUSIA ZOEA var. SCAPULARIS Ortmann

Gnathophausia scapularis ORTMANN, 1906, p. 50, pl. 2, figs. 3a-c.
Gnathophausia zoea var. *scapularis* TATTERSALL, 1939a, p. 226, figs. 1, 2.

Occurrence.—CALIFORNIA COAST: *Albatross* station 2992*, identified by Ortmann, types.

Distribution.—Off Baja California and the Indian Ocean.

GNATHOPHAUSIA ELEGANS G. O. Sars

Gnathophausia elegans G. O. SARS, 1884, p. 7; 1885, p. 42, pl. 6, figs. 1–5.—ORTMANN, 1906, p. 51.—HANSEN, 1910, p. 18.—TATTERSALL, 1939a, p. 228.

Occurrence.—JAPAN: *Albatross* stations 4906, 1 female, 34 mm.; 5060, 1 female, 34 mm.; 3697*, identified by Ortmann (1906). PHILIPPINE ISLANDS: *Albatross* stations 5115, 1 female, 36 mm.; 5287, 1 immature, 16 mm.; 5359, 1 male, 52 mm.; 5449, 1 female, 38 mm.; 5463, 1 male, 43 mm.; 5466, 1 male, 46 mm.; 5468, 1 male, 42 mm.; 5471, 5 damaged specimens; 5619, 1 male, 45 mm., 1 female, 34 mm.; 5631, 1 female, 38 mm.

Distribution.—This species is not known from the waters off either the east or west coasts of America. It has a distribution comparable with that of *G. longispina*, confined to the western part of the Pacific Ocean and the Indian Ocean. Like *G. longispina*, too, it is found in the more moderately deep rather than the very deep waters of the area of its distribution. The present material comes from the waters to the south of Japan and the waters around the Philippine Islands. The previous records are from south of the Fiji Islands (Sars), off Japan (Ortmann), the waters of the East Indian Archipelago (Hansen), and the Indian Ocean (Tattersall).

Remarks.—In table 6 measurements are given similar to those for *G. gigas* and *G. zoea* to illustrate the changes in the relative lengths of the rostrum and posterolateral spines of the carapace which accompany growth. In all cases the total length given is measured from the eye to the end of the telson.

This is one of the rarest species of the genus and the present collection is twice as large as the sum of all previous records. It is, therefore, the first material on which any change of proportion with age could be demonstrated. Table 6 shows that this species conforms with the general rule established for other species: that the rostrum and the posterolateral spines of the carapace become relatively shorter with growth. These specimens agree with Ortmann's observations in that the branchiostegal lobe is angular and that the five anterior abdominal somites have flattened median dorsal posterior projections.

TABLE 6.—*Measurements of* Gnathophausia elegans *illustrating changes in relative lengths of rostrum and posterolateral spines of carapace that accompany growth*

Station No.	Total length in mm.	Rostrum (percent of total length)	Postero-lateral spines (percent of total length)	Extent of posterolateral spines
5359	52	25	10.0	End of segment 1
5466	46	30	14.0	Half way segments 2–3
5619	45	37	20.0	Half way segments 3–4
5463	43	33	16.0	End of segment 3
5468	42	33	16.0	End of segment 3
5449	38	34	18.0	End of segment 3
5631	38	37	18.0	End of segment 3
5115	36	42	25.0	End of segment 4
4906	34	(1)	26.0	End of segment 5
5060	34	(1)	21.0	End of segment 3
5919	34	47	26.0	End of segment 5
5287	16	50	37.5	End of segment 6

1 Broken.

Family EUCOPIIDAE Dana

Eucopidae DANA, 1852a, p. 19.

Definitions.—Carapace very large and membranous; second to the fourth pairs of thoracic limbs developed as gnathopods; fifth to the seventh pairs of thoracic limbs very long and slender, subchelate; eighth pair of thoracic limbs developed as normal pereiopods.

Remarks.—Only one genus, *Eucopia*, is included in this subfamily. Four species have been described. Hansen (1910, p. 20) has given a key for their identification.

Genus EUCOPIA Dana, 1852

Chalaraspis WILLEMOES-SUHM, 1874a, p. xiv; 1875, p. 39.
Eucopia DANA, 1852a, p. 19.

EUCOPIA SCULPTICAUDA Faxon

Eucopia sculpticauda FAXON, 1893, p. 218; 1895, p. 219, pl. K, figs. 2, 2d; pl. 53, figs. 1–10; 1896, p. 164.
Eucopia intermedia HANSEN, 1905a, p. 5, figs. 2–3.
Eucopia australis (pars) G. O. SARS, 1884, p. 10; 1885, p. 55, pls. 9, 10.

Occurrence.—EAST COAST OF NORTH AMERICA: *Albatross* stations 2083, 1 specimen; 2094, 1 specimen. WEST AMERICAN COAST: *Alba-*

tross station 3413*, identified by Faxon (1895) (cotype); material identified by Hansen (1912) was taken at *Albatross* stations 4648*, 4657*, 4664*, 4667*, 4676*, 4715*, 4724*. HAWAIIAN ISLANDS: *Albatross* stations 4005*, 4144*, identified by Ortmann (1905).

Distribution.—This species has hitherto only once been recorded from the deep water off the Atlantic coast of North America, namely, by Faxon (1896), who recorded one specimen from 968 fathoms in the Caribbean Sea area. I suspect that the *"Lophogaster"* with a bathymetrical range of 1,022 to 2,949 fathoms mentioned by Smith (1884) and Verrill (1885) really refers to this species and probably to the actual specimens here recorded. On the Pacific coast of America this species has been recorded from the Gulf of Panama by Faxon (1893 and 1895).

EUCOPIA AUSTRALIS Dana

Eucopia australis DANA, 1852a, p. 28; 1852b, p. 609; 1855, pl. 40, figs. 10*a–m.*— FAXON, 1895, p. 218.—ORTMANN, 1906, p. 53.

Occurrence.—WEST AMERICAN COAST: Material was identified by Faxon (1895) from *Albatross* dredging station 3406* and hydrographic station H2627*; Ortmann (1906) identified material from *Albatross* station 3308*, 3604*, 4397*, 4403*. Off KAMCHATKA: 3783*, identified by Ortmann (1906). ALASKA: *Albatross* station 4793*, identified by Rathbun (unpublished). EAST COAST OF AMERICA: *Albatross* station 2751*, identified by Ortmann (1906). JAPAN: *Albatross* station 3696*, identified by Ortmann (1906).

Distribution.—Northern, tropical, and southern Atlantic, Antarctic, Indian Ocean, East Indian Archipelago, central and northern Pacific.

Remarks.—Many of the above records are from American waters. Hansen (1912) has suggested that the specimens recorded by Ortmann are probably *E. major* or an undescribed species, but that it cannot be *E. australis*, which is an Antarctic species. The same remarks also probably apply to Faxon's records of *E. australis* from off the west coast of America. The material in the Museum collection should be reexamined.

EUCOPIA MAJOR Hansen

Eucopia major HANSEN, 1910, p. 21, pl. 1, figs. 4*a, b.*

Occurrence.—BERING SEA: *Albatross* station 3603, 1 specimen. JAPAN: *Albatross* stations 4953, 3 specimens; 4954, 4 specimens. WEST COAST OF SOUTH AMERICA: *Albatross* stations 4645*, 4651*, identified by Hansen (1912).

Distribution.—These specimens are from the western part of the Pacific Ocean off Japan and from the Bering Sea. Hansen (1912) recorded the species off the west coast of South America. It is not known from the deep water off either coast of North America, unless some of the material recorded as *E. australis* should prove on reexamination to belong to this species.

EUCOPIA UNGUICULATA (Willemoes-Suhm)

Chalaraspis unguiculata WILLEMOES-SUHM, 1875, p. 40.
Eucopia australis (pars) G. O. SARS, 1884, p. 10; 1885, p. 55, pls. 9, 10.
Eucopia unguiculata HANSEN, 1905b, p. 3; 1910, p. 20, pl. 1, figs. 3a, b.—WATERMAN ET AL., 1939, p. 266, fig. 4d.—STEPHENSEN, 1933, p. 9.
Eucopia biunguiculata LEAVITT, 1938, p. 384 *(lapsus calami)*.

Occurrence.—EAST COAST OF NORTH AMERICA: *Albatross* stations 2083, 1 specimen; 2427, 3 specimens; 2535, 7 specimens; 2709, 1 specimen. EAST COAST OF THE UNITED STATES: *Fish Hawk* station 1123, latitude 39°59'45'' N., longitude 68°54' W., 787 fathoms, August 26, 1882, 1 specimen; *Albatross* stations 2034, 2 specimens; 2036, 1 specimen; 2039, 1 specimen; 2044, 1 specimen; 2094, 1 specimen; 2098, 1 specimen; 2099, 2 specimens; 2101, 2 specimens; 2103, 1 specimen; 2104, 1 specimen; 2149, 2 specimens; 2190, 2 specimens; 2203, 1 specimen; 2215, 1 specimen; 2226, 1 specimen; 2235, 1 specimen; 2674, 1 specimen; 2715, 1 specimen; 2716, 1 specimen; 2728, 1 specimen; *Bache station* 10166, off South Carolina, latitude 32°33' N., longitude 72°14' W., 1,100-0 m., January 30, 1914, 1 specimen. CALIFORNIA: *Albatross* station 4307, 1 specimen; 4352, 1 specimen, 4380, 3 specimens; 4383*, identified by Ortmann (1906); 4389, 4 specimens; 4390, 2 specimens; 4393, 1 specimen; 4400, 1 specimen; 4401, 1 specimen; 4406, 1 specimen; 4415, 1 specimen; 4428, 4 specimens; 4429, 1 specimen; 4528, 1 specimen. BERING SEA: *Albatross* stations 3325, 1 specimen; 3327, 1 specimen; 3603, 1 specimen; 4765, 9 specimens; 4766, 11 specimens; 4767, 3 specimens; 4780, 1 specimen; 4785, 3 specimens; 4793, 1 specimen. WEST COAST OF CANADA: *Albatross* stations 4759, 11 specimens; 4760, 16 specimens. SEA OF OKHOTSK: *Albatross* station 4800, 12 specimens. PHILIPPINE ISLANDS: *Albatross* station 5544, 1 specimen. WEST COAST OF SOUTH AMERICA: Hansen (1912) identified specimens from *Albatross* stations 4646*, 4650*, 4652*, 4655*, 4664*, 4668*, 4671*, 4672*, 4676*, 4679*, 4716*.

Distribution.—The long list of records of this species shows that it is an abundant and widely distributed species in the deep water off both coasts of North America and in the Japanese and neighboring seas. It has been recorded from the eastern coast of America also by Tattersall (1926), Leavitt (1938), and Waterman et al. (1939), and from the coast of California also by Ortmann (1906). Faxon (1895) records it from the Gulf of Panama.

Suborder MYSIDA

Carapace generally small, its posterior part generally leaving one or more of the thoracic somites exposed; second pair of thoracic limbs modified as gnathopods; no branchiae on any of the thoracic limbs; oöstegites of the female sometimes seven pairs but mostly only two or three pairs; pleopods in the female generally rudimentary and not natatory; pleopods of the male sometimes biramous and natatory, more often one or more pairs modified as accessory copulatory organs.

Family PETALOPHTHALMIDAE Czerniavsky

Petalophthalmidae CZERNIAVSKY, 1882a, p. 56.

Maxillule without palp; first thoracic limbs without exopod; second thoracic limbs with a lamellalike expansion of the merus; penultimate joint of the endopodites of the third to the eighth thoracic limbs not jointed; seven pairs of oöstegites; pleopods of the female slender, biramous or uniramous; pleopods of the male robust, biramous, natatory; no statocyst on the inner uropods.

Four genera have been referred to this family, *Ceratomysis*, *Hansenomysis*, *Petalophthalmus*, and *Scolophthalmus*, of which the first three are represented in the National Museum collection.

Genus PETALOPHTHALMUS Willemoes-Suhm

Petalophthalmus WILLEMOES-SUHM, 1874a, p. xiv; 1875, p. 40.

PETALOPHTHALMUS ARMIGER Willemoes-Suhm

FIGURES 3, 4

Petalophthalmus armiger WILLEMOES-SUHM, 1875, p. 44, pl. 7.—G. O. SARS, 1884, p. 34; 1885, p. 174, pl. 32, figs. 1–9.—FAXON, 1895, p. 221; 1896, p. 164.—HOLT and TATTERSALL, 1906b, p. 22.—TATTERSALL, 1911, p. 25; 1925, p. 4, pl. 1, figs. 1–3; 1939a, p. 229.—HANSEN, 1927, p. 22, pl. 1, fig. 6a.
Petalophthalmus pacificus FAXON, 1893, p. 218; 1895, p. 223, pl. 54, figs. 1–1e.—ORTMANN, 1905, p. 971.

Occurrence.—CARIBBEAN SEA: *Albatross* station 2140, 2 adult females, 36 mm. BERING SEA: *Albatross* station 3308, 1 adult male, 48 mm. CALIFORNIA: *Albatross* stations 4390, 1 female, 50 mm.; 4544, 1 female, 42 mm.

Distribution.—Tropical Atlantic, 2,500 fathoms (*Challenger*); Gulf of Mexico, 955 fathoms (Faxon); west coast of Ireland, 900 to 1,200 fathoms (Holt and Tattersall, and Tattersall); off the coast of Morocco, 1,590 meters (Hansen) ; off South Africa, 500 fathoms (Tattersall) ; Gulf of Aden, 1,270 meters (Tattersall) ; Gulf of Panama, 700 fathoms (Faxon) ; off Hawaii, 762 to 1,000 fathoms (Ortmann). The present material comes from the Caribbean Sea, from off the coasts of California, and from the Bering Sea. The latter record extends the geographical range of the species very considerably. The species is bathypelagic rather than bottom living, and most of the specimens already recorded were taken in nets and trawls working in deep water but above the bottom. Younger specimens are, as a rule, found in lesser depths than older ones.

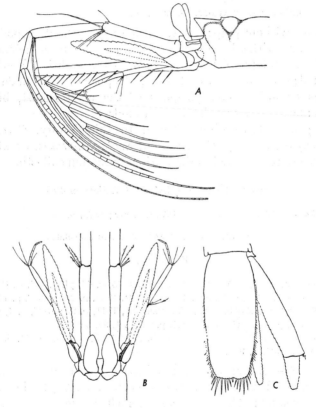

FIGURE 3.—*Petalophthalmus armiger* Willemoes-Suhm: *a*, Lateral view of anterior end to show carapace, rostrum, eye, antennule, antennal scale, and mandibular palp; *b*, dorsal view of anterior end to show rostral plate, eyes, and antennal scale; *c*, telson and uropods.

Remarks.—These five specimens came from three widely separated geographical regions—the Caribbean Sea, off the coast of California, and the Bering Sea—yet I can find no valid differences between the specimens which could be regarded as of specific value, unless it be in the pleopods, to be discussed later. I regard all the specimens as belonging to one species, the genotype.

In the female specimens the outer flagellum of the antennule is thinner than the inner, but in the male the basal portion of this flagellum is considerably thickened and is thicker than the inner flagellum. It does not, however, assume the excessively stout appearance of the outer flagellum in *Hansenomysis* and *Ceratomysis*.

The flagellum of the antenna in the female is about the same length as the last joint of its peduncle and is divided into from 6 to 8 joints, which are all cylindrical in shape and longer than broad. The flagellum is, in fact, as described by Faxon in *P. armiger* and *P. pacificus* and by me in *P. armiger*. In the male, however, it is considerably longer, being more than twice as long as its peduncle, and is, moreover, multiarticulate; that is, it is composed of a large number of joints, and these joints are all short joints scarcely as long as broad. There is a group of very long and very delicate richly plumose setae arising from the distal end of the peduncle at the base of the flagellum.

The mouth parts of *Petalophthalmus* have never been investigated. I dissected these appendages from a female and figure them herewith. They present no very unusual features, but are constructed on the same general plan as in the Mysidacea, with minor modifications to be described below.

In the right mandible (fig. 4, *a*) the cutting edge consists of a single chitinous ridge with one broad terminal tooth and a smaller one behind it. The lacinia mobilis is present but reduced and beside it is a short stout rodlike spine. The spine row is absent. The molar process is well developed with three chitinous ridges separated by somewhat deep grooves. In the left mandible (fig. 4, *b*) the cutting edge is composed of two strong chitinous ridges with a narrow deep groove between them. Each ridge has two bluntly pointed teeth at the free end. The lacinia mobilis and rodlike spine are absent but there is a single curved spine, which represents the spine row. The molar process resembles that of the right side. The mandibles, therefore, differ mainly from those of typical Mysidacea in the reduction or absence of the lacinia mobilis and the spine row, and, in these respects, would appear to be specialized, doubtless in correlation with the special development of the mandibular palp.

The maxillule (fig. 4, *c*) is built on the typical mysidacean plan, with lobes from the first and third joints.

The maxilla (fig. 4, *d*) has the usual lobes from the second and third joints but on the whole they are smaller than is usual in the Mysida. The lobe from the second joint is simple and appears to lack entirely the posterior setiferous expansion with its setose margin such as is figured for *Praunus flexuosus* by Hansen (*Mysis flexuosa*, 1925, pl. vi, fig. 1b). The division of the lobe from the third joint into two parts is barely indicated. The second joint of the endopod

is long and narrow, about three times as long as broad. The exopod is likewise rather long and narrow compared with other members of the group Mysida.

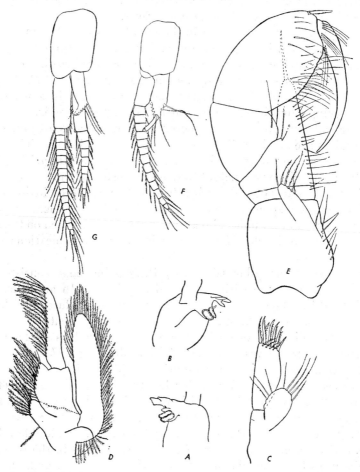

FIGURE 4.—*Petalophthalmus armiger* Willemoes-Suhm: *a*, Right mandible, × 24⅘; *b*, left mandible, × 24⅘; *c*, maxillule, × 24⅘; *d*, maxilla, × 24⅘; *e*, endopod of first thoracic limb, × 24⅘; *f*, first pleopod of male; × 10⅖; *g*, second pleopod of male, × 10⅖.

The first thoracic limb (fig. 4, *e*) (maxilliped) has a small but distinct gnathobasic lobe on the second joint and the large lobe from the fourth joint appears to be more pointed and narrower than is figured by Sars (1885), and terminates in a single strong spine. There is a well-developed epipodite present on this appendage. Sars (1885) stated that it was absent.

I have nothing to add to the existing descriptions of the remaining thoracic appendages, except to note that the last thoracic limb of the male has a well-developed genital appendix of the normal mysidacean type. This does not appear to have been noted in *Petalophthalmus* previously, though it is present in *Hansenomysis*.

The pleopods of the female are all uniramous and conform to the figure given by Faxon (1895). In the male, however, all the pleopods are biramous and agree closely with those of the male of *Hansenomysis fyllae*, figured by Hansen (1908a, fig. 4). I give herewith figures of the pleopods of the male (figs. 4, *f* to 4 *g*). The pleopods of the female consist of a sympod of one joint and an endopod which appears to be 2-jointed, a long basal joint and a short terminal joint. The exopod is absent. In the pleopods of the male the sympod is greatly enlarged compared with that of the female. In the first pleopod of the male the endopod is rather similar to the endopod of the female pleopods except that the terminal joint is more elongate. The exopod is a long appendage with the basal part undivided and the terminal portion composed of about 19 joints. In the remaining pleopods of the male the exopod is slightly longer than the endopod and is similar to the exopod of the first pleopod. The endopods have the terminal part divided into about 10 joints. In the endopods of the male pleopods the form of the female pleopods can be detected and it appears that the only change is in the small terminal portion of the female pleopod. This remains as a single joint in the first pleopod of the male but becomes greatly elongated and subdivided into 10 joints in the second to the fifth pleopods of the male.

This condition of the pleopods of the male in the genus *Petalophthalmus* has not previously been noted and, as the specimen from which it is described came from the Bering Sea, a new geographical record, and one far from the other known localities for the species, it might at first be supposed that we are dealing with a new species. I do not accept this interpretation of the facts for two reasons. In the first place, the male specimen agrees in every other detail with the females from California and the Caribbean Sea except for the pleopods. In the second place, I do not think that a fully adult male specimen of the genus has hitherto ever been seen. The *Challenger* specimen measured 40 mm., it is true, but it appeared to have lacked the secondary sexual characters of a male, namely, the thickened outer flagellum of the antennule, the multiarticulate flagellum of the antenna, and the genital appendix of the eighth thoracic limbs. The present specimen measures 48 mm. and has all the above criteria of the adult male. I interpret the matter thus: that Sars' specimen was immature, and that the condition of the pleopods of the specimen must, therefore, be regarded as that of immaturity. The pleopods of the *Challenger* specimen differ from those here described in the narrowness of the sympod, in the unjointed condition of the exopod, and in the unjointed condition of the terminal part of the endopod. If I am right in my interpretation of the facts it is evident that the fully developed condition of the pleopods in the male comes very late and is coincident with the attainment of sexual maturity.

There now arises the question of the status of *Petalophthalmus pacificus* Faxon. I have already shown (1925) that this species agrees with *P. armiger* in every character except that of the pleopods, and that the other points of difference pointed out by Faxon disappear on examination of the *Challenger* type. The pleopods of *P. pacificus* differ from those of the *Challenger* specimen of *P. armiger* only in the much more rudimentary condition of the exopod, virtually absent in the first pleopod and appearing as a very small rudiment on the remaining pleopods. Apart from the type only one other specimen has been referred to *P. pacificus*, that recorded from Hawaii by Ortmann (1905). The type specimen measured 31 mm., but Ortmann gives no size for his specimen. Hansen (1927) suggested that the differences between the pleopods of *P. pacificus* and *P. armiger* were due to the immature state of Faxon's specimens. From what has emerged above from the study of a really adult male there is considerable evidence to show that Hansen's suggestion is correct. If the *Challenger* specimen is immature at 40 mm. a specimen at 31 mm. would obviously be still more immature. I think there can be no doubt that *P. pacificus* was founded on a very young male specimen of *P. armiger*, in which the secondary sexual characters of the pleopods had hardly begun to manifest themselves. I have therefore united Faxon's species with *P. armiger* on these grounds.

The telson of these specimens has from 40 to 50 spines on each lateral margin and five large barbed spines on each side of the slightly emarginate apex with a single median spine between the two series. Between the central spine and the inner spine of the lateral series at the apex there are five small spinules. The telson shows variation in its armature correlated with age. I have examined two small specimens taken off the west coast of Ireland, measuring 14 and 15 mm., in which the number of spines on the lateral margins is only 10 and 13 respectively. The number of spines on the lateral margins increases as growth proceeds. So does the number of spines at the apex. In the smaller of the above mentioned specimens there are only three spines on each half of the apex and the number of spinules on each side of the central spine is only three.

PETALOPHTHALMUS OCULATUS Illig

FIGURE 5

Petalophthalmus oculatus ILLIG, 1906a, p. 194, fig. 1; 1930, p. 411, figs. 20, 21.—
 TATTERSALL, 1937, p. 1; 1939a, p. 229, fig. 3.

Occurrence.—PUERTO RICO: Johnson-Smithsonian expedition station 99, series number 573, latitude 18°40′ N., longitude 64°51′ W., 220 fathoms, March 3, 1933, 1 adult male, 14 mm.; 1 adult female, 15 mm.; 1 immature female, 10 mm.

Distribution.—This species has been recorded from the Gulf of Aden (Illig) and the Indian Ocean (Tattersall). The occurrence of the species in the Caribbean Sea is therefore a matter of great interest from the point of view of geographical distribution.

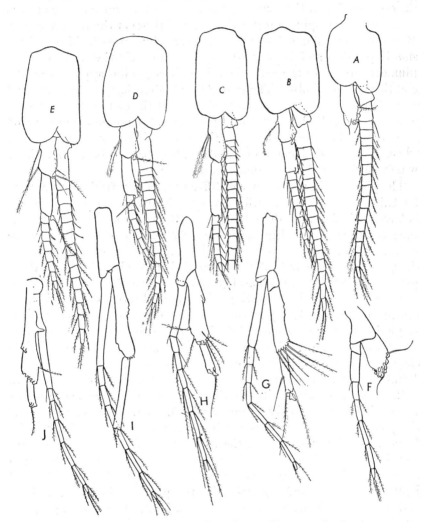

FIGURE 5.—*Petalophthalmus oculatus* Illig: *a-e,* First to fifth pleopods of male, × 33; *f-j,* first to fifth pleopods of female, × 33.

Remarks.—I have already recorded (1937) these specimens, and I now add the following notes on them. On the whole they agree very well with Illig's description and figures except for the pleopods. The carapace leaves only the last two thoracic somites completely free, not three as in Illig's figure. The eyes are somewhat differently shaped. The stalk is not so long as Illig shows and the corneal portion is more expanded. The flagellum of the antenna has four or five joints and is apparently similar in both male and female. The telson has 12 to 14 spines on each lateral margin. At each corner of the slightly emarginate apex are three long spines, each armed with small spinules, the center spine of the three the longest. In the center of the apex is a single median spine, shorter than any of those at the lateral angles. Between the median spine and the lateral spines at each side are three small spinules, and between the spinules are a series of eight long plumose setae. In the male there is a short genital appendix on the eighth thoracic limbs. The first thoracic limb has a well-developed epipodite as in *P. armiger*. Illig states that the endopods of the posterior thoracic limbs have the expanded basal portion composed of two joints. I am unable to detect this feature in the present specimen, where the exopods have the normal single expanded basal joint from which the flagellalike part takes origin.

The pleopods in my specimens differ profoundly from those figured by Illig for the female. Illig gives no description of the pleopods, but from his figure of the adult female the pleopods in this sex conform to the type found in the female of *P. armiger;* that is, they are uniramous and composed of three joints. From a consideration of the pleopods of the male of *P. armiger* it is possible to interpret these pleopods as consisting of a basal sympod and an endopod of two joints. In the adult female in the National Museum collection all the pleopods are biramous (fig. 5, *f–j*). In pleopod 1 the endopod consists of a single joint and the exopod of six joints. In the remaining pleopods the endopod has two joints and the exopod seven to nine joints. The exopods are not flagellalike, the joints being long, slender, and cylindrical in form. The exopod in all cases is longer than the endopod.

In the male specimen all the pleopods are again biramous and the exopod is longer than the endopod (fig. 5, *a–e*). The sympod of all the pleopods of the male is much stouter and broader than in the female. In the first pleopod the endopod consists of one joint only and the exopod of about 16 joints. In the remaining pleopods of the male the endopod is composed of nine joints and the exopod of 16 joints. The exopods are flagellalike, the joints all being quite short and stout with the exception of the basal joint. In the endopods the two basal joints are exactly as in the female pleopods and the remaining joints form a flagellalike termination of seven joints added to the normal endopod of the female. Although Illig had a male specimen of his species he makes no special mention of the structure of the pleopods. The structure of the pleopods is the one point which makes the reference of these specimens to *P. oculatus* doubtful. Illig does not mention the pleopods in his type beyond the general statement that they are the same as those in *P. armiger*, and it is inconceivable that he should have overlooked the biramous nature of the pleopods in the female unless the exopods, which are slender and very delicate, were broken off in his specimens. This is what I assume, for the moment, to have happened. The other characters of my specimens are so similar to those of *P. oculatus* that I hesitate to institute a new species on characters which may possibly be due to injury to the type specimens. Further material must be awaited before the matter can be satisfactorily cleared up.

Genus HANSENOMYSIS Stebbing

Arctomysis HANSEN, 1887, p. 210.
Hansenomysis STEBBING, 1893, p. 268.

HANSENOMYSIS FYLLAE (Hansen)

Arctomysis fyllae HANSEN, 1887, p. 210, pl. 7, figs. 5–51.
Hansenomysis fyllae HANSEN, 1908a, p. 96, pl. 4, figs. 4a–k.—TATTERSALL, 1911b, p. 25.

Occurrence.—EAST COAST OF THE UNITED STATES: *Albatross* station 2186, 1 adult female with young in the brood pouch, 18 mm.

Distribution.—This is the first record of this species from the waters of eastern America. It is known from Greenland, Iceland, and the Atlantic slope of the west of Ireland in 80 to 795 fathoms.

Genus SCOLOPHTHALMUS Faxon

Scolophthalmus FAXON, 1893, p. 219.

The only species of this genus so far found in American waters is *Scolophthalmus lucifugus* Faxon.

SCOLOPHTHALMUS LUCIFUGUS Faxon

Synonymy and distribution records of this species will be found on page 243.

Genus CERATOMYSIS Faxon

Ceratomysis FAXON, 1893, p. 220.

CERATOMYSIS SPINOSA Faxon

Ceratomysis spinosa FAXON, 1893, p. 220; 1895, p. 228, pl. 55, fig. 2; pl. 56.

Occurrence.—WEST COAST OF NORTH AMERICA: *Albatross* station 2859, 1 male, 30 mm. JAPAN: *Albatross* stations 4915, 1 female, 28 mm.; 5050, 1 female, 28 mm.; 5082, 1 male, 35 mm.

Distribution.—*C. spinosa* was known previously only from the type specimen from 782 fathoms off the Gulf of Panama. The specimens here recorded are from deep water at three points off the coasts of Japan and from deep water off the coast of British Columbia. The species is thus widely distributed in the deep waters of the Pacific Ocean. *C. egregia* is also a Pacific species from waters of the East Indian Archipelago.

Remarks.—These specimens agree very closely with Faxon's description and figures. The number of spines among the setae of the antennal scale varies from 8 to 10. In the male the basal portion of the outer flagellum of the antennule (14 joints) is very considerably thickened, and beyond it is a normal flagellum of 24 joints. From the basal joint of the thickened flagellum on the right side is a dense tuft of delicate plumose setae. It was not present on the left side, but it may have been rubbed off.

The immature male from Station 2859 has the large dorsal spine of both the first and second abdominal somites bifid, as in *C. egregia*, but otherwise this specimen appears to belong to *C. spinosa*. I could detect no suture on the outer uropod marking off a distal portion. Faxon says there is no suture in *C. spinosa*, but it is stated to be present in *C. egregia*. The number of spines among the setae of the outer uropod appears to be very variable. In the large adult male there are 10, in the small male and in one of the females 6, and in the other female I could not detect more than 3.

The telson was not complete in any of the specimens, but it agreed with Faxon's figure in that the apex is not shortly truncate as in *C. egregia* but slightly before the apex gradually tapers to an apex armed with two stout spines.

The pleopods of the female are all uniramous and agree with Faxon's figures except that neither of the fifth pairs had a lateral branch. I think that the biramous fifth pleopod on one side only of the type must be regarded as an abnormality. The pleopods of the male agree in essentials with those in *Hansenomysis*, but the exopods are longer and more slender than in that genus.

C. spinosa is closely allied to *C. egregia*, but, according to Hansen's description and figures (1910, p. 21, pl. 1, figs. 5a–c; pl. 2, figs. 1a–d), the latter species is to be distinguished by the truncate apex to the telson and the suture on the outer uropod. The other characters pointed out by Hansen as separating the two species were the number of spines on the antennal scale and uropods and the bifid character of the dorsal spine on both the first and second abdominal somites. The latter character cannot be regarded as anything more than a casual variation in the light of the small male specimen in this collection. The number of spines on the scale and outer uropod, particularly the latter, would also seem to be subject to considerable variation. The two species are very closely allied and more material of *C. egregia* is necessary to determine their exact relationship.

Family MYSIDAE Dana

Mysidae DANA, 1852b, p. 636.

Maxillule without palp; first thoracic limbs as a rule with a well-developed exopodite; second thoracic limbs without a lamellalike expansion of the merus; propodus or carpopropodus of the endopods of the third to the eighth thoracic limbs as a rule divided into a number of subjoints; generally two or three, rarely seven, pairs of oöstegites; pleopods of the female rudimentary, rarely biramous, generally consisting of a small unjointed plate; pleopods of the male either well-developed, biramous, natatory appendages, or one or more pairs reduced as in the female, and one or more pairs secondarily modified as accessory sexual appendages; statocyst on the inner uropods.

Hansen in his survey of the crustacean limbs has shown that in the Mysidae the carpal joint of the endopods of the thoracic limbs is distinct in some forms and the propodal joint alone divided into subjoints, or in other species, the carpus and propodus are fused and the fused joints divided into subjoints.

The family is divided into six subfamilies to which Hansen (1910, p. 11) has provided a useful key. Four of these subfamilies are represented in this collection, the subfamilies Rhopalophthalminae and Mysidellinae being absent.

Subfamily BOREOMYSINAE

Seven pairs of oöstegites in the female; labrum broader than long, without frontal process; endopods of the third to the eighth thoracic limbs with the carpus distinct and the propodus divided into two or three subjoints; pleopods of the male well developed, biramous; exopod of the second and third pairs elongated; exopod of the uropods with the proximal part of the outer margin naked, and generally with one or two spines and a transverse rudimentary articulation at the end of the naked part; telson distally cleft, cleft armed with teeth.

Only one genus, *Boreomysis*, is included in this subfamily. About 20 species have been described, of which 10 are listed below.

Genus BOREOMYSIS G. O. Sars

Boreomysis G. O. SARS, 1869, p. 330.
Petalophthalmus (pars) WILLEMOES-SUHM, 1874a, p. xv.
Arctomysis CZERNIAVSKY, 1882a, pp. 61, 69; 1887, p. 6.
Pseudanchialus CAULLERY, 1896, p. 368.

I have examined the type specimen of *Pseudanchialus megalolepis* Caullery in the Paris Museum and find that it is a specimen of *Boreomysis tridens* G. O. Sars. *Pseudanchialus* therefore becomes a straight synonym of *Boreomysis*.

BOREOMYSIS INERMIS (Willemoes-Suhm)

Petalophthalmus inermis WILLEMOES-SUHM, 1874a, p. xv; 1876a, p. 575.
Petalophthalmus armiger WILLEMOES-SUHM, 1875 (female), p. 41, pl. 7, figs. 1, 3–14.
Boreomysis scyphops G. O. SARS, 1884, p. 34; 1885, p. 178, pl. 32, figs. 10–20.—CALMAN, 1901, p. 23.
Boreomysis suhmi FAXON, 1893, p. 218, footnote.
Boreomysis distinguenda HANSEN, 1908a, p. 100, fig. 2a-b.—TATTERSALL, 1913, p. 869.

Occurrence.—WEST COAST OF NORTH AMERICA: *Albatross* stations 2839, 5 specimens; 2860, 13 specimens; 2919, 4 specimens; 2927, 1 speciman; 2928, 1 specimen; 3071, 2 specimens; 3073, 2 specimens; 3074, 4 specimens; 3075, 2 specimens; 3126, 1 specimen; 3342, 16 specimens; 3343, 1 specimen; 3346, 2 specimens; 3348, 12 specimens; 4307, 4 specimens; 4317, 5 specimens; 4334, 2 specimens; 4337, 1 specimen; 4351, 2 specimens; 4353, 1 specimen; 4380, 2 specimens; 4389, 1 specimen; 4400, 1 specimen; 4401; 4 specimens; 4405, 3 specimens; 4407, 3 specimens; 4415, 10 specimens; 4427, 2 specimens; 4428, 1 specimen; 4429, 4 specimens; 4516, 7 specimens; 4536, 4 specimens; 4540, 2 specimens; 4541, 1 specimen. BERING SEA: *Albatross* stations 3307, 6 specimens; 3607, 4 specimens; H3784, 8 specimens; 4781, 1 specimen. SEA OF OKHOTSK: *Albatross* station 5015, 1 specimen.

Distribution.—This species has been recorded by Sars (1885) from three localities in the South Pacific and by Tattersall (1913) from the Weddell Sea. The long list of records here published shows that the species, far from being a southern form, has a very extensive distribution in the deep waters of the Pacific as far north as the Bering Sea and the Sea of Okhotsk. I have carefully examined all these specimens and can find no characters on which they can be separated among themselves or from the published descriptions. The distribution rivals that of other deep-sea species of Mysidacea, especially those belonging to the genera *Gnathophausia* and *Petalophthalmus.*

Remarks.—This species is very closely allied to *B. scyphops* G. O. Sars, but as Hansen (1908a) has pointed out it differs in having the eye more quadrangular in shape, with a thicker marginal rim. These specimens agree with Sars' figure (1885, pl. 32, fig. 13) rather than with Hansen's figure (1908a, p. 100, fig. 2) in that the dorsal rim of the eye cup is not so thick as Hansen represents it. Otherwise there is the closest agreement.

The decision as to which name should be applied to this species has been a matter of some difficulty. Willemoes-Suhm (1874a) applied the name *Petalophthalmus inermis* to a mysid from *Challenger* station 147, and it is clear that the specimens so called were afterward identified by Sars as *Boreomysis scyphops*. Willemoes-Suhm also described the female of this species as the female of *Petalophthalmus armiger* (1875), and Faxon (1893), recognizing that the supposed females of *P. armiger* were in reality specimens of *Boreomysis*, suggested the name *Boreomysis suhmi* for the species. Hansen (1908a) arrived at the conclusion that the *Challenger* specimens attributed to *B. scyphops* were in reality different from that species and he renamed them *B. distinguenda*, without reference, apparently, to the history of the species. It is true that Willemoes-Suhm did not publish any description of the species to which he gave the name *Petalophthalmus inermis*, and it would, perhaps, be legitimate to ignore his name as a nomen nudum. In my view, however, since it is possible to identify

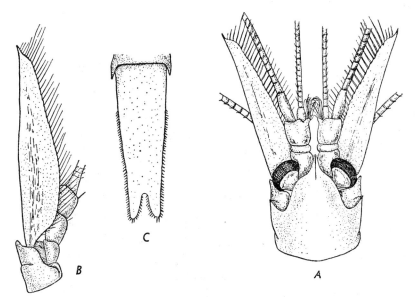

FIGURE 6.—*Boreomysis nobilis* G. O. Sars: *a*, Dorsal view of anterior end; *b*, antennal scale; *c*, telson. (Afer G. O. Sars.)

the specimens to which the name was given definitely with those described and recorded in the *Challenger* report as *B. scyphops*, the name *inermis* should be applied to the species, and, since it is the earliest name it should be given priority over the later names *suhmi* and *distinguenda*. Hansen (1910, p. 26) described a new species of *Boreomysis* as *B. inermis*, and if the specific name *inermis* is used for *B. distinguenda*, Hansen's species will require a new name (see p. 58).

BOREOMYSIS NOBILIS G. O. Sars

FIGURE 6

An American species not represented in the National Museum collection. The species is recorded on page 243.

BOREOMYSIS TRIDENS G. O. Sars

FIGURE 7

Boreomysis tridens G. O. SARS, 1870a, p. 153.—VERRILL, 1882, p. 364; 1884, p. 653; 1885, p. 557.
Pseudanchialus megalolepis CAULLERY, 1896, p. 368, pl. 13.
Boreomysis tricornis G. O. SARS, 1885, p. 183 (*lapsus calami*).

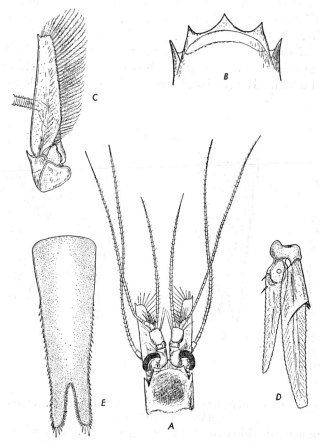

FIGURE 7.—*Boreomysis tridens* G. O. Sars: *a*, Dorsal view of anterior end; *b*, rostral plate; *c*, antennal scale; *d*, uropods, *e*, telson. (After G. O. Sars.)

Occurrence.—EAST COAST OF THE UNITED STATES: *Fish Hawk* stations 952, latitude 39°55′ N., longitude 70°28′ W., 396 fathoms, August 23, 1881, 15 specimens; 994, latitude 39°40′ N., longitude 71°30′ W., 368 fathoms, September 8, 1881, 3 males, 3 females; 997, latitude 39°42′ N., longitude 71°32′ W., 335 fathoms, September 8, 1881, 1 male, 1 female; 1029, latitude 39°57′6″ N., longitude 69°16′ W., 458 fathoms, September 14, 1881, 4 males, 4 females, 4 immature; 1093, latitude 39°56′ N., longitude 69°45′ W., 349 fathoms, August 11, 1882, 1 immature; 1143, latitude 39°29′ N., longitude 72°1′ W., 452 fathoms, September 8, 1882, 1 male; 1122* (identified by S. I. Smith); *Albatross* stations 2046, 39 specimens, mostly immature; 2213, 5 specimens, immature; 2230, 1 male; 2233, 1 male, 1 female; 2237, 1 female. S. I. Smith identified specimens from *Albatross* stations 2171*, 2179*, 2180*, 2201*, 2202*, 2429*, 2546*, 2689*. As far as I can ascertain the records of specimens identified by S. I. Smith have not been published.

Distribution.—This species is quite common off the northeast coast of the United States in depths of 335 to 1,168 fathoms. Its distribution extends across to Norway, the west coast of the British Isles, and to the Bay of Biscay, in the deep and warmer waters of the Atlantic and Arctic Oceans.

Remarks.—The type specimen of *Pseudanchialus megalolepis* Caullery proves on examination to be a specimen of *Boreomysis tridens.* Sars, in the *Challenger* report (1885, p. 183), inadvertently refers to this species as *B. tricornis.* Verrill's records of this species in 1882 and 1884 refer to the specimens from *Fish Hawk* station 1122, which were identified by S. I. Smith. Verrill (1885) records this species as follows: "–B. range, 351–500 fathoms, 1880, 1882, 1883. Common in the trawl wings." The records for 1882 and 1883 refer to specimens from *Albatross* stations 1122, 2171, 2179, and 2180, all identified by S. I. Smith, but I cannot trace the records for 1880. There are no specimens in the material submitted to me for examination nor are there any specimens in the National Museum collections that were collected in that year. Figure 7 shows the salient characters of this species and will help in its identification.

BOREOMYSIS ARCTICA (Krøyer)

FIGURE 8

Mysis arctica KRØYER, 1861, p. 34, pl. 1, fig. 5a–f.
Boreomysis arctica G. O. SARS, 1869, p. 330, 1879a, p. 10, pls. 11–13.—S. I. SMITH, 1881, p. 445.—FOWLER, 1912, p. 540.—STEPHENSEN, 1913, p. 67; 1933, p. 11.— TATTERSALL, 1939b, p. 282.
Arctomysis arctica CZERNIAVSKY, 1887, p. 7.

Occurrence.—EAST COAST OF NORTH AMERICA: *Fish Hawk* stations 952, latitude 39°55′ N., longitude 70°28′ W., 396 fathoms, yellow mud and sand, August 23, 1881, 3, immature; 994, latitude 39°40′ N., longitude 71°30′ W., 368 fathoms, brown mud, September 8, 1881, 1 adult male, 1 immature; 1029, latitude 39°57′6″ N., longitude 69°16′ W., 458 fathoms, yellow mud and sand, September 14, 1881, 1 female; 1093, latitude 39°56′ N., longitude 69°45′ W., 349 fathoms, sand and blue mud, August 11, 1882, 1 immature; S. I. Smith identified specimens from *Fish Hawk* stations 891*, latitude 39°46′ N., longitude 71°10′ W., 6 a. m., October 2, 1880, 310 fathoms, trawl; and 937*, latitude

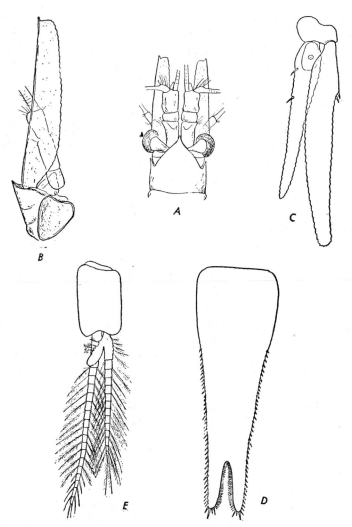

Figure 8.—*Boreomysis arctica* (Kroyer): *a*, Dorsal view of anterior end; *b*, antennal scale; *c*, uropods; *d*, telson; *e*, third pleopod of male. (After G. O. Sars.)

39°49′25″ N., longitude 69°49′ W., 12:45 p. m., August 4, 1881, 516 fathoms; *Albatross* stations: 2046, 25 specimens, mostly immature; 2078, 2 males; 2213, 1 adult female and 7 immature specimens; 2215, 3 immature specimens; 2235, 1 adult female and 1 immature specimen; 2654, 1 adult female. S. I. Smith identified specimens from *Albatross* station 2550*. BERING SEA: *Albatross* station 3307, 1 male and 1 female; 3326, 2 adult females; 3327, 3 males and 4 females, 28 mm.; 3329, 3 males and 3 females; 3330, 2 males and 1 female, 4781, 1 immature female, 19 mm. SEA OF OKHOTSK: *Albatross* station H3710, 2 females. CALIFORNIA: *Albatross* station 4541, 1 immature female.

Distribution.—A widely distributed species in the boreal waters of the Arctic Ocean, extending southward on the eastern slope of the Atlantic to the British Isles, Bay of Biscay, and the Mediterranean, and on the western slope to the deep water off the coasts of New England. All the known Pacific records are listed here.

Remarks.—Smith's original record of this species from the American coast probably refers to the specimens from *Fish Hawk* station 891, which are the only specimens collected in 1880 of which I can find any trace. Smith, however, gives the depth from which his specimens were collected at 500 fathoms, whereas the depth at station 891 was only 310 fathoms. Fowler's note (1912) of this species is based on Smith's record.

The most interesting records in the list are those from the Bering Sea, the Sea of Japan, and the coast of California. The occurrence of this species in the Bering Sea area is perhaps not unexpected, as several Arctic species are known to have penetrated into the northern part of the Pacific as well as into the Atlantic. I could not detect any differences from the typical form in the specimens from this region. The specimens from *Albatross* station 3710, in the Sea of Japan, are doubtfully identified with this species. They are much smaller in size, 16 mm., as against 28 mm. for adult *B. arctica*, and moreover they are badly damaged. As far as I could see they presented no features at variance with *B. arctica*, and they are provisionally recorded as belonging to that species. The single specimen from the California coast, *Albatross* station 4541, is immature but again no special differences from *B. arctica* could be detected. I give a figure (fig. 8) showing the salient characters of this species as a means to its identification.

BOREOMYSIS SIBOGAE Hansen

Boreomysis sibogae HANSEN, 1910, p. 25, pl. 2, fig. 3 a–e.—ILLIG, 1930, p. 414.

Occurrence.—*Albatross* station H3710, 2 females.

Distribution.—Known heretofore only from the waters of the Dutch East Indies (Hansen, 1910) and the Indian Ocean (Illig, 1930) and now from the Sea of Okhotsk. It is probably a bathypelagic rather than a bottom-living form.

Remarks.—The two specimens are very defective but appear to belong to this species. They differ from *B. arctica* in the very much shorter rostral projection and in their smaller size. They were taken in company with both *B. arctica* and *B. rostrata*.

BOREOMYSIS CALIFORNICA Ortmann

FIGURES 9, 10

Boreomysis californica ORTMANN, 1894, p. 106, figs. 4–14.
Boreomysis media HANSEN, 1912, p. 190, pl. 1, figs. 2a–2b.

Description.—The rostral plate (fig. 9, *b*) is considerably produced and has rather prominent shoulders. In lateral view (fig. 9, *a*) it is somewhat upturned. The front margin of the plate is produced in the median line into an acutely pointed rostrum, which, however, does not extend in front of the eyes.

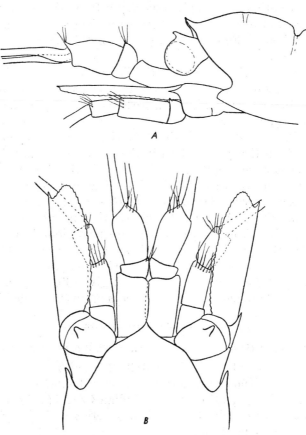

FIGURE 9.—*Boreomysis californica* Ortmann: *a*, Lateral view of anterior end to show eye and rostral plate, × 18; *b*, dorsal view of anterior end to show eye, rostral plate, antennules, antennae, and scale, × 18.

The eyes (figs. 9, *a–b;* 10, *a*) are small to moderate in size, with the cornea scarcely as broad as the distal end of the eye stalk and the pigment light golden-brown. The eye stalk has a well-marked triangular process on the upper surface, which is very prominent in lateral view.

The antennal scale (fig. 10, *b*) extends somewhat beyond the distal end of the antennular peduncle. It is about three times as long as broad, with the outer margin straight and terminating in a strong spine beyond which the apex of the scale barely projects.

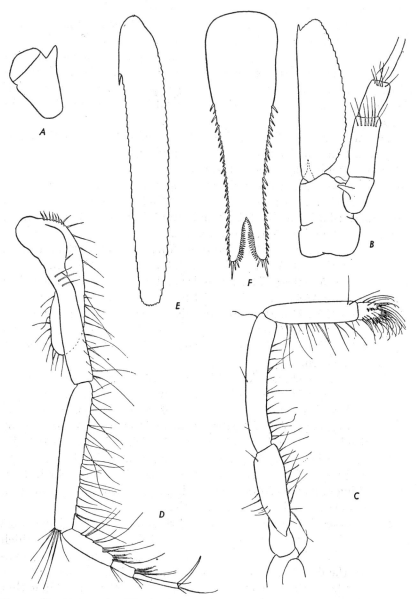

FIGURE 10.—*Boreomysis californica* Ortmann: *a*, Eye in lateral view, × 22½; *b*, antennal scale and peduncle, × 22½; *c*, endopod of second thoracic limb, × 22½; *d*, endopod of third thoracic limb, × 22½; *e*, outer uropod, × 22½; *f*, telson, × 22½.

The telson (fig. 10, f) is about three times as long as broad at its base and the cleft is about one-sixth of the total length. The proximal third of each lateral margin is unarmed. The distal two-thirds of the lateral margins are armed with from 30 to 32 spines, which show a suggestion of an arrangement into short series of one, two, or three smaller spines between larger spines. The larger spines are, however, not very much larger than the smaller spines and the arrangement into series is not nearly so well marked as in *B. rostrata*, where the large spines are considerably larger than the small spines between them and the arrangement into series much more pronounced. Each apical lobe of the telson has three moderately large spines on its border. The cleft is armed with teeth and there is no "dilation" such as is seen in *B. rostrata*.

The outer uropod (fig. 10, e) has the proximal sixth of the outer margin unarmed and terminating in a single spine.

Length of adult specimens 19 mm.

Occurrence.—CALIFORNIA: *Albatross* stations 4406, 3 males and 3 females; 4407, 1 male; 4415, 1 male; 4427, 1 female; 4429, 1 male; 4461, 1 male; 4493, 1 male; 4513, 1 male and 1 female; 4529, 1 immature male; 4536, 1 male; 4541, 1 male and 2 females; 4544, 1 specimen. BRITISH COLUMBIA: *Albatross* station 4759, 1 female. BERING SEA: *Albatross* stations 3307, 2 females: 4763, 3 males and 6 females; 4765, 8 females and 5 males; 4766, 7 females and 4 males; 4775, 2 females; 4785, 1 female; 4793, 5 females and 1 male. SEA OF OKHOTSK: *Albatross* station 4800, 11 males and 9 females, none fully mature. SOUTH OF GUAYMAS, GULF OF CALIFORNIA, types*, identified by A. E. Ortmann (1894). OFF PERU: *Albatross* stations 4652*, 4675*, identified as *B. media* by Hansen.

Distribution.—Ortmann's specimens were collected off the coast of California and Hansen's a little farther to the south off the coasts of South America. The extensive list of records given here shows that the species is widely distributed in the Pacific from latitude 13° S. to latitude 55° N. and from longitude 79° W. to longitude 153° E., off Peru to British Columbia and the Bering Sea. It is a bathypelagic species and most of the specimens here recorded were caught in townets working at 200 to 400 fathoms. Illig has recorded *B. media* from the Indian Ocean and from the Atlantic.

Remarks.—From an examination of these specimens I have come to the conclusion that there is no really valid character by which to separate *B. californica* Ortmann and *B. media* Hansen. A comparison of the figures given herewith with those illustrating *B. media* shows the closest agreement between them and leaves no doubt that the identity of my specimens with *B. media* is complete. Hansen (1910, p. 24) had already dismissed *B. californica* Ortmann as being too inadequately described to be recognizable, so that when, in

1912, he founded the species *B. media,* he made no reference to Ortmann's species nor any attempt to compare the two. It is true that Ortmann's description is very meager, and, in itself, is insufficient to identify his species, but a close examination of his figures reveals very close agreement with Hansen's species. The details of the telson in Ortmann's figure are incomplete, but the general form of the telson, uropods, and antennal scale is the same in the two forms. Ortmann's figure of the anterior end from the lateral aspect agrees very closely with the one I give here, while the dorsal view of the anterior end here given agrees closely with that given by Hansen for *B. media.* It is impossible to point to any character that separates the two supposed species, and I have united them under Ortmann's name, *B. californica.* The species may be recognized by the combination of the characters of the eye, the antennal scale, the telson, and the uropods.

BOREOMYSIS FRAGILIS Hansen

Boreomysis fragilis HANSEN, 1912, p. 191, pl. 1, fig. 3a; pl. 2, fig. 1a.

Occurrence.—OFF PERU: *Albatross* stations 4652*, 4655*, 4676*, 4679* (type), all identified by Hansen.

Distribution.—Eastern Pacific (Hansen, 1912); Indian Ocean (Illig, 1930).

BOREOMYSIS OBTUSATA G. O. Sars

Boreomysis obtusata G. O. SARS, 1884, p. 35; 1885, p. 182, pl. 33, figs. 1–6.— ORTMANN, 1905, p. 971.

Occurrence.—HAWAIIAN ISLANDS: *Albatross* stations 4014*, 4018*, identified by Ortmann (1905).

Distribution.—Pacific Ocean, off Japan (Sars, 1884, 1885); Hawaii (Ortmann, 1905).

BOREOMYSIS MICROPS G. O. Sars

Boreomysis microps G. O. SARS, 1884, p. 35; 1885, p. 184, pl. 33, figs. 7–10.— STEPHENSEN, 1913, p. 67; 1933, p. 11.—WATERMAN et al., 1939, p. 266, fig. 4c.
Boreomysis subpellucida HANSEN, 1905a, p. 8, figs. 5–8.

Occurrence.—EAST COAST OF NORTH AMERICA: *Fish Hawk* stations 952, latitude 39°55′ N., longitude 70°28′ W., 396 fathoms, August 23, 1881, 19 specimens; 994, latitude 39°40′ N., longitude 71°30′ W., 368 fathoms, September 8, 1881, 2 immature; 1093, latitude 39°56′ N., longitude 69°54′ W., 349 fathoms, August 11, 1882, 1 immature; 1122, latitude 40°2′ N., longitude 68°50′ W., 351 fathoms, August 26, 1882, 3 immature; *Albatross* stations 2034, 1 adult female and 1 immature specimen; 2044, 1 male, 1 female, and 1 immature specimen; 2045, 6 immature specimens; 2046, 1 immature specimen; 2047, 1 immature male; 2083, 2 adult females; 2104, 1 immature female; 2190, 2 immature specimens; 2193, 1 adult female and 1 immature specimen; 2195, 1 immature specimen; 2215, 1 immature specimen; 2229, 2 adult females; 2535, 2 adult females; 2428*, identified by S. I. Smith.

Distribution.—The first actual record of this species from the eastern coasts of America is that of the type specimen, which was taken by the *Challenger* south of Nova Scotia in 1,250 fathoms. The species was actually known to S. I. Smith as an American species, for the unrecorded specimens in the National Museum collection from station 2428 were identified by him. It will be seen from the above long list of records that the species is by no means rare in the deeper waters off the eastern American coasts. It frequents deeper water than the other two common species of the genus and it is probably bathypelagic rather than bottom living. Waterman and his colleagues (1939) investigated the bathymetric distribution of this species at various times of the day and night and found that it had a daily vertical migration of 400 meters.

Remarks.—In the bottle containing the specimen from *Fish Hawk* station 1122 there is a label stating that the specimens were "coloured orange." The adult female from *Albatross* station 2034 measures 28 mm. in length, larger than any specimen yet recorded. It differs from the other specimens in that the rostral spine is almost obsolete and the rostral plate has much more prominent shoulders than in more normal specimens. I take these features to be a sign of old age. The characteristic endopod of the second thoracic limbs of this species is present in this specimen.

BOREOMYSIS ROSTRATA Illig ?

Figures 11–13

Boreomysis rostrata Illig, 1906a, p. 196, fig. 2; 1930, p. 414, figs. 22–35.
Boreomysis inermis Hansen, 1910, p. 26, pl. 2, figs. 4a–c.

Occurrence.—Alaska: *Albatross* station 4765, 1 immature male, 16 mm. Japan: *Albatross* stations 3710, 2 adult females, 21 to 22 mm., and 1 immature specimen, 14 mm.; 4909, 1 adult male, 22 mm.; 5063, 4 adult females, 25 mm.

Distribution.—Hansen's specimen of *B. inermis* was taken in the waters of the Dutch East Indies. The specimens which Illig referred to *B. rostrata* were taken in widely separated localities in the Atlantic and Indian Oceans. The type specimen was collected in latitude 30°6′7″ S., longitude 87°50′4″ E., northeast of New Amsterdam. The species is thus at least widely distributed in the western Pacific as far north as the Aleutian Islands, and has an even wider distribution if all the specimens referred to it by Illig really belong to this species.

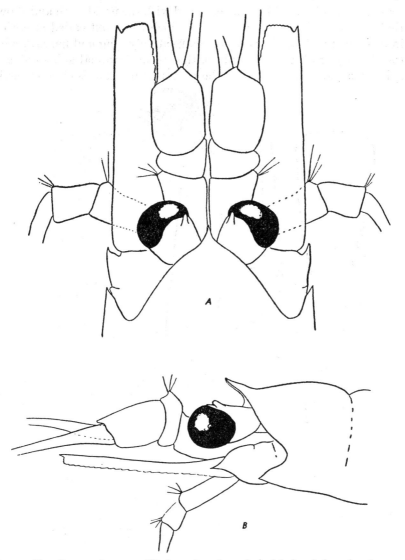

FIGURE 11.—*Boreomysis rostrata* Illig ? : *a*, Anterior end of adult female from dorsal aspect; *b*, anterior end of adult female from lateral aspect.

Remarks.—The determination of these specimens has presented some difficulty. The telson (fig. 12, *c*) is very characteristic. It is comparatively long and narrow, and the spines on the lateral margins are sharply graded and grouped. There are about eight relatively large spines on each lateral margin, between which are to be found groups of much smaller spines, from 4 to 6 in number. At the apex of each terminal lobe there is one conspicuous large spine, inside which are two smaller spines.   The cleft is armed with the usual teeth and shows that peculiar dilation at the base to which Sars first called attention in *B. microps*.   This form of telson, relatively long and narrow, with the sharply graded lateral spines, the strong terminal spine on each apical lobe, and the cleft with the proximal dilation is characteristic

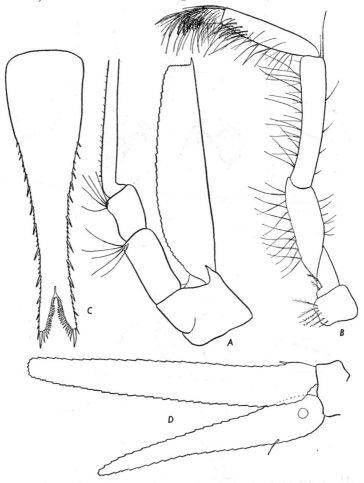

FIGURE 12.—*Boreomysis rostrata* Illig ♀ : *a*, Antennal scale and peduncle, × 19; *b*, endopod of second thoracic limb, × 19; *c*, telson, × 19; *d*, uropod, × 19.

of *B. microps* G. O. Sars, *B. rostrata* Illig, *B. inermis* Hansen, and *B. verrucosa* Tattersall, to the exclusion of all other described species. *B. microps* is distinguished by the curious subchelate character of the endopod of the second thoracic limb and *B. verrucosa* by the tubercles on the carapace.   The two remaining species, *B. rostrata* and *B. inermis*, are extremely closely allied and in my judgment should be united.   They differ from each other mainly in the length of the rostral spine.   In *B. rostrata* it is comparatively long while in *B.*

inermis it is very short. I suggest that this difference is sexual. The type of *B. rostrata* is a female and that of *B. inermis* a male. In the present collection are specimens of both sexes and the male specimens, especially the older ones, agree with Hansen's figures of *B. inermis*. The female specimens have a longer rostral process than the male though in no case is it as long as shown by Illig. Incidentally the rostral plate is relatively longer in young specimens than in adults (figs. 11, *a*, *b*; 13) and appears to undergo progressive reduction with growth. The two species are otherwise in the closest agreement,

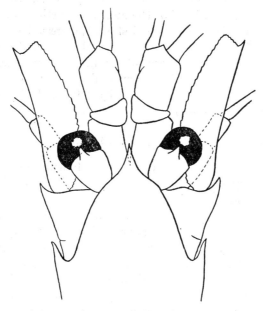

FIGURE 13.—*Boreomysis rostrata* Illig ♀ : Anterior end of young specimen to show the rostral plate, eye, antennular peduncle, and antennal scale and peduncle.

especially in the form and armature of the telson, the very short un-armed portion of the outer margin of the outer uropod (fig. 12, *d*), and in the shape and proportions of the antennal scale (fig. 12, *a*). The question of the identity of the two species is rendered more difficult by the fact that Illig's specimens of *B. rostrata* would appear to include more than one species. The male specimen figured by Illig (1930, figs. 28–35) appears to me to belong to a different species from those representing the female (Illig, 1930, figs. 22–27). No type specimen is indicated and for the purposes of this paper I have regarded the specimens figured by Illig in figures 22 to 27 as the types. I am convinced that my specimens can be referred to *B. inermis* Hansen, and I would record them under that name were it not for the fact that as stated above the specific name *inermis* is preoccupied within the genus. I think it is very probable that some, at least, of the speci-

mens referred to *B. rostrata* by Illig are the same as those here recorded, and I have preferred classifying them under Illig's name to
introducing a new name into literature. I figure the telson, uropods,
antennal scale, and endopod of the second thoracic limb of a large
female specimen (fig. 12, *a-d*), as well as the anterior end of a female
both from the dorsal and lateral aspects (fig. 11, *a, b*). Hansen gave
the specific name *inermis* to his specimens in reference to the very
short unarmed portions of the outer margin of the outer uropod.
Hansen describes it as apparently without spines at the junction of
the unarmed and armed parts. In all my specimens there is a single
spine marking the distal end of the unarmed portion and Illig figures
a similar spine in his specimens. I should suggest that it had become
broken off in Hansen's specimen. It should be noted that there is a
single spine on the inner margin of the inner uropod near the statocyst (fig. 12, *d*). The fully grown males measure 29 mm., a size
considerably in excess of that given by Illig and Hansen for their
species, namely 16 to 18 mm.

Subfamily SIRIELLINAE

Three pairs of oöstegites in the female; labrum much longer than
broad, with a very long frontal process; thoracic limbs with the carpal
joint of the endopods distinct and the propodus either undivided or,
generally, divided by a single articulation and terminating in a brush
of stiff peculiarly serrated setae surrounding the "claw," usually consisting of the dactylus and the real claw, and very strong (except
in the first pair in *Hemisiriella*) ; pleopods of the male well developed,
with biramous pseudobranchiae, exopodites or endopodites or both, of
the third or fourth or both, male pleopods with some of the terminal
setae modified; exopods of the uropods divided by a feeble articulation, the proximal part of the outer margin armed with more or fewer
spines but no setae; telson entire, without distal cleft.

Remarks.—Two genera, *Siriella* and *Hemisiriella*, are included in
this subfamily and both are represented in this collection. The genus
Siriella is enormously abundant in the tropical inshore waters and no
fewer than 14 species and one variety are here listed.

Genus SIRIELLA Dana

Siriella DANA, 1850, p. 130.

SIRIELLA THOMPSONII (H. Milne-Edwards)

Cynthia thompsonii H. MILNE-EDWARDS, 1837, p. 462.
Siriella thompsoni G. O. SARS, 1884, p. 40; 1885, p. 205, pl. 36, figs. 1–24.
Siriella thompsonii HANSEN, 1910, p. 31.—TATTERSALL, 1926, p. 9.

Occurrence.—EAST COAST OF NORTH AMERICA: *Bache*, George Bank,
11 a. m., September 15, 1872, 1 immature female; *Bache* stations 10194,

northeast of the Bahamas, latitude 28°51′ N., longitude 75°13′ W., 600–0 m., February 28, 1914, 10 plus specimens; 10180, off Bermuda, latitude 31°32′ N., longitude 65°14′ W., surface, February 18 to 19, 10 plus specimens; off Marthas Vineyard, latitude 38°25′ N., longitude 72°40′ W., electric light, 1 male; *Albatross*, 75 miles south of Gay Head, surface, 8 p. m., September 20, 1883, 3 females; *Albatross* stations 2096, 1 immature male; 2174, 18 males and 12 females; 2210, 20 males and 9 females; 2569, 3 males, 2 females, and 6 immature specimens; 2585, 1 female; 2728, 1 male and 1 female; 2742, 10 males and 7 females. NORTH ATLANTIC OCEAN: Specimen identified by S. I. Smith, not published; *Grampus*, August 16, 1890, 1 male. WEST INDIES: Johnson-Smithsonian expedition stations 86, series number 495, latitude 19°30′30″ N., longitude 65°14′00″ W., 500 to 3,000 fathoms, February 27, 1933, 10 plus specimens; 98, series number 567, latitude 18°39′30″ N., longitude 64°56′00″ W., 290 to 340 fathoms, March 3, 1933, 1 specimen. WEST COAST OF NORTH AMERICA: *Albatross* stations 4571*, 4576*, identified by Hansen (1912). WEST COAST OF CENTRAL AMERICA: 4615*, 4617*, 4619*, 4635*. WEST COAST OF SOUTH AMERICA: *Albatross* station 4640*; *Albatross* survey stations 16 (H2670), 50 specimens of both sexes, breeding; 28 (H2682), 1 male; U. S. S. *Wachusett*, latitude 29°33′ S., longitude 81°34′ W., surface, Dr. W. Jones collector, August 10, 1887, 6 males and 3 females; Hansen (1912) identified specimens from *Albatross* stations: 4646*, 4648*, 4667*, 4671*, 4677*, 4678*, 4682*, 4683*, 4685*, 4688*, 4692*, 4694*, 4695*, 4696*, 4698*, 4700*, 4702*, 4704*, 4706*, 4709*, 4710*, 4718*, 4720*, 4723*, 4725*, 4727*, 4729*, 4741*. HAWAIIAN ISLANDS: *Albatross* station 4145, 1 male; A. E. Ortmann (1905) identified specimens from *Albatross* stations: 3797*, 3799*, 3801*, 3802*, 3829*, 3867*, 3889*, 3912*, 3926*, 3927*, 3929*, 3930*, 3980*, 4011*, 4086*, 4145*. CALIFORNIA TO HAWAIIAN ISLANDS: Ortmann (1894) identified specimens from *Albatross* survey stations 74* (H2728), 133* (H2788), and 165* (H2820). PHILIPPINE ISLANDS: *Albatross*, Nasugbu Bay Anchorage, Luzon, surface, electric light, 7:30 p. m., January 21, 1908, 2 immature specimens; *Albatross* station 5597, 1 immature specimen.

Distribution.—This species is an oceanic form widely distributed in the tropical Atlantic and Pacific Oceans. It was actually first recorded from American waters by the *Challenger*, which collected it in the North Atlantic Ocean off the American coast and also off the coast of Chile. In 1926 I gave a further list of localities in the western Atlantic between Chesapeake Bay and the Bermudas, all near the American coast. The above list of captures shows that the species is not rare in the oceanic waters off the east coast of America, where it is generally caught at or near the surface at night.

SIRIELLA GRACILIS Dana

Siriella gracilis DANA, 1852b, p. 658 ; 1855, pl. 44, figs. 1a–g, 2a–c.—G. O. SARS, 1884, p. 41 ; 1885, p. 209, pl. 36, figs. 25–28.—HANSEN, 1910, p. 31.

Occurrence.—PHILIPPINE ISLANDS : *Albatross*, Naso Point, Panay, electric light, surface, 7 p. m., February 3, 1908, 1 immature female. WEST COAST OF CENTRAL AND SOUTH AMERICA : *Albatross*, Galápagos Islands to Charles Island*, 1891, identified by A. E. Ortmann (1894) ; H. J. Hansen (1912) identified specimens from *Albatross* stations 4592*, 4607*, 4619*, 4716*, 4720*, 4723*, 4725*, 4729*, 4733*. HAWAIIAN ISLANDS : *Albatross* stations 3867*, 4009*, 4086*, all identified by A. E. Ortmann (1905).

Distribution.—An oceanic surface species widely distributed in the tropical and subtropical parts of the Pacific and Indian Oceans. It is not known from the Atlantic.

SIRIELLA VULGARIS Hansen

? *Siriella suluensis* CZERNIAVSKY, 1882a, p. 108 ; 1887, p. 29.
Siriella vulgaris HANSEN, 1910, p. 34, pl. 3, figs. 2a–k.

Occurrence.—PHILIPPINE ISLANDS : The *Albatross* collected material at several Philippine localities without station numbers, all at the surface, by electric light : Nasugbu Bay Anchorage, January 21, 1908, 19 females, 9 males ; Jolo Anchorage, February 7, 1908, 4 females, 11 males ; Romblon Anchorage, March 25, 1908, 1 female ; Cataingan Bay, Masbate, April 19, 1908, about 200 of both sexes ; Port San Miguel Anchorage, Ticao Island, April 21, 1908, 2 females ; Port Busin Anchorage, Burias Island, April 22, 1908, 4 females ; Santa Cruz Harbor, Marinduque, April 23, 1908, 2 females ; Mansalay Anchorage, Mindoro, June 3, 1908, about 250 of both sexes, 11 specimens parasitized by *Dajus ? siriellus* G. O. Sars ; Looc Bay Anchorage, July 18, 1908, 17 females, 11 males ; Port San Pio Quinto, Camiguin Island, November 10, 1908, 3 females and 1 male ; Port Matalvi Anchorage, November 22, 1908, 5 females, 2 males ; Sablayan Bay Anchorage, Mindoro, December 13, 1908, 11 males, 29 females ; Tara Island Anchorage, December 14, 1908, 2 males, 7 females ; Endeavour Straight, anchorage between Bando and Endeavour Point, December 23, 1908, 1 male, 1 female ; Capulaan Bay, Pagbilao, Chica Island, anchorage, February 23, 1909, 8 males ; Catanduanes Island, Cabugao Bay, June 9, 1909, 1 male, 10 females ; Butauanan Island, June 12, 1909, several hundreds of both sexes ; Mahinog Anchorage, Camiguin Island, 2 males, 3 females ; Opol, Macajalar Bay, Mindanao, 20 males, 8 females ; Talisse Island, East, November 9, 1909, about 200 of both sexes ; the *Albatross* collected several hundreds of both sexes at Jolo Anchorage, March 5, 1908 (no further data) ; additional specimens were taken by the *Albatross* at stations 5233, 1 male ; 5435, 4 males, 4 females ;

5596, 1 male, 1 female. CHINA SEA: Vicinity of Formosa, *Albatross* station 5320, 1 female.

Distribution.—Waters of the Dutch East Indies (Hansen, 1910); India (Tattersall, 1922); Arabian Sea (Colosi, 1924); Hong Kong and Peru (Coifmann, 1937); Queensland and the Barrier Reef (Tattersall, 1928 and 1936b), and the Philippine Islands. It is thus an abundant species in the tropical waters of the western Pacific and Indian Oceans. It is an inshore form, always taken near land, never oceanic. Coifmann's record of this species from Peru is somewhat surprising. The records for the stations given under "Occurrence" are interesting as showing the abundance of this species at the surface during hours of darkness.

Remarks.—Breeding appears to go on all the year around in the waters of the Philippine Islands. Practically all the above records include breeding females. Several specimens were infested with a dajid parasite, which appears to me to be very close to, if not actually, *Dajus siriellae* G. O. Sars.

Dana (1852b, p. 569), records a specimen of *Siriella* that resembled *S. gracilis* but that had a prominent tooth or spine on the lower side of the sixth abdominal segment, a character not observed in *S. gracilis*. Czerniavsky (1882a) named this specimen *S. suluensis*. The species has not since been seen. I suggest that *S. suluensis* is the same as *S. vulgaris* Hansen, though I am unable to suggest what the spine noted by Dana really is. The two species are otherwise very similar.

SIRIELLA VULGARIS ROSTRATA, new variety

FIGURE 14

Description.—The specimens here recorded agree very closely in all their characters with Hansen's description of *S. vulgaris* except that the rostral plate (fig. 14, *a*) is very much longer, acutely produced into a long spiniform rostrum which extends forward just beyond the cornea of the eyes. In *S. vulgaris* the rostral plate is short, acute, and extends forward only to the base of the eye stalks. The close resemblance in all the other characters leads me to regard these specimens as only a variety of the typical form. I give herewith figures of the main appendages of the variety for comparison with those of the type (figs. 14, *a-f*).

Type lot.—U.S.N.M. No. 81254, from Arno Atoll, Marshall Islands.

Occurrence.—Several hundreds of specimens of both sexes were taken by the *Albatross* by electric light at the surface of a lagoon, January 24–26, 1900, at the type locality. The *Albatross* likewise took 3 males and 2 females at Kusac, Caroline Islands, electric light, surface, February 7, 1900. PHILIPPINE ISLANDS: *Albatross*, Bagacay

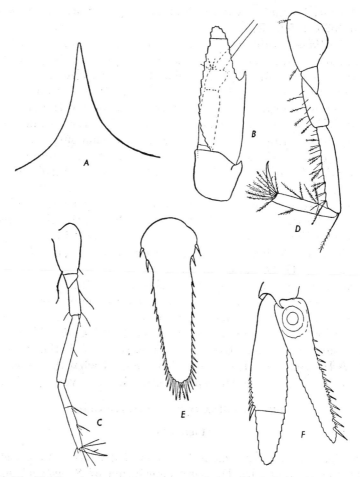

FIGURE 14.—*Siriella vulgaris* var. *rostrata*, new variety: *a*, Rostral plate; *b*, antennal scale and peduncle, × 37½; *c*, endopod of third thoracic limb, × 37½; *d*, endopod of eighth thoracic limb, × 37½; *e*, telson, × 37½; *f*, uropods, × 37½.

Bay, Escarparda Island, electric light, surface, March 12, 1909, 157 females, 23 males; *Albatross*, Mahinog Anchorage, Camiguin Island, surface, August 3, 1909, 2 males, 1 female.

SIRIELLA AFFINIS Hansen

Siriella affinis HANSEN, 1910, p. 35, pl. 3, figs. 3a–i.

Occurrence.—PACIFIC: *Albatross*, Kusac, Caroline Islands, electric light, surface, 2 males, 1 female, February 7, 1900. PHILIPPINE ISLANDS: The *Albatross* collected specimens at various Philippine localities, without station numbers, all by electric light from the surface: Port Binanga Anchorage, January 8, 1908, 4 males, 4 females; Nasugbu Bay Anchorage, January 21, 1908, 1 male, 2 females; Tumindao Anchorage, February 26, 1908, 1 male; Looc Bay Anchorage, July 18, 1908, 1 male, 2 females; Varadero Bay Anchorage, July 22, 1908, 6 males, 14 females; Port San Pio Quinto, Camiguin Island, November 10, 1908, 3 males, 16 females; Tara Island Anchorage, December 14, 1908, 5 females, 11 males; Pasaco, Ragay Gulf, Luzon, March 8, 1909, 24 females, 5 males; Mahinog Anchorage, Camiguin Island, August 3, 1909, 2 males, 8 females; Opol, Macajalar Bay, Mindanao, August 4, 1909, 1 male; Catanduanes Island, Cabugao Bay, June 9, 1909, 26 females, 23 males; the *Albatross* collected 1 female and 3 males from station 5435.

Distribution.—Waters of the Dutch East Indies (Hansen, 1910); India (Tattersall, 1922), the Caroline and Philippine Islands. This species has a distribution very similar to that of *S. vulgaris* and the two species are often taken together.

SIRIELLA INORNATA Hansen

Siriella inornata HANSEN, 1910, p. 36, pl. 4, figs. 2a–k.—TATTERSALL, 1928, p. 106; 1936b, p. 146.

Occurrence.—PHILIPPINE ISLANDS: The *Albatross* took specimens from several localities, without station number, by electric light, at the surface: Nasugbu Bay, Luzon, 7:30 p. m., January 21, 1908, 2 adult females, breeding, 4 immature females; Cataingan Bay, Masbate, 8 p. m., April 19, 1908, 3 males, 3 females; Looc, Lubang Island, China Sea, 8:45 p. m., July 18, 1908, about 40 specimens; Port Matalvi, western Luzon, 7:45 p. m., November 23, 1908, about 30 specimens; Sablayan Bay, Mindoro, 7 p. m., December 12, 1908, 12 specimens; Tara Island Anchorage, Mindoro, 7 p. m., December 14, 1908, 12 males, 102 females, breeding; Taal Anchorage, Luzon, 7:30 p. m., February 20, 1909, 1 adult female, breeding; Ragay Bay, Luzon, 7 p. m., March 9, 1909, 1 adult male; Batauanan Island, eastern Luzon, 7:30 p. m., June 12, 1909, about 200 specimens; Talisse Island, north of Celebes, November 8, 1909, 400 specimens; the *Albatross* likewise collected 4 breeding females at Cebu, March 13, 1909, by electric light, depth not stated, and 1 breeding female from station 5287.

Distribution.—Known only from the eastern Pacific in the waters of the Dutch East Indies and the Philippines, from the coast of Queensland (Tattersall, 1928 and 1936b). As the above records show the species is abundant at the surface at night and appears to be a coastal form not taken far from land.

SIRIELLA MEDIA Hansen

Siriella media HANSEN, 1910, p. 38, pl. 4, figs. 3a–k; 1912, p. 194.

Occurrence.—PHILIPPINE ISLANDS: The *Albatross* made collections at various Philippine stations by electric light, at the surface: Subig Bay, southern Luzon, 7 p. m., January 6, 1908, 2 immature males, 3 breeding females, 2 young; Caldera Bay, Sulu Sea, 7 : 30 p. m., February 6, 1908, 1 male, 1 female; Tumindao Island Anchorage, Sulu Sea, 7 : 30 p. m., February 25, 1908, 2 males, 2 females; Jolo Anchorage, March 5, 1908, 8 breeding females; Looc, Lubang Island, China Sea, July 18, 1908, about 40 specimens; Varadero Harbor, Mindoro, 8 p. m., July 22, 1908, 4 males, 3 females; Port San Pio Quinto, Camiguin Island, Nov. 10, 1908, 7 breeding females, 5 males; Port Matalvi, Luzon, 7 : 45 p. m., November 23, 1908, 30 specimens; Sablayan Bay, Mindoro, 7 p. m., December 12, 1908, 80 specimens; Sablayan Bay, Mindoro, 9 p. m., December 13, 1908, 50 specimens; Capulaan Bay Anchorage, February 23, 1909, 4 males, 1 female; Pasacao Anchorage, Ragay Gulf, 7 p. m., March 8, 1909, 4 males, 4 females; Catanduanes Island, Cabugao Bay, 7 p. m., June 9, 1909, 3 males and 2 females; Opol, Macajalar Bay, Mindanao, August 4, 1909, 18 males, 12 breeding females; the *Albatross* likewise collected 5 males and 6 females from the ship's side, at the surface (electric light not stated) at 9 p. m., June 3, 1908, and additional specimens from stations 5595, about a thousand specimens, and 5596, 20 breeding females and 16 males. Two of these females had an epicarid very closely allied to *Dajus siriellae* G. O. Sars on the carapace. GILBERT ISLANDS*: H. J. Hansen (1912) identified specimens from these islands.

Distribution.—The Philippine and Gilbert Islands.

Remarks.—Very similar to *S. inornata*, and like *inornata* an inshore species, abundant at the surface at night, and a coastal rather than an oceanic form.

SIRIELLA CHIERCHIAE Coifmann

FIGURES 15, 16

Siriella chierchiae COIFMANN, 1937 (March), p. 3, fig. 1.
Siriella occidentalis TATTERSALL, 1937 (May), p. 6, figs. 3, 4.

Description.—In his *Siboga* report Hansen (1910, p. 30) divides the species of *Siriella* into four groups. Using his grouping as a basis, this species belongs to the second group, characterized as follows: End of the telson with three small spines and a single pair of more lateral long spines. Proximal joint of the exopod of the uropods with much more than half of its outer margins furnished with spines, and at least about twice as long as broad. Proximal widened part of the telson with three pairs of marginal spines; spines along the distal third of the lateral margins of the telson closely set but irregular as to length, as several long spines are found, and between each two of these some, or near the end of the telson only one or two, smaller or small spines are inserted. Both rami of the fourth pair of male pleopods terminating in very modified setae. Pseudobranchial rami of the second to fourth pleopods of the male spirally twisted.

Within this group the species may further be described as follows:

Carapace somewhat produced but leaving the eyes and eyestalks completely uncovered, frontal plate a broad, low triangle with the apex slightly produced into an acute point.

Eyes large and black.

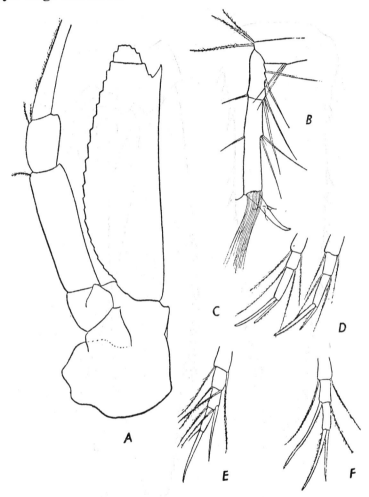

FIGURE 15.—*Siriella chierchiae* Coifmann: *a*, Antennal scale and peduncle, × 64; *b*, distal three joints of endopod of one of the posterior thoracic limbs, × 64; *c*, distal extremity of endopod of third pleopod of male, × 64; *d*, distal extremity of exopod of third pleopod of male, × 64; *e*, distal extremity of exopod of fourth pleopod of male, × 64; *f*, distal extremity of endopod of fourth pleopod of male, × 64.

Antennal scale (fig. 15, *a*) extending forward as far as the distal end of the antennular peduncle, three and one-fourth times as long as broad, terminal lobe broader than long.

Endopod (fig. 15, *b*) of the third to the eighth thoracic limbs with the carpus distinct and the propodus undivided; in the third limbs the carpus is half as long as the propodus and the dactylus is more than one-third but less than one-half the length of the carpus and propodus combined.

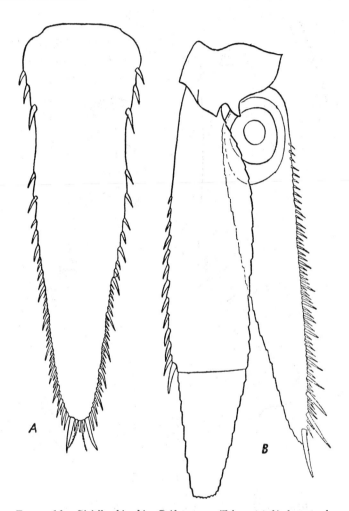

A

B

FIGURE 16.—*Siriella chierchiae* Coifmann: *a*, Telson, × 64; *b*, uropods.

Telson (fig. 16, *a*) rather narrowly lanceolate, three and one-third times as long as broad at the base, lateral margins with three large proximal spines separated by an unarmed interval from the distal series of spines in which the larger spines are separated by groups of three, four, or five smaller spines, apex armed with a single pair of long stout spines, between which are three equal small spines and a pair of plumose setae.

Uropods (fig. 16, *b*) with the exopod longer than the endopod; proximal joint of the exopod twice as long as the distal joint, with about 13 spines on the outer margin occupying more than half the margin; distal joint of the exopod almost twice as long as broad; endopod with a closely set row of spines on the inner margin extending from the statocyst to the apex, arranged as large spines separated by groups of smaller spines.

Pleopods of the males with both rami and both the third and fourth pairs with modified setae on the terminal and penultimate joints. In the third pair the terminal joint of the endopod (fig. 15, *c*) bears two modified setae, a large, blunt simple one and a smaller, more acute plumose one. The exopod of the third pair (fig. 15, *d*) has a pair of similarly modified setae, both plumose, on the terminal joint. In the fourth pair the endopod (fig. 15, *f*) has the terminal joint furnished with two modified setae, the longer very closely and finely feathered but much stouter than the normal plumose setae arming the rest of the limb, the shorter stout and simple; the penultimate joint has one of its plumose setae modified in the same way as the longer of the two setae on the terminal joint; that is, it is stouter and more closely and finely feathered. The exopod (fig. 15, *e*) of the fourth pair has the terminal joint armed with one long, stout, simple spiniform seta and a rather short, fine, simple seta; the penultimate joint, in addition to the normal plumose seta at each corner, has a single long, stout, simple seta inserted some little way behind the distal margin on each side. Length of adult specimens of both sexes 10 mm.

Occurrence.—WEST INDIAN REGION: The *Albatross* collected material by electric light at the surface in 1884 at Kingston, Jamaica, about 50 specimens; Monos Island, Trinidad, about 50 specimens; Key West, Fla., 3 specimens; the *Albatross* likewise collected two lots at the surface in 1886, at San Salvador, 25 specimens; and New Providence Island, 5 specimens. John B. Henderson and Dr. Paul Bartsch, on the *Tomas Barrera* expedition to Cuba, collected at the following localities: Los Arroyas, station 8, collection numbers 192 and 197, May 12–20, 25 males and 6 breeding females; off Santa Lucia, collection number 28, May 12, 1914, 6 breeding females and 9 males; Ensenada Santa Rosa, station 7, collection numbers 184, 185, 1 to 3 fathoms, on sand, shell, weed, and sponge, 40 specimens; Cabanas, station 16, collection 518, on sand, shell, grass, or mud, 2 to 25 fathoms, June 8–9, 1 adult female and 1 young; Punta Colorado, station 1C, collection 240, 2 to 3 fathoms, from shell and grass, 11 females; Esperanza between anchorage and entrance, collection 396, station 13, 2 fathoms, mud and gravel, 3 males and 6 females; Ensenada de Cajón, off Cape San Antonio, station 11, collection numbers 351–353, May 22–23, 1914, several hundreds. The Johnson-Smithsonian expedition is represented by three localities: Gangway at Santa Barbara, Samaná Bay, Dominican Republic (series number 310B), surface, February 17, 1923, 5 specimens; anchorage off Playa de Fajardo, Puerto Rico, series number 358A, surface, February 23, 1933, 10 plus specimens; Luispena Channel, Puerto Rico, series number 406, February 25, 1933, 10 specimens.

Distribution.—The species is evidently a very abundant one in the tropical parts of the western Atlantic. It is not an oceanic species but it frequents waters near land, either among the islands of the Caribbean Sea or near the mainland. May and June seem to be its breeding season, for nearly all the females recorded above had either eggs or embryos in the marsupium.

Remarks.—On May 7, 1937, I described this species under the name *Siriella occidentalis* from specimens collected by the Johnson-Smithsonian expedition in 1933 in the Caribbean Sea. Earlier in the same year a paper appeared by Coifmann describing a new species of *Siriella* under the name *S. chierchiae*, which was collected on a journey from Pernambuco to Rio de Janeiro. The date of Coifmann's paper is March 1937. I think there can be no doubt that *S. chierchiae* and *S. occidentalis* are synonymous. It is true that Coifmann makes no mention of the modified third pleopods of the male, but in all other characters the resemblance is so close as to leave no doubt as to the identity of the two forms. Since Coifmann's paper has priority, the species must be known as *S. chierchiae* and the name *S. occidentalis* must be canceled.

The species is very closely related to the other American species, *S. pacifica*, *S. roosevelti*, and *S. panamensis*, and can be identified with certainty only from the examination of adult males. All four species have both the third and fourth pleopods of the male modified and in this respect differ from all other species except *S. anomala*, from which all can be distinguished by the pseudobranchial rami of the male pleopods, which are not spirally twisted in *S. anomala*.

SIRIELLA PACIFICA Holmes

FIGURE 17

Siriella pacifica HOLMES, 1900, p. 227.—HANSEN, 1913b, p. 175, pl. 9, figs. 1a–f.— TATTERSALL, 1932a, p. 302.

Description.—For the sake of completeness I give here a transcription of Hansen's redescription of this species. The species belongs to the second group of Hansen's classification, for the definition of which see under *S. chierchiae*, and within this group may be defined as follows:

Carapace in both sexes somewhat produced, the frontal plate being a broad, rather low triangle with the vertex somewhat produced, acuminate and acute (fig. 17, a).

Eyes in the male (fig. 17, b) considerably smaller than in allied forms, seen from above conspicuously shorter and narrower than the last joint of the peduncle, the posterior margin of which is rather convex; eyes in the female (fig. 17, f) distinctly larger than in the

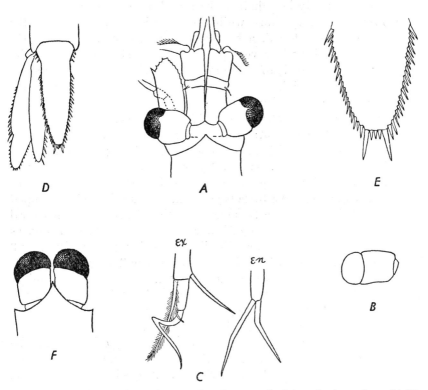

FIGURE 17.—*Siriella pacifica* Holmes: a, Anterior part of adult male, from above, $\times$ 22; b, left eye of male, from outer side, $\times$ 22; c, terminal parts of both rami of fourth right pleopod of male, $\times$ 82 (ex = exopod, en = endopod); d, end of abdomen with left uropod of male, from above, $\times$ 20; e, distal portion of telson shown in d, from above, $\times$ 67; f, front end of carapace with eyes of female, from above, $\times$ 22.

male, seen from above conspicuously shorter but slightly broader than the peduncular joint.

Antennule in the male (fig. 17, a) with third peduncular joint only a little longer than broad; flagellum in the male extremely long, reaching beyond the hind margin of fourth abdominal segment.

Antennal scale (figs. 17, a and 17, f) subequal in both sexes, with the terminal lobe much broader than long.

Both rami of third pair of male pleopods terminating in a robust, spiniform, nearly straight, seemingly naked seta not longer than the normal setae on the preceding joint and with the end obtuse. Each ramus of fourth pair of pleopods (fig. 17, c) with peculiar setae; the endopod terminates in two strong, naked, spiniform setae, the outer seta almost straight, about as long as the sum of the three distal joints, the inner seta distinctly shorter and less thick than the outer and somewhat angularly bent before the middle; the exopod terminates in two setae, one very short, while the other is nearly as long as the long seta on the endopod, naked, robust, and, somewhat before the middle, strongly bent in a very peculiar way. These setae are quite similar in both uropods of the fourth pair. Finally the inner angle of the penultimate joint has a nearly straight, naked, strong seta scarcely as long as the long terminal seta.

Uropods moderately slender (fig. 17, d). The exopod overreaches conspicuously the endopod; its proximal joint is almost three times as long as the distal, with 14 or 15 spines occupying somewhat more than half its outer margin; distal joint not fully twice as long as broad. Telson (fig. 17, d–e) somewhat less than three times as long as broad, reaching a little beyond the articulation of the exopod of the uropods; along a little more than the distal half each lateral margin has an arrangement of spines nearly as in S. inornata, as above 9 or 10 long spines are distributed so that proximally 4 or 3 shorter spines are found in each interval between 2 long spines, while distally 3 or 2 (or only 1) are found in each interval. The terminal margin of the telson has 3 somewhat small spines placed between the single pair of very long and strong spines.

Length of both sexes 9 mm. (Hansen, 1913b).

Occurrence.—Three lots from La Jolla, Calif., collected by the Scripps Institution, have been examined: Haul 432, October 3, 1916, 1 specimen; haul 2308, August 23, 1917, 2 specimens; haul 2425, September 15, 1917, 1 specimen.

Distribution.—This species is known only from the coast of California, from which it has been recorded by Holmes (1900), Hansen (1913b), and Tattersall (1932a).

Remarks.—This species is distinguished from S. chierchiae, S. roosevelti, and S. panamensis by the form of the third and fourth pleopods of the male. Females of all these species are extremely alike and very difficult to separate from one another.

SIRIELLA ROOSEVELTI Tattersall

FIGURES 18, 19

Siriella roosevelti TATTERSALL, 1941, p. 2, figs. 1, 2.

Description.—A Siriella belonging to group II (Hansen, 1910) in which the apex of the telson is armed with three small spines in the center and a single pair of long lateral spines; the exopod of the uropods longer than the endopods with more than half of the margin of the proximal joint furnished with spines; spines along the distal third of the lateral margins of the telson irregular, with smaller spines in series between the larger spines; *both* rami of *both* the third and fourth pairs of pleopods of the male with modified distal setae;

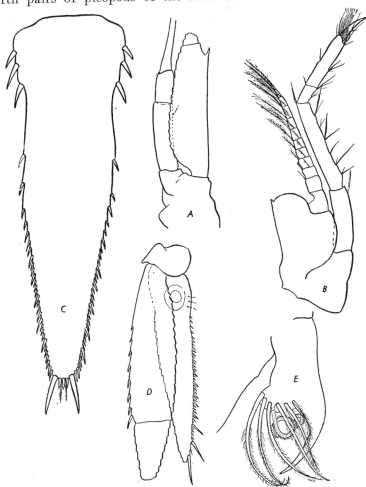

FIGURE 18.—*Siriella roosevelti* Tattersall: *a*, Antennal scale and peduncle, × 45; *b*, third thoracic limb, × 45; *c*, telson, × 83; *d*, uropods, × 45; *e*, copulatory appendage of the eighth thoracic limb of male, × 80.

pseudobranchial rami on the second to the fourth pleopods of the male spirally twisted; distal joint of the outer uropod less than twice as long as broad; antennal scale without spines on the outer margin.

Carapace similar in both sexes, only slightly produced into a short triangular rostral plate with a pointed apex, which extends scarcely beyond the base of the eyestalks; eyes of moderate size, pigment black.

Antennal scale (fig. 18, *a*) extending as far forward as the distal end of the antennular peduncle, four times as long as broad, terminal lobe rather broader than long, extending beyond the distal spine of the outer margin, apex of the lobe marked off by a distinct suture.

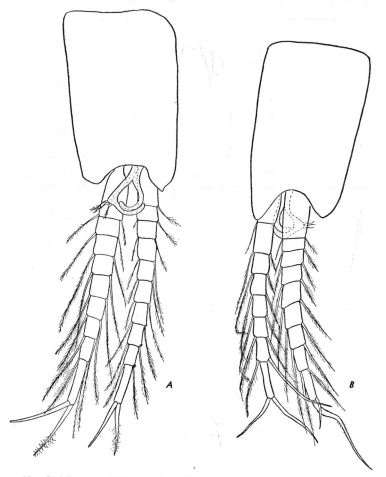

FIGURE 19.—*Siriella roosevelti* Tattersall: *a*, Third pleopod of male, × 85; *b*, fourth pleopod of male, × 85.

Endopods of the third to the eighth thoracic limbs (fig. 18, *b*), with the carapace distinct and the propodus undivided, the carpus rather less than one-third of the whole propodus.

Both rami of the third pleopods (fig. 19, *a*) of the male with two modified setae at the distal end, the outer seta is stout and smooth, the inner seta slightly more slender than the outer and plumose at the distal end.

The endopod of the fourth pleopod of the male (fig. 19, *b*) has two strong, smooth, modified setae at the apex, set at a widely divergent angle, which is constant and characteristic; the penultimate joint has a long stout and smooth seta on the outer angle; the exopod has two modified setae at the apex, one of which is very long and characteristically bent about one-third the distance from the base, the other short, less than half the length of the other seta, and smooth.

Endopod of the uropods (fig. 18, *d*) distinctly shorter than the exopod, with a row of spines extending from the statocyst to the distal end, rather irregular and arranged in groups distally; among them near the distal end are three or four specially long, strong, and prominent spines.

Exopod of the uropods (fig. 18, *d*) with the proximal joint three times as long as the distal, with eight or nine spines somewhat widely spaced occupying more than half of its outer margin; distal joint one and a half times as long as broad.

Telson (fig. 18, *c*) three times as long as broad at the base, of the form and shape characteristic of the genus, apex armed with one pair of long and stout spines between which are three small equal spinules and a pair of plumose setae; lateral margins armed with three strong spines near the base followed by a short smooth portion and then a more or less continuous row of spines to the distal end, the spines arranged in series, especially distally, where there are about five graded smaller spines between each pair of larger spines.

The copulatory lobe of the eighth thoracic limbs of the male has a rather special form which is best described by a figure (fig. 18, *e*).

Length of adult specimens of both sexes, 8 mm.

Remarks.—Among the many species of *Siriella*, this species is most closely allied to *S. pacifica* Holmes. Indeed females of the two species are difficult, if not impossible, to distinguish from one another, but males are readily separated on examination of the third and fourth pleopods. Hansen (1913b) has given a full description and figures of *S. pacifica*. On comparing this description and figures with those here given for *S. roosevelti*, the following differences between the two forms emerge:

1. Third pleopod of the male. In *S. pacifica* both rami terminate in a *single* robust spiniform naked seta. In *S. roosevelti* both rami terminate in *two* modified setae, one robust, spiniform, and smooth, the other robust and plumose, much stouter than the plumose setae on the other joints.

2. Fourth pleopod of the male. Endopod in *S. pacifica* has two strong spiniform setae at the apex set at an acute angle to one another, one straight and the other slightly bent. In *S. roosevelti* there are

two strong smooth spiniform setae set at a widely divergent angle which is constant and characteristic in all the specimens I have examined. The exopod in *S. pacifica* bears two setae, one short and simple, the other long and very curiously bent in an acute angle. In *S. roosevelti* there are also two setae, one quite short and simple, the other longer and more robust and not bent in the same way as in *S. pacifica*.

The most easily observed character for distinguishing the females of the two species is the number and spacing of the spines on the outer margins of the proximal joint of the outer uropods. In *S. pacifica* there are 14 or 15 spines, rather closely set, whereas in *S. roosevelti* there are only 8 or 9 spines somewhat distantly spaced so that, although fewer in number, they occupy about as much of the margin as they do in *S. pacifica*.

S. pacifica and *S. roosevelti* agree with each other and differ from all other species of the genus with the exception of *S. anomala* Hansen, in having *both* rami of *both* the third and fourth pleopods of the male terminating in modified setae. They can both be distinguished from *S. anomala* by the antennal scale, which in the latter species is of very special and peculiar shape in the male.

Occurrence.—GALÁPAGOS ISLANDS: The *Albatross* expedition of 1887–89 collected two lots: Chatham Island, April 4 and 14, 1888, several thousand specimens; Albemarle Island, April 10, 1888, 3 specimens; from the Presidential cruise of 1938 there is the material upon which I reported in 1941.

Distribution.—This species is known only from the waters of the Galápagos Islands, where it would appear to be very abundant.

SIRIELLA PANAMENSIS, new species

FIGURE 20

Description.—This new species is very closely allied to the other American species, *S. pacifica, S. roosevelti,* and *S. chierchiae,* and females are almost impossible to distinguish from those of the other three species. The males, on the other hand, are readily separated by the form of the modified setae on the third and fourth pleopods. The species belongs to the second group of Hansen's classification, for the definition of which see under *S. chierchiae,* and within this group may be further defined as follows:

Carapace somewhat produced but leaving the eyes and eye stalks completely uncovered, similar in both sexes, rostral plate a short triangle with an acute point, not extending forward beyond the base of the eye stalks.

Eyes of moderate size, pigment black.

Antennal scale (fig. 20, *a*) extending forward as far as the distal end of the antennular peduncle, 3¼ times as long as broad, terminal lobe broader than long, extending slightly beyond the spine of the outer margin, apex of the lobe marked off by a distinct suture.

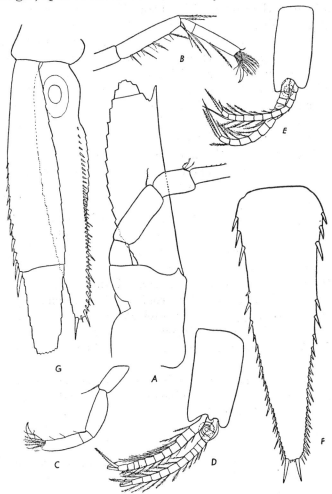

FIGURE 20.—*Siriella panamensis*, new species: *a*, Antennal scale, × 67½; *b*, endopod of third thoracic limb, × 45; *c*, endopod of eighth thoracic limb, × 45; *d*, third pleopod of male, × 45; *e*, fourth pleopod of male, × 45; *f*, telson, × 90; *g*, uropods, × 67½.

Endopod (fig. 20, *b*) of the third to the seventh thoracic limbs with the carpus distinct and the propodus undivided, the carpus about one-quarter of the propodus, nail about half as long as the combined length of the carpus and propodus. Endopod of the eighth thoracic limbs (fig. 20, *c*) shorter and more robust than that of the remaining limbs, but of similar form.

Endopod of the uropods (fig. 20, g) distinctly shorter than the exopods with a row of spines extending from the statocyst to the distal end, rather irregular, and arranged in groups distally.

Exopods (fig. 20, g) of the uropods with the proximal joint $2\frac{1}{2}$ times as long as the distal, with 10 spines occupying more than half of its outer margin; distal joint twice as long as broad.

Telson (fig. 20, f) three times as long as broad at its base, of the form and shape characteristic of the genus, apex armed with one pair of long stout spines between which are three small equal spinules and a pair of plumose setae; lateral margins armed with three strong spines near the base, followed by a short unarmed portion and then a more or less continuous row of spines to the distal end, the spines arranged in groups, especially distally.

Pleopods of the male with modified setae on both rami of both the third and fourth pair; third pair (fig. 20, d) with both rami terminating in two modified setae, one stout and straight, the other almost equally stout but bent into a strong hook; penultimate joint of the exopod with a short spine at the outer corner; fourth pair (fig. 20, e) with the endopod terminating in two stout straight plumose setae, one slightly shorter than the other; exopod terminating in a single straight plumose spine and a short simple seta.

Length of adult specimens of both sexes, 7 mm.

Type lot.—U.S.N.M. No. 81255, from San José, Panama.

Occurrence.—The type lot, San José, Panama, 5 fathoms, January 25, 1916, collected by Dr. Th. Mortensen, 3 females, 2 males.

Distribution.—Known only from the coasts of Panama on the Pacific side.

Remarks.—*S. panamensis* is distinguished from the other American species by the strongly hooked spine on the distal end of both rami of the third pleopod of the male.

SIRIELLA AEQUIREMIS Hansen

Siriella aequiremis HANSEN, 1910, p. 40, pl. 3, figs. 4a–c; pl. 4, figs. 1a–1; 1912, p. 194.—TATTERSALL, 1911a, p. 122.—COLOSI, 1919, p. 6; 1920, p. 236, pl. 18, fig. 1a.—COIFMANN, 1937, p. 3.

Occurrence.—PHILIPPINE ISLANDS: The *Albatross* collected 1 immature specimen at Busin Harbor, Burias Island, by electric light at the surface, April 22, 1908; material was received from *Albatross* stations 5195, surface, 20 females, 18 males, adult, breeding (one specimen with an epicarid parasite resembling *Dajus siriellae*); 5435, surface, 5 immature specimens; 5540, surface, 7 females, 3 males. CELEBES: *Albatross* station 5601, 3 males, 2 females; 5611, 9 males, surface, 16 females, breeding. SOUTHWEST COAST OF MEXICO: *Albatross* station 4592, identified by H. J. Hansen. PACIFIC:* A specimen was identified by H. J. Hansen that was collected by the *Albatross* at latitude 1°45′ N., longitude 137° W.

Distribution.—This species is more oceanic in its habit than are *S. vulgaris* and *S. affinis*, as Hansen (1910) has already observed and as the present records indicate. The species is widely distributed in the tropical waters of the Pacific and Indian Oceans from the Arabian Sea to China.

Remarks.—From the fact that females bearing eggs or embryos in the brood pouch occurred in April, August, and November it would appear that this species breeds all the year around.

SIRIELLA ANOMALA Hansen

Siriella anomala HANSEN, 1910, p. 41, pl. 5, figs. 1*a*–1*l*.—TATTERSALL, 1936b, p. 146.

Occurrence.—PACIFIC: The *Albatross* collected material at two localities, without station numbers: Kusac, Caroline Islands, surface tow net with electric light, February 7, 1900, 66 males, 35 females, breeding; Arno Atoll, Marshall Islands, surface tow net in the lagoon with electric light, January 24–26, 1900, 3 males and 10 females, breeding. PHILIPPINE ISLANDS: The *Albatross* collected at one locality, without station number, Port Matalvi, Luzon, electric light, surface, 7:45 p. m., November 23, 1908, 6 males, 4 females, breeding.

Distribution.—Known heretofore only from the waters of the East Indian Archipelago (Hansen) and the Great Barrier Reef (Tattersall), range here extended to the Caroline, Marshall, and Philippine Islands. The breeding season of the species extends from November to the beginning of February at least, since most of the females in this material have either eggs or embryos in the brood pouch. It appears to be a coastal form, abundant at the surface during hours of darkness.

SIRIELLA DISTINGUENDA Hansen

Siriella distinguenda HANSEN, 1910, p. 42, pl. 5, figs. 2*a*–e.

Occurrence.—PHILIPPINE ISLANDS: The *Albatross* collected material from Sablayan Bay, Mindoro, electric light, surface, 7 p. m., December 12, 1908, 1 male, 9 females.

Distribution.—Known from the original record by Hansen from the waters of the Dutch East Indies; range here extended to the Philippine Islands.

SIRIELLA DUBIA Hansen

Siriella dubia HANSEN, 1910, p. 44, pl. 5, figs. 4*a*–e.—TATTERSALL, 1922, p. 455, figs. 5*a*–b; 1936b, p. 146, fig. 1.

Occurrence.—PHILIPPINE ISLANDS: The *Albatross* collected material from Nasugbu Bay Anchorage, Luzon, electric light, surface, 7:30 p. m., January 21, 1908, 1 immature male.

Distribution.—The species has been recorded from the waters of the East Indian Archipelago (Hansen), Andaman Islands (Tattersall), and the Great Barrier Reef, Australia (Tattersall), range now including the Philippine Islands. It is one of the rarer species of the genus and I was able to detect only one specimen in the large amount of material of this genus in the National Museum collection.

Remarks.—This specimen agrees with those that I recorded from India in having three small equal spines at the center of the apex of the telson between the median pair of long spines. Otherwise the specimen, which is not in good condition, agrees with Hansen's description and figures.

Genus HEMISIRIELLA Hansen

Hemisiriella HANSEN, 1910, p. 45.

HEMISIRIELLA PARVA Hansen

Hemisiriella parva HANSEN, 1910, p. 47, pl. 6, figs. 2a–e.—ZIMMER, 1918, p. 16, figs. 5–7.—COLOSI, 1919, p. 6; 1920, p. 236, pl. 18, fig. 2a.—TATTERSALL, 1922, p. 456; 1936b, p. 147.—DELSMAN, 1939, p. 167.

Occurrence.—PHILIPPINE ISLANDS: The *Albatross* collected a specimen at Opol, Macajalar Bay, Mindanao, by electric light, at the surface, August 4, 1909; other *Albatross* collections are from stations 5435, 1 specimen; 5456, 19 specimens; 5568, 9 specimens.

Distribution.—Originally described from the *Siboga* collections made in the waters of the Dutch East Indies, this species has since been recorded from Malaysia (Colosi), Java (Zimmer and Delsman), east coast of India (Tattersall), and the Barrier Reef, Australia (Tattersall); Philippine Islands included by present record. It is apparently widely distributed in the tropical waters of the west Pacific and Indian Oceans.

HEMISIRIELLA ABBREVIATA Hansen

Hemisiriella abbreviata HANSEN, 1912, p. 195, pl. 2, figs. 2a–c.

Occurrence.—GILBERT ISLANDS: The type, identified by H. J. Hansen.

Distribution.—Not known from any but the type locality.

Subfamily GASTROSACCINAE

Two pairs of oöstegites in the female; labrum much longer than broad, with a very long frontal process; in the endopods of the third to the eighth thoracic limbs either the carpus is distinct and only the propodus divided into subjoints, or the carpus and propodus are fused and the combined joints subdivided into subjoints; third pleopod of the male with the exopod elongate, its endopod and the other pairs of pleopods either well developed or reduced in varying degree; first abdominal somite of the female with a pair of lateral lamellae, which take part in the formation of the brood pouch; exopod of the uropod undivided, its outer margin with one, two, or several spines, but without setae between the spines and the base; telson with a distinct apical cleft.

Remarks.—Five genera are included in this subfamily—*Archaeomysis, Gastrosaccus, Anchialina, Paranchialina,* and *Pseudanchialina.* The first three occur in the National Museum collection.

Genus ARCHAEOMYSIS Czerniavsky

Archaeomysis CZERNIAVSKY 1882a, pp. 62, 71, 73.—HANSEN, 1910, p. 50.—TATTERSALL, 1932a, p. 303.
Callomysis HOLMES, 1894, p. 582.

This interesting genus was established in 1882 by Czerniavsky for a mysid found in the stomach of a gadoid fish caught at Bering Island, Alaska, by Grebnitzky in 1880. Its outstanding characteristic is that the pleopods of the female, while feebly developed and nonnatatory, are all biramous. In 1894 Holmes founded the genus *Callomysis,* describing the pleopods of the female as rudimentary but biramous. In 1910 Hansen, without having seen specimens, suggested that the genera *Archaeomysis* and *Callomysis* were identical, and, in 1932 I was able to confirm Hansen's suggestion from the examination of specimens that I referred to *Callomysis maculata* Holmes. Czerniavsky's species *Archaeomysis grebnitzkii* has not been recorded since its description, but specimens in the collection of the United States National Museum, which I refer with some confidence to this species, have enabled me to redescribe the species and to confirm Czerniavsky's description. The genus is very closely allied to *Gastrosaccus* and to be distinguished only by the biramous pleopods of the female.

ARCHAEOMYSIS GREBNITZKII Czerniavsky

FIGURES 21, 22

Archaeomysis grebnitzkii CZERNIAVSKY, 1882a, p. 73; 1887, p. 1, pl. 30, figs. 17–24; pl. 32, figs. 19–20.—ZIMMER, 1904, p. 428, figs. 26, 27.

Description.—Carapace without reflected lobes or fringe or filaments on the posterior margin; produced in front into a short, broadly triangular rostral plate with a bluntly rounded apex, the whole rostral plate shorter than the eyestalk, apex slightly depressed.

Eye somewhat pyriform in shape; whole eye including the stalk rather less than twice as long as broad, cornea occupying about one-half the entire eye, pigment black.

Antennular peduncle with the first joint about equal to the remaining joints combined; second joint with two strong short spines on the outer margin.

Antennal peduncle (fig. 21, *a*) longer than its scale but shorter than the antennular peduncle; terminal joint one-third the length of the preceding joint.

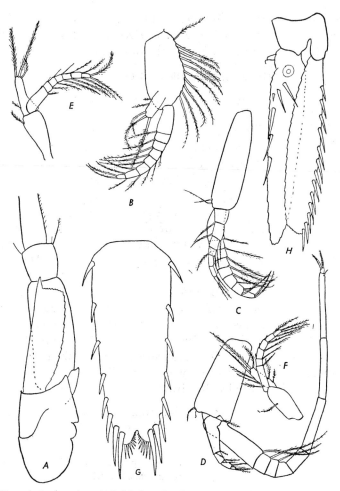

FIGURE 21.—*Archaeomysis grebnitzkii* Czerniavsky: *a*, Antennal scale and peduncle, × 45; *b*, first pleopod of male, × 45; *c*, second pleopod of male, × 45; *d*, third pleopod of male, × 45; *e*, fourth pleopod of male, × 45; *f*, fifth pleopod of male, × 45; *g*, telson, × 45; *h*, uropods, × 45.

Antennal scale (fig. 21, *a*) extending to the distal end of the penultimate joint of its peduncle, three and a half times as long as broad, apex of the scale somewhat squarely truncate, terminal spine very strong and projecting wholly beyond the truncate apex, so that there is no terminal lobe to the scale; no distal suture on the scale.

Mouth parts and thoracic limbs very similar to the appendages in the genus *Gastrosaccus;* endopod of the third to the eighth thoracic limbs (fig. 22, *a*) with the carpopropodus divided into 10 subjoints; basal joint of the exopods with an acute outer distal corner; oöstegite attached to the seventh thoracic limb of the female essentially of the same form as figured by Sars for *G. normani.*

Fifth abdominal somite without a dorsal spine.

Outer uropod (fig. 21, *h*) slightly shorter than the inner, with 13 spines on its outer margin; inner uropod (fig. 21, *h*) with 6 spines on its inner lower margin, 3 placed in an oblique row near the statocyst, the other 3 longer and stronger spines about the center of the inner margin.

Telson (fig. 21, *g*) 2½ times as long as broad at the base, with eight or nine spines on each margin, the last two of which are longer and stronger than the remainder and placed close together.

Pleopods of the female (fig. 22, *b-f*) all biramous; the first pair (fig. 22, *b*) with the sympod twice as long as the exopod and endopod, with a group of long plumose setae at the proximal and distal ends of the outer margin; exopod and endopod more or less equal in size; second to fifth pairs (fig. 22, *c-f*) of pleopods more or less all alike, sympod short, about half or less than half the length of the endopod, exopod in all only about half as long as the endopod.

First pleopod (fig. 21, *b*) of the male with the sympod somewhat ovate in shape, twice as long as broad, outer margin fringed with 10 long plumose setae; endopod of one joint; exopod of 8 joints.

Second pleopod (fig. 21, *c*) of the male with the sympod about as long as the exopod, four times as long as broad; exopod longer than the endopod, 8-jointed; endopod of seven joints.

Third pleopod (fig. 21, *d*) of the male with the sympod slightly longer than the endopod, twice as long as broad; exopod very long and slender, of nine joints, first joint rather long, second, third, and fourth joints short and subequal, fifth joint longer than the fourth; sixth, seventh, and eighth joints long and narrow, ninth joint quite small and terminated by two short plumose setae; endopod of four joints.

Fourth pleopod (fig. 21, *e*) of the male with the sympod shorter than the exopod and only slightly longer than the endopod; exopod of seven joints; endopod 1-jointed.

Fifth pleopod (fig. 21, *f*) of the male very similar to the fourth, sympod about as long as the endopod; exopod 6-jointed; endopod 1-jointed.

Length of adult specimens of both sexes, 15 mm.

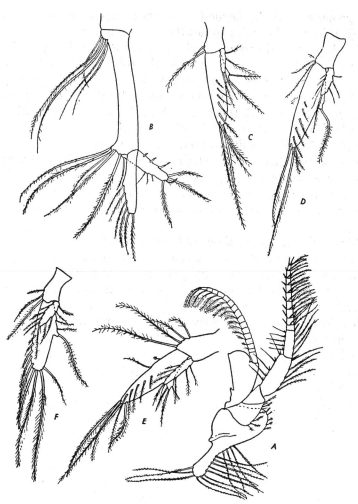

FIGURE 22.—*Archaeomysis grebnitzkii* Czerniavsky: *a*, Seventh thoracic limb, × 15; *b*, first pleopod of female, × 45; *c*, second pleopod of female, × 45; *d*, third pleopod of female, × 45; *e*, fourth pleopod of female, × 45; *f*, fifth pleopod of female, × 45.

Occurrence.—NORTH PACIFIC REGION: Bering Island, from mouth of cod, N. Grebnitzky collector, 2 adult females (? cotypes), breeding, 17 mm.; St. Paul Island, Bering Sea, W. Palmer, collector (No. 30e), July 18, 1890, 1 adult female, breeding, 14 mm.; the *Albatross* collected material at Unalaska, shore, May 26, 1906, 1 adult female, breeding, 15 mm., and from Kiska Island, Aleutian Islands, remains of 2 females from the stomach of an eider duck (*Oidemia deglandii*). CALIFORNIA: The *Albatross* collected 2 adult breeding females from Half Moon Bay, April 23. 1890. BRITISH COLUMBIA: Gabriola Island,

Nanaimo, collector Dr. Th. Mortensen, June 25 and July 10, 1915, several hundreds of both sexes.

Distribution.—The original material of this species was collected in the Bering Sea and the present material includes four additional records from that area. In addition there are records from British Columbia and California so that the species is now known to occur all along the Pacific coast of America from Alaska to California. The specimens from California are unfortunately all females and there are no males from which to substantiate the record. The specimens are, however, so completely in agreement with Alaskan specimens that, in the absence of males, I must include them in this species.

Remarks.—The above description agrees very closely with that of Czerniavsky, and in spite of some discrepancies I think there can be no doubt of the identity of these specimens with *Archaeomysis grebnitzkii.* The main points of difference concern the number of joints in the pleopods, though the form of these appendages agrees very closely with that described by Czerniavsky. In the female the third pair of pleopods is described as having the exopod showing division into three subjoints, and the endopods of the third and fourth pairs terminating in minute joints, two in the third and one in the fourth. I am unable to make out these structures in my specimens, both exopod and endopod of all the pleopods consisting of a single joint.

In the male, while the general form of the pleopods is in close agreement with Czerniavsky's description, the numbers of joints in the various exopods and endopods show some variation from his figures. The differences are set out in table 7. I have not regarded these differences as of specific value.

TABLE 7.—*Variation in numbers of joints in exopods and endopods in* Archaeomysis grebnitzkii

Author	Pleopods									
	I		II		III		IV		V	
	Exo-pod	Endo-pod	Exo-pod	Endo-pod	Exo-pod	Endo-pod	Exo-pod	Endo-pod	Exo-pod	Endo-pod
Czerniavsky	10	1	11	6	12	5	9	1	9	1
Tattersall	8	1	8	7	9	4	7	1	6	1

It is a matter of great interest that this species, which has so long remained obscure, should have been rediscovered so that its structure and affinities can be definitely established. Czerniavsky's original description is substantially accurate and he justly realized the primitive nature of the genus in having biramous pleopods, in the female. It is clear, also, that the genus apart from the female pleopods is essentially a *Gastrosaccus*.

This species was originally described from specimens taken from a gadoid fish. In this collection there are two specimens from the same locality as the type, collected by the same collector, also from the stomach of a gadoid fish. It is possible that they are really cotypes from Czerniavsky's original material. The record above of this species from the stomach of *Oidemia deglandii* probably means that the bird had acquired them from fish on which it had been feeding.

ARCHAEOMYSIS MACULATA (Holmes)

FIGURES 23, 24

Callomysis maculata HOLMES, 1894, p. 582, pl. 20, figs. 36–44; 1900, p. 224.
Archaeomysis maculata TATTERSALL, 1932a, p. 304, figs. 1–13.

Description.—In order to make this account of the American Mysidacea complete I reproduce the description and figures that I published in 1932:

Length.—Adult female, 12 mm.

Description.—Carapace (fig. 23, *a*) produced in front into a moderately long, acutely pointed rostral projection, extending anteriorly to the distal margin of the eyes; posterior dorsal margin of the carapace without a fringe of lappets but with two simple digitate lobes, not forwardly directed.

Fifth abdominal somite with the median dorsal posterior margin drawn out into a laterally compressed acute spine overlapping the sixth somite for about one-quarter of its length. Sixth abdominal somite one and a half times as long as the fifth.

Antennular peduncle (fig. 23, *a*) with two spines on the outer margin of the second joint. Antennal peduncle (figs. 23, *a*, 24, *a*) as long as the first two joints of the antennular peduncle; distal joint quite short. Antennal scale (figs. 23, *a*, 24, *a*) shorter than its peduncle, slightly longer than the first joint of the antennular peduncle, four times as long as broad, with a distinct distal joint marked off by an articulation; outer margin entire and terminating in a very pronounced spine projecting well beyond the apex of the scale. Labrum produced into a well-marked forwardly projecting spine.

Carpopropodus of the endopod (fig. 23, *d*) of the third to the eighth thoracic limbs divided into from 8 (in the third) to 12 (in the eighth) subjoints; expanded basal plate of the exopods of the thoracic limbs with 2 small spines on the outer distal corner in the second to the seventh pairs, rounded in the first and last.

Telson (fig. 23, c) as long as the sixth abdominal somite, two and a quarter times as long as broad at the base; cleft for one-sixth of its length, the cleft armed with serrations; lateral margins armed with 9 or 10 spines; each lobe of the apex armed with two closely placed, long powerful spines about one-sixth of the telson in length.

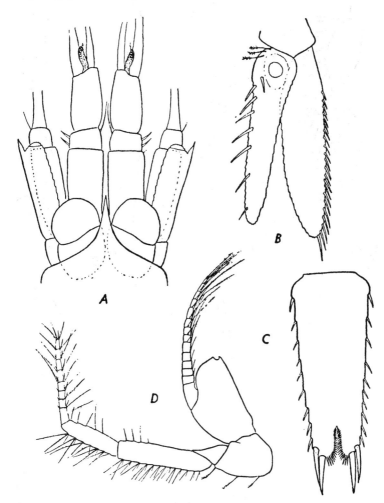

Figure 23.—*Archaeomysis maculata* (Holmes): *a*, Anterior end of young male showing rostral plate, antennules, antennal peduncle, and scale, × 78; *b*, uropod, × 78; *c*, telson, × 78; *d*, third thoracic limb, × 62.

Uropods (fig. 23, *b*) subequal in length, one-sixth longer than the telson; inner uropod with eight rather stout, widely spaced spines on the inner margin; outer uropod with 22 closely set spines on the distal three-quarters of the outer margin.

Pleopods of the female all biramous; in the first pair (fig. 24, *g*) the rami are less than half as long as the peduncle, equal in length, and armed with a few plumose setae; the distal margin of the basal joint armed with several very long plumose setae; in the remaining

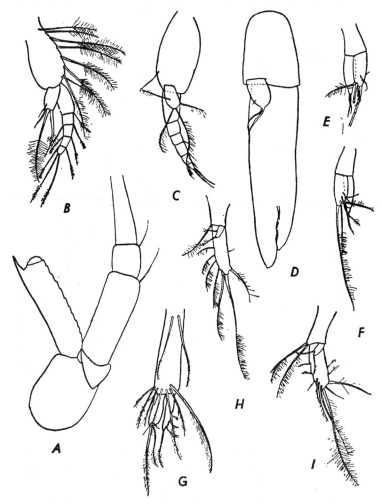

FIGURE 24.—*Archaeomysis maculata* (Holmes): *a*, Antennal scale and peduncle, × 78; *b*, first pleopod of male, × 100; *c*, second pleopod of male, × 100; *d*, third pleopod of male, × 100; *e*, fourth pleopod of male, × 100; *f*, fifth pleopod of male, × 100; *g*, first pleopod of female, × 100; *h*, second pleopod of female, × 100; *i*, third pleopod of female, × 100.

pairs (fig. 24, *h-i*) the exopod is a very minute lobe tipped with two setae, the endopod 1-jointed, longer than the peduncle, and armed with several very long plumose setae.

First pleopod of the male (fig. 24, *b*) with the peduncle equal in length to the outer ramus and armed with several very long plumose setae on the outer margin; endopod small and 1-jointed; exopod 5-jointed.

Second pleopod of the male (fig. 24, c) similar to the first but without plumose setae on the outer margin of the peduncle, the outer ramus 6-jointed.

Third pleopod of the male (fig. 24, d) (in an immature specimen) with a short peduncle; endopod single-jointed; exopod greatly developed and divided at the distal end into two digitate lobes.

Fourth and fifth pleopods (figs. 24, e-f) of the male similar; rami slightly longer than the peduncle; endopod single-jointed; exopod slightly longer than the endopod and 3-jointed.

Occurrence.—La Jolla, Calif., Scripps Institution: Haul 137, September 13, 1916, 1 specimen; Haul 1720, April 26, 1917, 1 specimen; Haul 1966, June 16, 1917, 2 specimens; Haul 3005, January 8, 1918, 2 specimens.

Distribution. — Known only from California (Holmes and Tattersall).

Remarks.—Having examined specimens that I believe represent the true Archaeomysis grebnitzkii it is now possible to state that the specimens which I recorded in 1932 as A. maculata are in reality very distinct from A. grebnitzkii and may be separated by the following characters: (1) The rostral projection is long and acutely pointed, extending in front beyond the eye; (2) there is a prominent spine on the dorsal posterior margin of the fifth abdominal somite; (3) there are 12 spines on the telson whereas in A. grebnitzkii there are only 8; (4) there are 22 spines on the outer uropod whereas in A. grebnitzkii there are only 13.

Genus GASTROSACCUS Norman

Gastrosaccus NORMAN, 1868, p. 438.
Acanthocaris SIM, 1872, p. 185.
Haplostylus KOSSMANN, 1880, p. 94.
Pontomysis CZERNIAVSKY, 1882a, pp. 61, 70, 77.
Chlamydopleon ORTMANN, 1893, p. 25.

This genus is represented in the United States National Museum by several species, but only three are found in American waters—Gastrosaccus johnsoni, G. dissimilis, and the new species, G. mexicanus. All three are characterized by the curious and greatly modified third pleopod of the male but they may be separated by the following characters: G. johnsoni has no reflected lobes on the carapace and no spine on the fifth abdominal somite; G. dissimilis has no reflected lobes on the carapace but it has a prominent spine on the fifth abdominal somite; G. mexicanus has reflected lobes on the carapace but no spine on the fifth abdominal somite.

GASTROSACCUS SPINIFER (Goës)

Mysis spinifera GOËS, 1863, p. 174.

Occurrence.—SCOTLAND: Banff*, identified by A. M. Norman. ENGLAND: south of Start Point, Devonshire*, identified by G. E. Bullen.

Distribution.—Atlantic coasts of southern Europe.

GASTROSACCUS SANCTUS (van Beneden)

Mysis sancta VAN BENEDEN, 1861, pp. 17, 141, pl. 6, figs. 1–3.
Gastrosaccus sanctus NORMAN, 1868, p. 438.

Occurrence.—Cornwall, Helgoland*, identified by G. E. Bullen.

Distribution.—Atlantic coasts of southern Europe, Black Sea, Sea of Azov.

GASTROSACCUS PACIFICUS Hansen

Gastrosaccus pacificus HANSEN, 1912, p. 198, pl. 2, figs. 3a–3g.—TATTERSALL, 1922, p. 461, fig. 8a, b.

Distribution.—Gilbert Islands (Hansen); coasts of India (Tattersall); Philippine Islands.

Occurrence.—PHILIPPINE ISLANDS: *Albatross* station 5568, 2 males, 1 female. GILBERT ISLANDS (type)*, identified by H. J. Hansen (1912).

GASTROSACCUS sp. ?

Occurrence.—JAVA, 30 miles west of Tandjoeng Prioek Station, near Batavia, September 10, 1920, 1 immature male.

Remarks.—This specimen is too immature to identify with certainty. It belongs to the same group as *G. indicus*, *G. pacificus*, and *G. parva*, and it is almost certainly one of these species.

GASTROSACCUS INDICUS Hansen

Gastrosaccus indicus HANSEN, 1910, p. 56, pl. 8, figs. 2a–r.—TATTERSALL, 1911a, p. 125.—DELSMAN, 1939, p. 167.

Occurrence.—PHILIPPINE ISLANDS: *Albatross* station 5595, surface, 5 males, 2 females.

Distribution.—Waters of the Dutch East Indies (Hansen and Delsman); coasts of India (Tattersall); Philippine Islands.

GASTROSACCUS PHILIPPINENSIS, new species

FIGURE 25

Description.—Carapace produced in front into a short triangular pointed rostral plate, not extending forward as far as the cornea of the eye; no trace of reflected lobes on the dorsal median posterior margin.

Fifth abdominal somite without a dorsal spine.

Eyes small, pyriform, cornea occupying rather less than half of the entire eye including the eyestalk.

Antennular peduncle with two spines on the outer margin of the second joint.

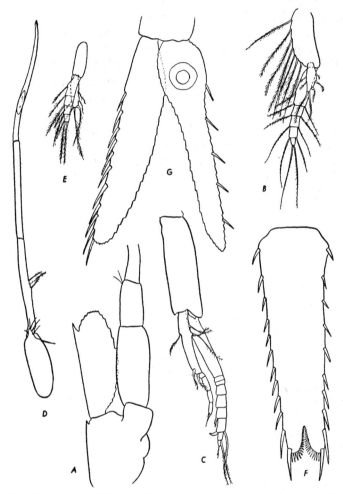

FIGURE 25.—*Gastrosaccus philippinensis*, new species: *a*, Antennal scale and peduncle, × 65¼; *b*, first pleopod of male, × 65¼; *c*, second pleopod of male, × 65¼; *d*, third pleopod of male, × 39; *e*, fourth pleopod of male, × 65¼; *f*, telson, × 65¼; *g*, uropods, × 65¼.

Antennal scale (fig. 25, *a*) 2½ times as long as broad, increasing in breadth toward the apex, terminal lobe one and a half times broader than long, overreaching the terminal spine of the outer margin and reaching a little beyond the end of the second joint of the antennal peduncle and halfway along the second joint of the antennular peduncle; antennal peduncle (fig. 25, *a*) extends halfway along the third joint of the antennular peduncle.

Carpopropodus of the endopod of the third to the eighth thoracic limbs divided into about 12 subjoints, dactylus absent.

Inner uropods (fig. 25, *g*) with five spines along the inner margin, widely spaced from the statocyst to near the apex.

Outer uropod (fig. 25, *g*) with eleven spines on the outer margin.

Telson (fig. 25, *f*) rather long and narrow, somewhat more than three times as long as broad at the base, with 10 to 12 spines on each lateral margin, the last two of which are longer than the remainder; cleft about one-tenth of the length of the telson with the usual serrated margins.

First pair of pleopods of the male (fig. 25, *b*) with the sympod rather narrowly ovate, with seven long setae on the outer margin; endopod one-jointed and shorter than the first joint of the exopod; exopod five jointed, the first joint as long as the remaining four combined.

Second pair of pleopods of the male (fig. 25, *a*) with the sympod three times as long as broad, about equal in length to the endopod and considerably shorter than the exopod; endopod 5-jointed, the first joint 1½ times as long as the remaining joints combined, a strong seta near the distal end of the first joint, another at the junction of the first and second joints, and two setae, one shorter than the other, on the terminal joint; exopod longer than the endopod, composed of nine joints, the first joint as long as the combined length of the remaining joints, sixth joint with a short seta on the inner corner, seventh joint with a long plumose seta on the outer corner and a short stout hooklike spine on the inner corner, ninth joint terminated by a short straight seta.

Third pleopod of the male (fig. 25, *d*) very long and styliform, reaching backward almost to the end of the telson, sympod three times as long as broad; endopod very short and one jointed; exopod very long and three jointed, the first and second joints subequal in length and nearly one and a half times as long as the sympod, both joints narrow, first joint with three setae about the middle of the outer margin, third joint half as long as the second and terminated by a single very long and strong spine one and a half times as long as the third joint, which appears to fit into a kind of socket on the third joint.

Fourth and fifth pairs of pleopods of the male (fig. 25, *e*) similar, with the sympod shorter than the endopod, latter 1-jointed, exopod longer than the endopod and 3-jointed.

Length of adult specimens of both sexes, 6 mm.

Type lot.—U.S.N.M. No. 81256, 58 males, 13 females, breeding, Nato Anchorage, Lagonoy Gulf, Luzon.

Occurrence.—The *Albatross* collected material from several Philippine localities: Nasugbu Bay Anchorage, electric light, surface, 7:30 p. m., January 21, 1908, 11 males, 2 females; Pasacao Anchorage, Ragay Gulf, Luzon, electric light, surface, 7 males, March 8, 1909, 3 males; Cabugao Bay, Catanduanes Island, Luzon, electric light, surface, 7 p. m., June 9, 1909, several hundreds of both sexes; Nato Anchorage, Lagonoy Gulf, Luzon, electric light, surface, 8 p. m., June 18, 1909, 58 males, 13 females, breeding (type lot); Talisse Island, north of Celebes, electric light, surface, November 8, 1909, 4 females, 2 males.

Distribution.—Known only from the waters around the Philippine Islands.

Remarks.—This species is closely allied to *G. indicus*, *G. pacificus*, and *G. parvus*, but it may be distinguished by the form of the male pleopods, especially that of the second and third pairs.

GASTROSACCUS JOHNSONI Tattersall

FIGURES 26–28

Gastrosaccus johnsoni TATTERSALL, 1937, p. 9, figs. 5–7.

Description.—Carapace (fig. 26, *a*) produced in front into a short triangular rostral plate with a subacute apex; dorsal posterior margin (fig. 26, *b*) of the carapace with a median triangular lobe and a broad rectangular lobe on each side of it, none of the lobes reflexed.

Eyes small (fig. 26, *a*), including the eyestalks twice as long as broad, cornea occupying the distal third of the whole eye and wider than long.

Antennular peduncle (fig. 26, *a*) with the first joint equal to the combined length of the second and third; two spines on the outer margin of the second joint and a similar spine near the distal end of the outer margin of the third joint.

Antennal peduncle (fig. 26, *a*) extending forward to the level of the distal end of the second joint of the antennular peduncle.

Antennal scale (fig. 26, *a*) shorter than the first two joints of the antennular peduncle, about three and a half times as long as broad, terminal joint marked off by a distinct suture.

Mouth parts and thoracic limbs essentially as in *G. sanctus;* carpopropodus of the endopod of the third to the eighth thoracic limbs (fig. 27, *f–g*) divided into 7 to 12 subjoints, dactylus very reduced; basal plate of the exopod of the first thoracic limb with the outer corner rounded, those of the remaining limbs with a distinct tooth at the outer corner.

Uropods (fig. 28, *b*) with 13 spines on the outer margin of the exopod and 2 spines on the inner margin of the endopod.

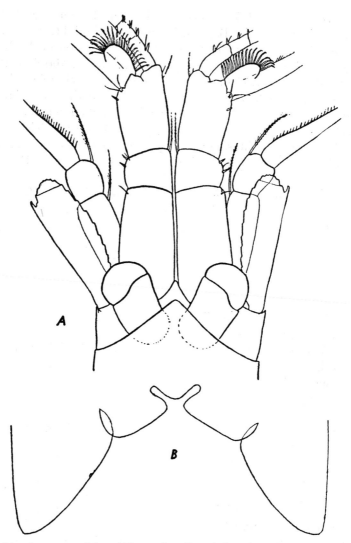

FIGURE 26.—*Gastrosaccus johnsoni* Tattersall: *a*, Dorsal view of anterior end to show rostral plate, eyes, antennular peduncle, and antennal scale, × 50; *b*, outline of posterior margin of carapace, × 50.

Telson (fig. 28, *a*) including the terminal spines, slightly shorter than the inner uropods, 2½ times as long as broad at the base, cleft of the usual type and with the usual armature, lateral margins with nine spines extending throughout their entire length, the distal pair of spines on each margin much larger than the rest, about three times as long as the antepenultimate spines, subequal in length and placed close together.

Male pleopods very distinctive, especially those of the second and third pairs; the endopod of all the pleopods of the male is composed of a single short joint; the exopod of the first pair (fig. 27, *a*) is much longer than the endopod and is composed of four joints; in the second pair (fig. 27, *b*) the sympod is very long and stout, 1½ times as long as the exopod, the endopod is single jointed and furnished with 8 or 9 delicate plumose setae, the exopod is 7-jointed, the terminal joint furnished with 2 long plumose setae; in the third pair (fig. 27, *c*) the sympod is about 2½ times as long as broad, shorter and not so stout as the sympod of the second pair and shorter than its own exopod, endopod single jointed and furnished with 2 short curved spines at the apex, the exopod is long and modified in the most extraordinary way into a very complicated copulatory organ (fig. 27, *c*);

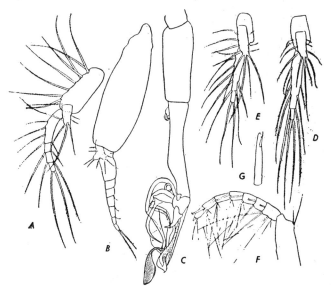

FIGURE 27.—*Gastrosaccus johnsoni* Tattersall: *a*, First pleopod of male, × 33⅓; *b*, second pleopod of male, × 33⅓; *c*, third pleopod of male, × 25; *d*, fourth pleopod of male, × 33⅓; *e*, fifth pleopod of male, × 33⅓; *f*, carpopropodus of endopod of one of posterior thoracic limbs, × 33⅓; *g*, one of setae of carpopropodus of one of posterior thoracic limbs, enlarged.

fourth and fifth pleopods of the male (figs. 27, *d–e*) very similar to one another, with a short rectangular sympod, a single-jointed endopod and a 2-jointed exopod, all furnished with the usual long plumose setae.

Length of adults of both sexes, 10 mm.

Occurrence.—EAST COAST OF THE UNITED STATES: *Albatross* station 2272, 2 adult females, 1 adult male. WEST INDIES: The Johnson-Smithsonian Expedition collected two lots of material from Luispena

Channel, Puerto Rico, surface, February 25, 1933, 10 specimens (series number 406) and 7 specimens (series number 521), and 1 specimen from Brewers Bay, St. Thomas, Virgin Islands, surface, March 1, 1933.

Distribution.—Known only from the original records from the waters of the West Indies, this record extends the known distribution of the species considerably northward to the American coast off North Carolina.

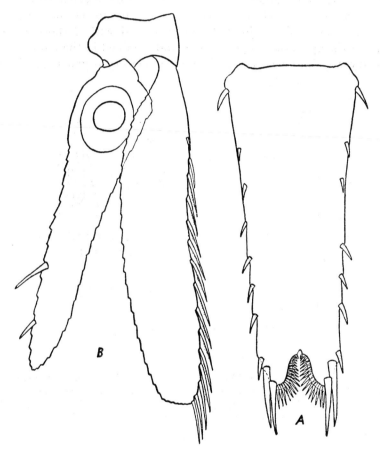

FIGURE 28.—*Gastrosaccus johnsoni* Tattersall: *a*, Telson, × 62½; *b*, uropods, × 62½.

Remarks.—This species is distinguished by the absence of reflected lobes on the carapace, the absence of a spine on the fifth abdominal somite, and the form of the third pleopod of the male. The specimens here recorded have been dried up at some time or other, and they are not in very good condition. Fortunately there is an adult male among them and the peculiar development of the third pleopod allows the specific determination of the specimens.

GASTROSACCUS DISSIMILIS Coifmann

FIGURE 29

? *Chlamydopleon aculeatum* ORTMANN, 1893, p. 25, pl. 2, fig. 1.
Gastrosaccus dissimilis COIFMANN, 1937, p. 5, fig. 2.

Occurrence.—Gulf of Mexico, Calcasieu Pass, La., No. 18, W. H. Spaulding collector, November 1906, 1 adult male.

Distribution.—Off the coast of South America, between Pernambuco and Rio de Janeiro (Coifmann) ; ? mouth of the River Tocantins (Ortmann). The present record is from the north side of the Gulf of Mexico, off the coast of Louisiana. All these localities suggest that the species is a shallow-water coastal form, probably brackish water in habit.

Remarks.—This species is very closely related to *G. johnsoni* but may be distinguished by the presence of a prominent median dorsal spine on the fifth abdominal somite, the longer and more acute rostral plate which extends forward as far as the distal end of the eye, and the somewhat different form of the modified third pleopod of the male. The present specimen agrees closely with the description and figures given by Coifmann (1937). The third pleopod of the male appears somewhat different from that figured by Coifmann, but this appendage is very difficult to interpret, and, moreover, Coifmann's specimens may not have been quite adult. I give here a figure of the third pleopod (fig. 29) in the present specimen for comparison. For the rest the agreement is so close that I feel justified in identifying it with Coifmann's species.

In 1893 Ortmann described a mysid under the name *Chlamydopleon aculeatum*, captured at the mouth of the Tocantins River, on the north coast of South America. The species ought certainly to be referred to the genus *Gastrosaccus*, but Ortmann's description is so inadequate that it is impossible to identify the species. I suggest that it is the same as *G. dissimilis*.

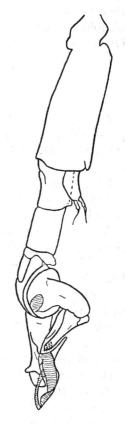

FIGURE 29.—*Gastrosaccus dissimilis* Coifmann: Third pleopod of male, × 34.

There is nothing in Ortmann's description and figures against this suggestion except the appearance of the third pleopod of the male in the figure of the whole animal from the lateral view given by Ortmann. The latter gives no detailed separate figure or description of this appendage, and in the figure referred to it appears as an elongate slender appendage which does not suggest the complicated third pleopod of *G. dissimilis*. It seems almost impossible that Ortmann could have overlooked the extraordinary structure of this appendage if it resembled in any way that which I figure here. Yet the agreement of the two forms is otherwise so close and the geographical localities in which they were found so approximate to one another that I tentatively put forward the suggestion that the two species are synonymous. The matter can be settled only if the type specimen of *C. aculeatum* is available for examination. If it is not, then Ortmann's name should be canceled as the species is unrecognizable. If my suggestion should eventually prove to be correct, then Ortmann's specific name *aculeatum* will take precedence over *dissimilis*.

GASTROSACCUS MEXICANUS, new species

FIGURE 30

Description.—Carapace produced into a short triangular rostral plate with an obtusely pointed apex, extending about halfway along the eye; a pair of reflected lobes on the dorsal posterior median margin.

Fifth abdominal somite without a dorsal spine.

Antennular peduncle with two spines on the outer margin of the second joint.

Antennal scale extending about halfway along the second joint of the antennular peduncle and slightly beyond the distal end of the second joint of its own peduncle, four times as long as broad, terminal lobe slightly overreaching the spine of the outer margin.

Carpopropodus of the endopod of the third to the eighth thoracic limbs divided into 7 to 9 subjoints, dactylus absent.

Inner uropod (fig. 30, *f*) with three spines on the inner margin, one near the statocyst, one near the tip and the third about two-thirds of the distance from the statocyst to the apex.

Outer uropod (fig. 30, *f*) with 14 to 16 spines on the outer margin.

Telson (fig. 30, *g*) rather long and narrow, about three times as long as broad; lateral margins with from 10 to 12 spines, the distal two of which are much larger than the others and placed quite close together; cleft about one-ninth of the length of the telson with the usual serrated margins.

First pair of pleopods of the male (fig. 30, *a*) with the sympod rectangular in shape, about twice as long as broad with the usual armature of seven long plumose setae; endopod 1-jointed, shorter than the first joint of the exopod; exopod 4-jointed, the first joint longer than the combined length of the other three.

Second pair of pleopods of the male (fig. 30, *b*) with the sympod three and a half times as long as broad and longer than the exopod;

endopod 1-jointed, shorter than the first joint of the exopod; exopod composed of six joints terminating in two long setae.

Third pair of pleopods of the male (fig. 30, c) stout, sympod four times as long as broad; endopod 1-jointed; exopod almost twice as

FIGURE 30.—*Gastrosaccus mexicanus*, new species: *a*, First pleopod of male, × 63; *b*, second pleopod of male, × 63; *c*, third pleopod of male, × 63; *d*, fourth pleopod of male, × 63; *e*, fifth pleopod of male, × 63; *f*, uropods, × 48; *g*, telson, × 63.

long as the sympod and profoundly and curiously modified in a manner that can best be described by a figure.

Fourth and fifth pairs of pleopods (figs. 30, *d–e*) of the male similar; endopod 1-jointed; exopod 3- or 4-jointed.

Length of adult specimen 7 mm.

Type lot.—U.S.N.M. No. 81257, numerous specimens, mostly immature, but one adult male, from Cape San Blas, Fla.

Occurrence.—GULF OF MEXICO: Cape San Blas, Fla., surface, electric light, March 7, 1885, numerous specimens, mostly immature, but one adult male (type lot). WEST COAST OF PANAMA: San José, Perlas Island, Gulf of Panama, Dr. Th. Mortensen collector, January 27, 1916, 2 males, 1 female.

Distribution.—The type specimens were collected off Cape San Blas, Fla., in the Gulf of Mexico. I have examined specimens taken by Dr. Th. Mortensen at San José, Perlas Islands, Gulf of Panama, which I am unable to separate from those collected off Florida. I cannot find any character by which they may be distinguished and must refer them to this species. If my identification is correct *G. mexicanus* is known from both sides of the Isthmus of Panama. It is the only mysid with such a distribution and is therefore of special interest. It seems probable that the species has reached the Pacific coast of Panama by migration through the Panama Canal and its probable brackish water habits would facilitate such migration.

Remarks.—This species is most closely related to *G. johnsoni* and to *G. dissimilis.* In all three species the exopod of the third pair of pleopods of the male is very stout and curiously modified, quite unlike that of any other species of the genus. The three species may be distinguished by the presence or absence of reflected lobes on the carapace and by the presence or absence of a spine on the fifth abdominal somite. *G. johnsoni* and *G. dissimilis* have no reflected lobes on the carapace, but in *G. mexicanus* reflected lobes are present on the carapace. *G. johnsoni* and *G. mexicanus* have no spine on the fifth abdominal somite, but *G. dissimilis* has a prominent spine on the fifth abdominal somite. These species also differ slightly in the form of the modified exopod of the third pleopods of the male. Otherwise the species are very similar in most details of their structure.

Genus ANCHIALINA Norman and Scott

Anchialus KRØYER, 1861, p. 58.
Anchialina NORMAN and SCOTT, 1906, p. 24.

ANCHIALINA TYPICA (Krøyer)

Anchialus typicus KRØYER 1861, p. 53, pl. 2, fig. 7a–1.
Anchialina typica HANSEN, 1910, p. 52, pl. 7, fig. 2a–k.—TATTERSALL, 1936a, p. 96.

Occurrence.—ATLANTIC OCEAN: Key West, Fla., electric light, surface, 1884, 1 male; Cape San Blas, electric light, surface, March 7, 1885, 32 males; John B. Henderson and Dr. Paul Bartsch collected material at four *Tomas Barrera* Expedition to Cuba stations: Off Santa Lucia, collection number 28, May 12, 1914, 6 males; Punta

Colorado, station 1C, collection number 240, 2 to 3 fathoms, from shell and grass, 3 females; Esperanza, between anchorage and entrance, station 13, collection number 396, 2 fathoms, mud and gravel bottom, June 2, 1914, 1 immature male; Ensenada de Cajon, off Cosmos, San Antonio, station 11, collection numbers 351–353, May 22-23, 1914, 1 male, 1 female; material was collected at six *Bache* stations: Station 10173, off Bermuda, latitude 32°27′ N., longitude 68°22′ W., 200–0 meters, April 2, 1914, 1 specimen; station 10178, off Bermuda, latitude 32°20′ N., longitude 64°21′ W., surface, February 17–18, 1914, 1 specimen; station 10182, off Bermuda, latitude 30°27′ N., longitude 66°05′ W., 1,800–0 meters, February 19–20, 1914, 1 specimen; station 10192, northeast of the Bahamas, latitude 28°35′ N., longitude 73°33′ W., 100–0 meters, February 26, 1914, 1 specimen; station 10203, Straits of Florida, latitude 25°34′ N., longitude 79°42′ W., 75–0 meters, March 20, 1914, 1 specimen; station 10208, north of Bahama Bank, latitude 27°46′ N., longitude 78°56′ W., 100–0 meters, March 21, 1914, 2 specimens; 6 lots were collected by the Johnson-Smithsonian expedition: Anchorage off Playa de Fajardo, Puerto Rico, series number 358A, surface, February 23, 1933, 10+ specimens; station 74, series number 387B, latitude 18°36′10′′ N., longitude 65°48′30′′ W., 360 fathoms, February 24, 1933, 15+ specimens; Luispena Channel, Puerto Rico, series number 406, surface, February 25, 1933, 25+ specimens; Luispena Channel, Puerto Rico, series number 407b, surface, February 25, 1933, 50 plus specimens; Brewers Bay, St. Thomas, Virgin Islands, series number 521, surface, March 1, 1933, 10+ specimens; station 109, series number 747, latitude 20°05′00′′ N., longitude 68°10′00′′ W., 2,900 fathoms, March 9, 1933, 1 specimen. PACIFIC OCEAN: Philippine Islands; Arno Atoll, Marshall Islands, electric light, surface, January 26, 1900, 46 males, 1 breeding female, 2 immature; the *Albatross* collected at 10 Philippine stations: China Sea, off Luzon, Port Binanga Anchorage, electric light, surface, 7 p. m., January 8, 1908, 85 males; China Sea off Luzon, Nasugbu Bay Anchorage, electric light, surface, 7 p. m., January 15, 1908, 22 males; China Sea, off Luzon, Nasugbu Bay Anchorage, electric light, surface, 7: 30 p. m., January 21, 1908, several hundreds, mostly males, a few breeding females; Tanon Strait, east coast of Negros, Balamban Anchorage, electric light, surface, 8 p. m., April 2, 1908, 1 male; China Sea, off southern Luzon, Veradero Bay Anchorage, electric light, surface, 8 p. m., July 22, 1908, 1 male, 1 female; station 5435, Cuyos Islands, Bisucay Island, 6 males; east coast of Luzon, Catanduanes Islands, Cabugao Bay, electric light, surface, 7 p. m., June 9, 1909, 43 males, 1 breeding female; east coast of Luzon, Lagonoy Gulf, Nato Anchorage, electric light, surface, 7: 30 p. m., June 18, 1909, several hundreds, mostly males, some breeding females; between Leyte and Mindanao, Mahinig Anchorage, Camiguin

Island, electric light, surface, August 3, 1909, 2 males; northern Mindanao, Opol, electric light, surface, August 4, 1909, 2 males. HAWAIIAN ISLANDS: *Albatross* station 3812*, 3829*, 3921*, identified by A. E. Ortmann (1905). GILBERT ISLANDS*, identified by H. J. Hansen (1912).

Distribution.—Western and tropical Atlantic, West Indies, Gulf of Siam, East Indies, Philippine Islands, Great Barrier Reef Lagoon, and Hawaii.

Remarks.—This species is abundant in the waters of the East Indies and Philippine Islands. Breeding females are recorded for January, June, and July, and it is probable that the species breeds all the year around. Most of the records from the Philippine Islands are of specimens captured in darkness at the surface by tow nets fitted with electric light. The majority of the specimens thus taken were males. In the large catches at Nasugbu Bay and Lagonoy Gulf I estimate that more than 90 percent of the specimens were males, while at all the other stations males alone were taken.

ANCHIALINA GROSSA Hansen

Anchialina grossa HANSEN, 1910, p. 54, pl. 7, figs. 3a–n; pl. 8, figs. 1a–d; 1912, p. 96.—TATTERSALL, 1922, p. 458, fig. 6; 1936b, p. 148.
Anchialina frontalis ZIMMER, 1915b, p. 159, figs. 1–6.

Occurrence.—PHILIPPINE ISLANDS: The *Albatross* collected specimens at six stations: Jolo Anchorage, surface, electric light, March 5, 1908, 1 female, breeding; Mansalay Anchorage, southeastern Mindanao, surface, electric light, June 3, 1908, 9 p. m., 1 adult male; Looc Bay Anchorage, southern Luzon, surface, electric light, July 18, 1908, 8:45 p. m., 8 males; Cabugao Bay, Catanduanes Island, east coast of Luzon, surface, electric light, June 9, 1909, 7 p. m., 1 adult, 2 immature males, 7 adult breeding females, 11 immature females; Opol, Macaljar Bay, Mindanao, surface, electric light, August 4, 1909, 4 adult males, 10 adult breeding females; Talisse Island, north of Celebes, surface, electric light, November 8, 1909, 7 males, none completely adult, 1 adult breeding female, 2 immature females. GILBERT ISLANDS*: Identified by H. J. Hansen (1912).

Distribution.—Bay of Bengal, Gulf of Siam, waters of the Dutch East Indies (Hansen, 1910); Gilbert Islands (Hansen, 1912); Bay of Bengal (Zimmer, 1915b); India (Tattersall, 1922); Barrier Reef (Tattersall, 1936b); Philippine Islands.

ANCHIALINA OBTUSIFRONS Hansen

Anchialina obtusifrons HANSEN, 1912, p. 197, pl. 2, figs. 4a–c.

Occurrence.—MARSHALL ISLANDS: Collected by the *Albatross* at Arno Atoll, surface of the lagoon, electric light, January 24–26, 1900,

4 males, 2 females. PHILIPPINE ISLANDS: Collected by the *Albatross* at Subig Bay Anchorage, China Sea, off southern Luzon, surface, electric light, January 6, 1908, 7 p. m., 2 males. GILBERT ISLANDS*: Identified by Hansen (type).

Distribution.—Known previously only from the Gilbert Islands, the present paper extends the range to the Marshall and Philippine Islands.

ANCHIALINA PENICILLATA Zimmer

Anchialina penicillata ZIMMER, 1915b, p. 161, figs. 7–12.

Occurrence.—MARSHALL ISLANDS: Arno Atoll, surface of the lagoon, electric light, 1 male, January 24–26, 1900. PHILIPPINE ISLANDS: *Albatross* station 5595, surface, 2 adult and 5 immature males, 6 adult breeding females.

Distribution.—Known from the type specimen captured during a voyage from Ceylon to Dampier Strait (Zimmer, 1915b); New South Wales (Tattersall, 1940); Marshall Islands; Philippine Islands.

ANCHIALINA ZIMMERI, new species

FIGURE 31

Description.—This new species is very closely allied to *A. penicillata* Zimmer, and it agrees with that species in the densely setose ornamentation of the inner margin of the antennular peduncle in the male. It should be emphasized that this character is definitely a secondary sexual feature, not present in the female. The new species differs from Zimmer's species in the following points:

(1) The presence of microscopic spinules on the outer part of the third joint of the antennular peduncle (fig. 31, *a*) and on the second joint of the antennal peduncle (fig. 31, *b*). (2) The antennal scale (fig. 31, *b*) is somewhat narrower than in *A. penicillata*, being three times as long as broad, whereas in the latter it is only slightly more than twice as long as broad. (3) The two joints of the propodus of the endopods of the 3 to 8 thoracic limbs are subequal to the carpal joint (fig. 31, *e*), whereas in *A. penicillata* the carpal joint is longer than the combined length of the two propodal joints. (4) In the form of the third pleopod of the male (fig. 31, *f*, *g*). The exopod is 11-jointed. The ninth joint has no lamellalike expansion on the outer side. The tenth joint is large and swollen and has a large strong spinelike process at each distal corner. The outer process is longer than the inner and gently curved into an S-shape, with tubercles on its outer margin. The inner process is slightly curved and is longer than the spines on the terminal joint. The latter is very small and almost embedded in the tenth joint, and bears three subequal spines all shorter than either of the long processes on the tenth joint.

The remaining characters of this species are closely similar to those of *A. penicillata*. I give figures of the first and second thoracic limbs (fig. 31, *c*, *d*), and the rostral process, telson, and uropods present no special points to distinguish them from the corresponding organs in

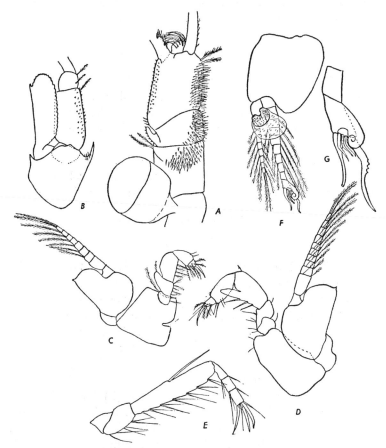

FIGURE 31.—*Anchialina zimmeri*, new species: *a*, Antennular peduncle and eye, × 39; *b*, antennal scale and peduncle, × 39; *c*, first thoracic limb, × 39; *d*, second thoracic limb, × 39; *e*, distal part of endopod of third thoracic limb, × 39; *f*, third pleopod of male, × 39; *g*, distal part of exopod of third pleopod of male, more highly magnified.

A. penicillata. The third pleopod of the male is the main distinguishing feature of the new species.

Type lot.—U.S.N.M. No. 81258, 13 adult and 4 immature males, 5 adult breeding females, Sablayan Bay Anchorage, Mindanao Strait, Philippine Islands.

Occurrence.—The *Albatross* collected only the type material, 13 adult and 4 immature males and 5 adult breeding females, from Sablayan Bay Anchorage, Mindanao Strait, surface, electric light, December 13, 1908, 9 p. m.

Distribution.—Known only from the specimens from the Philippine Islands.

ANCHIALINA AGILIS (G. O. Sars)

Anchialus agilis G. O. SARS, 1877, p. 78, pls. 26–28.

Occurrence.—Scilly Islands, Cornwall, England*. Identified by G. E. Bullen.

Distribution.—Mediterranean; eastern Atlantic from Spain to the English Channel and the coasts of Ireland.

Subfamily MYSINAE

Two pairs of oöstegites in the female; labrum generally broader than long, without frontal process, rounded behind; mandibles with the cutting lobe not expanded and its edge dentate; maxillules normal with oblique lacinia; maxillipeds with the sixth joint normal and without any free and aculeate terminal margin; endopod of the third to the eighth thoracic limbs with the carpus either distinct and undivided and the propodus alone subdivided into subjoints, or the carpus and propodus fused and the combined joints subdivided into several subjoints; fourth pleopod of the male with the rami either similar and well developed, or generally with one of the rami, most frequently the exopod, more or less elongated, while the remaining ramus and both rami of the second and third pair are either well developed, normal, or more or less reduced, sometimes all the pleopods in the male rudimentary; first abdominal somite in the female without lateral lamellae; exopod of the uropods undivided, its outer margin setose and without spines; endopod of the uropods generally considerably shorter than the exopod.

Tribe ERYTHROPINI

Endopods of the third to the eighth thoracic limbs with the carpus distinct and undivided and the propodus divided into a small number (usually two) of subjoints; four posterior pleopods of the male well developed, exopod of the fourth pair rarely and at most only slightly elongated, endopod of the same pair sometimes elongated, and in several genera one of the rami with modified setae; antennal scale nearly always with a pronounced external tooth, and, even if this is wanting, at most the distal half of the outer margin setose; scale may be styliform or wanting.

Remarks.—Twenty-six genera are included in this tribe, and 16 of these occur in the National Museum collection. In general, the species of this tribe inhabit moderately deep and deep water and are seldom actually littoral in habit.

Genus HOLMESIELLA Ortmann

HOLMESIELLA ANOMALA Ortmann

FIGURES 32, 33

Holmesiella anomala ORTMANN, 1908, p. 6, pl. 1, figs. 1–13.—ESTERLY, 1914, p. 14, pl. 1, figs. 11, 17.—TATTERSALL, 1933, p. 5.

Occurrence.—OFF CALIFORNIA: *Albatross* stations 2892, 1 adult female; 2896, 1 adult female; 2925, 1 adult female; 4307, 2 adult females, 26 to 32 mm.; 4334, 1 adult female, 32 mm.; 4351, 1 adult female; 4379, 2 adult females, 20 mm.; 4380, 1 adult male, 1 adult female, 35 mm.; 4399, 1 female, 20 mm., not quite adult; 4401, 1 adult female, 32 mm.; 4415, 1 adult female; 4423, 2 adult males, 32 mm., and 1 adult female, 35 mm.; 4429, 1 immature; 4435, 1 female, 25 mm.; 4461, 1 adult male, 31 mm., 2 adult females, 31–33 mm.; 4513, 2 adult males, 32 mm., 1 subadult male, 28 mm., 2 adult females, 28 mm.; 4515, 2 adult females, 33 mm., 2 immature females, 24 mm.; 4516, 1 adult male, 32 mm.; 4522, 1 immature female; 4533, 1 female, 25 mm.; 4540, 1 adult female, 35 mm., 2 specimens, 25–30 mm. WEST COAST OF THE UNITED STATES BETWEEN CALIFORNIA AND BRITISH COLUMBIA: *Albatross* stations 2890, 1 adult female; 3112, 2 adult males, 35 mm.; 3126, 1 adult female, 35 mm.; 3162, 1 adult female, 30 mm.; 3348, 3 adult females, 32–33 mm., 1 immature female; 3669, 1 adult female, 35 mm., 1 female not quite adult, 27 mm. OFF BRITISH COLUMBIA: *Albatross* stations 2860, 1 immature female, 20 mm.; 2861, 3 adult males, 20–23 mm., 3 immature specimens; 4192*, identified by Ortmann (1908); 4756, 3 immature males, 9 adult females with eggs in the brood pouch, 20–25 mm., 8 immature females; G. H. Wailes collected 1 specimen from Hecate Channel, Esperanza, Vancouver Island, No. 985, May 29, 1928 and 1 specimen from Sherringham, Barkley Sound. OFF ALASKA: *Albatross* stations 3211, 1 adult male, 37 mm., 1 adult female, 32 mm.; 3337, 1 adult female, 37 mm.; 4251*, 4257*, 4264* (types and cotypes) identified by Ortmann (1908). BERING SEA: *Albatross* stations 3227, 19 adult females, 13 adult males, up to 37 mm.; 3315, 1 immature female, 26 mm.; 3316, 1 adult male, 36 mm.; 3324, 1 adult male, 32 mm.; 3325, 1 adult female, 37 mm.; 3329, 2 adult females, 37–38 mm.; 3330, 2 adult males, 35–40 mm., 5 adult females, 35–40 mm.; 3331, 1 male, 3 females, 32 mm.; 3332, 1 immature female, 28 mm.; 3608, 1 adult male; 4781, 2 adult females, 33–37 mm., 8 immature females. OFF KOREA: *Albatross* station 4861, 1 adult female, 34 mm.

Distribution.—This species would appear to be widely distributed on the continental slope of the Pacific Ocean from California right around to the coasts of Korea. Previous records include the types from Alaska (Ortmann, 1908), specimens from California (Esterly, 1914), and specimens from British Columbia (Tattersall, 1933).

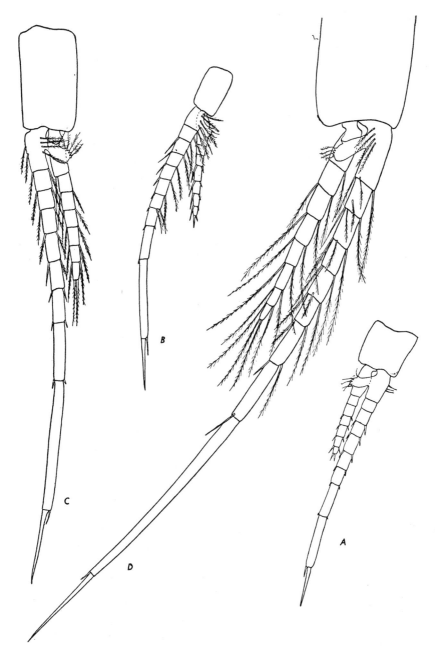

FIGURE 32.—*Holmesiella anomala* Ortmann: A series of fourth pleopods of male of large deep-water race to illustrate changes with growth: *a*, 27 mm.; *b*, 30 mm.; *c*, 33 mm.; *d*, 37 mm. (all × 20).

Remarks.—I give figures of four stages in the development of the fourth pleopod of the male. Figure 32, *a*, is from a male specimen, 27 mm. length, figure 32, *b*, from a male of the same length but showing a slightly advanced condition of development, figure 32, *c*, from a male measuring 30 mm. in length, and figure 32, *d*, from a fully adult

male, 37 mm. The general form of the pleopod is laid down quite early, and in the pleopod of the smallest male, 27 mm., the increase in length of the distal joints of the endopod is already indicated. This confirms Ortmann's observation on this point. Progress to full maturity is marked by the greater relative increase in length of the distal joint of the endopod and its terminal spine, and in the gradual increase in length of the setae of the whole pleopod and their change from simple setae to plumose setae. In the smallest pleopod figured none of the setae are plumose, and they are all quite short and spine-like. In the largest pleopod the setae are much longer, and all but two or three on the distal joints of the endopod have become plumose. This series of pleopods is interesting as suggesting a means whereby it is possible to judge the state of maturity of male specimens of Mysidae, namely, the degree to which the setae have become plumose.

I also give a figure (fig. 33) of the fourth pleopod of a male, 20 mm. in length, from *Albatross* station 4756, off the coast of British Columbia in 115 fathoms. It will be seen that it agrees in every way with the pleopod from a male of 37 mm. taken off Alaska. Nine females from this station averaged only 22 mm. in length but all carried eggs or embryos in the brood pouch. I have already noted (1933) that specimens from British Columbia, col-

FIGURE 33.—*Holmesiella anomala* Ortmann: Fourth pleopod of adult male, 20 mm., from *Albatross* station 4756, × 20.

lected in depths from 50 to 120 fathoms, were much smaller than Ortmann's types and were mature at 24 mm. I could not find any character, except size, to distinguish these smaller specimens from the large specimens from Alaska. Esterly (1914), in noting this species from California, says that the largest specimens measured 20 to 21 mm., but he does not give any details as to the depth at which they were captured, nor was he quite sure whether they were adult. It may be that there is a more coastal race of this species, smaller than the deep-water race, extending down the whole western coast of America from British Columbia to California in depths of about 100 fathoms or so. The deep-water race also has a similar distribution, though in much deeper water, for specimens in the above list of records, measuring up to 37 mm., were found all along the coast from Alaska to California. An examination of these records does suggest that northern specimens of the deep-water race tend to be larger than the southern and that the species tends to get into deeper water in more southern latitudes. The average size of adult specimens from Alaska is 37 mm., and from California only 32 mm. The average depth of the Alaska stations is 300 fathoms, and of the California stations 406 fathoms. The evidence is not conclusive since, though there are over 150 specimens, they were collected over a very wide area and the number of adult specimens from any one locality or area is not large.

Ii (1937, p. 200) has described a new species of the genus, *H. affinis*, from Japan. It is separated from *H. anomala* on three characters: (1) The shape of the third joint of the antennal peduncle; (2) the presence of small epipodial processes on the basal joint of the endopods of the third to the eighth thoracic limbs; and (3) the form of the endopod of the fourth pleopod of the male, which is only slightly longer than the exopod and does not have the greatly elongate distal joints found in *H. anomala*. Of these differences the second disappears in the light of the present specimens in which epipodial processes are present on the endopods of the third to the eighth thoracic limbs. The other two characters would appear to be distinctive. Ii's specimens measured 15 mm., and at first sight it appeared as if *H. affinis* could be regarded as a smaller coastal race of *H. anomala* occurring off Japan, similar to the smaller coastal race occurring off the west coast of America. The difficulty of so regarding it lies in the form of the fourth pleopod of the male. In the American coastal race this appendage is in every way similar to the same appendage of the large deep-water race and, moreover, I have shown above that even in immature specimens the general plan of the adult pleopod is laid down. The fourth pleopod of the male of *H. affinis* is quite different from the same appendage in *H. anomala*, even of immature specimens. The latter species does occur off the coasts of Korea, as evidenced from the specimen recorded above from *Albatross* station 4861, which was a female measuring 34 mm., which I could not distinguish from *H. anomala*. Ii unfortunately does not give the depth at which his specimens were taken.

Genus ERYTHROPS G. O. Sars

Erythrops G. O. SARS, 1869, p. 325.

ERYTHROPS ERYTHROPHTHALMA (Goës)

FIGURE 34

Mysis erythrophthalma GOËS, 1863, p. 178.
Nematopus goesii G. O. SARS, 1866, p. 96.
Erythrops goësii G. O. SARS, 1870b, p. 24, pl. 1.—S. I. SMITH, 1879, p. 92.—M. J. RATHBUN, 1905, p. 28.
Erythrops erythrophthalma GARDINER, 1934, p. 560.—TATTERSALL, 1939b, p. 282.
Erythrops microphthalmus CALMAN, 1901 ?, p. 24.

Occurrence.—EAST COAST OF UNITED STATES : U. S. Fish Commission locality 221, Massachusetts Bay, off Salem, 1 female; U. S. Fish Com-

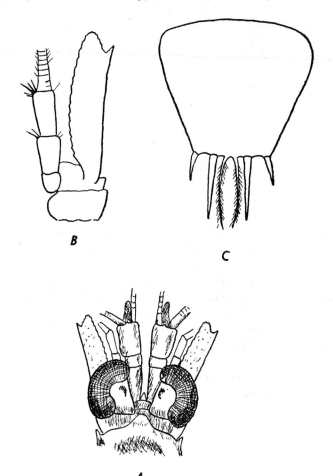

FIGURE 34.—*Erythrops erythrophthalma* (Goës): *a,* Dorsal view of anterior end; *b,* antennal scale and peduncle; *c,* telson. (After G. O. Sars.)

mission locality 321, off Cape Cod, 29½ fathoms, 1879, 1 male; U. S. Fish Commission locality 322, off Cape Cod, 67 fathoms, 1879, 1 female; *Fish Hawk* stations 993, latitude 40°28′ N., longitude 70°44′ W., 39 fathoms, September 7, 1881, 7 adults, 8 immature males; 1089, Cape Cod Lighthouse, 110 fathoms, August 3, 1882, 1 female; 1090*, off Cape Cod; *Speedwell* stations 5*, 25*, 30*, 81*, identified by Smith (1879); *Albatross* station 2453*.

Distribution.—This species is not uncommon off the east coast of North America. Smith (1879) recorded it from Massachusetts Bay, 20 to 48 fathoms. I have recorded it from several places in the Gulf of St. Lawrence from 40 to 275 meters and Gardiner (1934) from one locality in the Bay of Fundy.

ERYTHROPS MICROPS G. O. Sars

Nematopus microps G. O. SARS, 1864, p. 256.
Erythrops microphthalma G. O. SARS, 1870b, p. 30, pl. 2, figs. 13–19.
Erythrops microps ZIMMER, 1904, p. 447, figs. 99–101; 1909, p. 81, figs. 160–163.

Occurrence.—NORTHEAST COAST OF THE UNITED STATES: *Albatross* station 2046, 1 male.

Distribution.—New to the American fauna. Widely distributed in the boreal North Atlantic from the coasts of Ireland, Norway, and Greenland in deep water.

ERYTHROPS ABYSSORUM G. O. Sars

Erythrops abyssorum G. O. SARS, 1869, p. 326; 1870b, p. 36, pl. 5, figs. 1–12.

Occurrence.—NORTHEAST COAST OF THE UNITED STATES: *Albatross* stations 2046, 1 male, 1 female; 2179, 1 female; 2215, 1 female.

Distribution.—New to the American fauna. Its general distribution is similar to that of *E. microps*.

ERYTHROPS YONGEI Tattersall

Erythrops yongei TATTERSALL, 1936b, p. 149, fig. 2.

Occurrence.—*Albatross* station 5456, 1 female, 5.5 mm.

Remarks.—The single specimen is not in good condition, but it appears to agree in all essential characters with the type specimen. Unfortunately it does not throw any further light on this somewhat anomalous member of the genus *Erythrops*. One addition must be made to the characters given in my earlier description. There is a slender fingerlike process on the eye which originates on the inner upper surface of the eyestalk and projects over the cornea. It is as long as the cornea is deep.

Distribution.—This species was originally described from a single specimen collected off the Barrier Reef, Queensland, in 400 meters. Its occurrence off the Philippine Islands marks a considerable extension of its known geographical distribution. It appears to be a bathypelagic species, since both known specimens were taken by means of deep-water tow nets.

Genus EUCHAETOMERA G. O. Sars

Euchaetomera G. O. SARS, 1884, p. 41; 1885, p. 211.

EUCHAETOMERA TYPICA Tattersall, 1926

Euchaetomera typica G. O. SARS, 1884, p. 41; 1885, p. 211, pl. 37, figs. 1–20.—TATTERSALL, 1926, p. 10.

Occurrence.—BERMUDA: *Bache* stations 10173, 200–0 meters, February 4, 1914, 3 specimens; 10187, 200–0 meters, February 23, 1914, 1 female; both identified by Tattersall, 1926. GULF OF PANAMA: *Albatross* station H2619*, identified by Ortmann (1894). OFF GALÁPAGOS ISLANDS: *Albatross* station 4734*, identified by Hansen (1912).

Distribution.—The record of this species made by me in 1926 is the only one from American waters. I have also seen a specimen caught at Bermuda and kindly sent to me by Dr. R. Gurney, by whom it was collected; the range now includes the Gulf of Panama and the Galápagos Islands. The species is widely distributed in the tropical and subtropical waters of the world.

EUCHAETOMERA TENUIS G. O. Sars

Euchaetomera tenuis G. O. SARS, 1884, p. 42; 1885, p. 214, pl. 37, figs. 21–24.—ORTMANN, 1893, p. 23.—COLOSI, 1919, p. 7; 1920, p. 238.—TATTERSALL, 1926, p. 10; 1936a, p. 96.

Occurrence.—WESTERN ATLANTIC: *Bache* stations 10173, off Bermuda, latitude 32°27′ N., longitude 68°22′ W., 200–0 meters, February 4, 1914, 1 specimen; 10200, Straits of Florida, latitude 23°32′ N., longitude 81°48′ W., 500–0 meters, March 18, 1914, 1 specimen; 10211, North of Bahama Bank, latitude 28°08′ N., longitude 76°48′ W., 500–0 meters, March 22, 1914, 2 specimens. GALÁPAGOS ISLANDS: *Albatross* stations 4717*, 4719*, 4721*, identified by Hansen (1912).

Distribution.—The type specimen of this species was collected by the *Challenger* expedition at the surface off the coasts of Chile. Ortmann (1893) and Tattersall (1926 and 1936a) have recorded the species from the Atlantic slope of eastern America and Colosi's record is from the Galápagos Islands. No other previous American records are known, but Bermuda, Straits of Florida, and north of the Bahama Banks are now included. The species has a similar distribution in the warmer waters of the globe to *E. typica*.

EUCHAETOMERA PLEBEJA Hansen

Euchaetomera plebeja HANSEN, 1912, p. 202, pl. 3, figs. 1a–b.

Occurrence.—OFF PERU: *Albatross* station 4676* (type), identified by Hansen (1912).

Distribution.—Off Baja California and Peru.

Genus METERYTHROPS S. I. Smith

Meterythrops S. I. SMITH, 1879, p. 93.

METERYTHROPS PICTA Holt and Tattersall

Meterythrops picta HOLT and TATTERSALL, 1905, p. 116, pl. 19, figs. 5–7 ; pl. 25, figs. 8, 9.

Occurrence.—NORTHEAST COAST OF THE UNITED STATES : *Fish Hawk* station 994, latitude 39°40' N., longitude 71°30' W., 368 fathoms, September 8, 1881, 1 female.

Distribution.—New to the American fauna. This species is probably bathypelagic rather than bottom living, and it is widely distributed in the Atlantic Ocean mainly in temperate and boreal waters.

METERYTHROPS ROBUSTA S. I. Smith

FIGURE 35

Mysid nearest to *Erythrops* and *Parerythrops* WHITEAVES, 1874a, p. 4 ; 1874b, p. 191.

Meterythrops robusta S. I. SMITH, 1879, p. 93, pl. 12, figs. 1, 2.—WHITEAVES, 1901, p. 247.—STEPHENSEN, 1913, p. 71 ; 1933, p. 12.—KINDLE and WHITTAKER, 1918, p. 252.—TATTERSALL, 1933, p. 8 ; 1939 b, p. 283.

Parerythrops robusta M. RATHBUN, 1905, p. 28.

Occurrence.—EAST COAST OF THE UNITED STATES : U. S. Fish Commission localities 188, Gulf of Maine, 1878, 1 female; 322, off Cape Cod, 67 fathoms, 1879, 1 adult female; 355, off Cape Cod, 1879, 1 adult male. *Speedwell* stations 5* and 24* (types and cotypes) identified by S. I. Smith (1879). WEST COAST OF THE UNITED STATES : *Albatross* station 2842, 4 adult females, 2 adult males.

Distribution.—Except for Stephensen's Greenland records (1913, 1933), this species was not recorded from American waters after Smith's original records until 1933, in which year I recorded it from the west coast of America, off British Columbia. The record from *Albatross* station 2842 confirms the occurrence of the species in the Pacific. In 1939 I recorded the species from several localities in the Gulf of St. Lawrence and several localities off the east coast of the United States now extended the range. The bathymetric range of this species appears to be from 33–150 fathoms, and I am unable to trace any record from deeper water than this.

METERYTHROPS MICROPHTHALMA, new species

FIGURE 36

Description.—This new species is very similar to *M. robusta* Smith, but differs in the following characters:

(1) The eye (fig. 36, *a*) is considerably smaller. It is hardly wider than the basal joint of the antennular peduncle and scarcely as long

as this joint.   On the dorsal surface of the eyestalk there is a prominent tubercle.   The pigment is golden-brown.   In *M. robusta* the eye
is very large, more than twice as wide as the basal joint of the antennular peduncle and as long as the first two joints of the antennular
peduncle.   There is no tubercle on the dorsal surface of the eyestalk.

(2) The antennal scale (fig. 36, *b*), while substantially of the same
shape in the two species, is more slender in *M. microphthalma*, than in

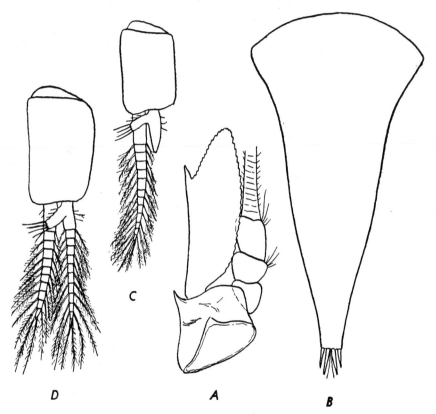

FIGURE 35.—*Meterythrops robusta* S. I. Smith: *a*, Antennal scale; *b*, telson; *c*, first pleopod
of male; *d*, second pleopod of male. (After G. O. Sars.)

M. robusta.   In the former species it is nearly four times as long as
broad, whereas in the latter species it is only three times as long as
broad.

(3) The inner uropod is without spines on its inner margin.   In
M. robusta there is a long series of spines, about 30 in number, extending from the statocyst almost to the apex.

Type lot.—Two adult males, two adult females, U.S.N.M. No. 81259,
from Japan, *Albatross* station 4800.

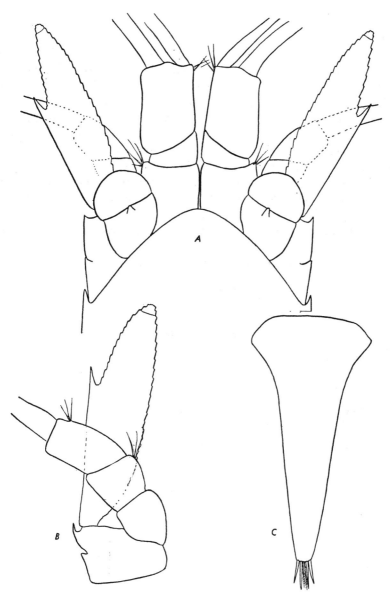

FIGURE 36.—*Meterythrops microphthalma*, new species: *a*, Dorsal view of anterior end to show eye, rostral plate antennular peduncle, and antennal scale, × 20; *b*, antennal scale and peduncle, × 25; *c*, telson, × 25.

Occurrence.—JAPAN: *Albatross* stations 4800, 2 adult males, 2 adult females (type lot); 4862, 1 male; 5030, 14 males, 13 females, 2 immature.

Distribution.—Known only from the present records from deep water off the east coasts of Korea and Japan.

Remarks.—This new species is remarkably similar to *M. robusta*, and apart from the points noted its characters are so very much the same as those of the latter species that the figures given by Sars and Smith for *M. robusta* will suffice for *M. microphthalma.* I give a figure of the telson (fig. 36, *c*) of the new species merely to emphasize the similarity of the two forms. The most conspicuous difference between the two forms is in the size of the eye. The difference is most marked even to the naked eye, and it may be correlated with depth, *M. microphthalma* living in deeper water, 200 to 1,000 fathoms, as against a maximum depth of 130 fathoms recorded for *M. robusta,* off Norway. The tubercle of the eyestalk of *M. microphthalma* may be a compensatory sensory development for the reduction in the size of the eye.

Genus METAMBLYOPS Tattersall

Metamblyops TATTERSALL, 1907, p. 106.

METAMBLYOPS MACROPS Tattersall

FIGURES 37, 38

Metamblyops macrops TATTERSALL, 1937, p. 15, figs. 9, 10.

Description.—I reproduce here the original description and figures of this species.

Carapace (fig. 37, *a*) hardly or not at all produced into a rostral plate, leaving the whole of the eye stalks and eyes, the antennular and antennal peduncles completely uncovered, front margin broadly and evenly arcuate, anterolateral corners rounded.

Eyes (fig. 37, *a*) relatively large and on enormous stalks; in lateral view the cornea is large and globular, without papilla, pigment reddish brown.

Antennal scale (fig. 37, *a*) extending for one-quarter of its length beyond the antennular peduncle, rather narrow, six times as long as broad; terminal lobe extending some distance beyond the spine of the outer margin, twice as long as broad, with a distal joint marked off by a suture.

Telson (fig. 37, *b*) narrowly triangular in shape, two and a half times as long as broad at its base, apex rounded and entire, lateral margins armed along the distal half with about 15 spines increasing somewhat in length toward the apex (spines on the apex broken away so that their exact arrangement cannot be established).

Uropods (fig. 37, *b*) both rather slender, inner one and a half times as long as the telson, with a single spine on the inner margin in the region of the statocyst; outer twice as long as the telson.

Length of an adult female 11 mm.

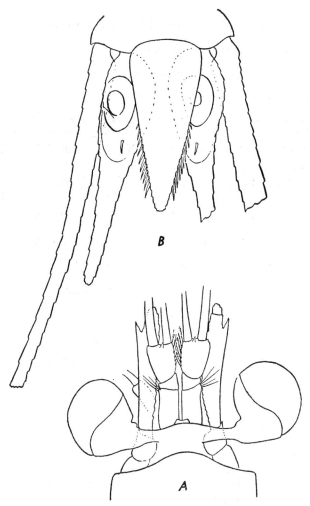

FIGURE 37.—*Metamblyops macrops* Tattersall: *a*, Dorsal view of anterior end to show rostral plate, eyes, antennular peduncle, and antennal scale, × 22½; *b*, uropods and telson, × 40.

The form of the endopods of the second and third thoracic limbs (figs. 38, *a*, *b*) are of the typical Erythropini form, rather long and slender, the carpus of the third endopod distinct and separated by a proximal oblique suture; propodus divided by a transverse suture into two subjoints.

Occurrence.—Johnson-Smithsonian expedition serial number 573, station 99, latitude 18°40′ N., longitude 64°51′ W., 200 fathoms, March 3, 1933, 1 female, 11 mm.

Distribution.—Known only from the above recorded type specimen from the Caribbean Sea.

Genus KATERYTHROPS Holt and Tattersall

Katerythrops HOLT and TATTERSALL, 1905, p. 117.

KATERYTHROPS OCEANAE Tattersall

Katerythrops oceanae TATTERSALL, 1926, p. 10.

Occurrence.—EAST COAST OF THE UNITED STATES: *Bache* stations 10211, latitude 28°8′ N., longitude 76°48′ W., 500 to 0 meters, February 22, 1914; 10166, latitude 32°33′ N., longitude 72°14′ W., 1,100 to 0 meters, January 30, 1914, 2 specimens.

Distribution.—The present record is the only one of this species in American waters. The species is a bathypelagic form widely distributed in the deep waters of the North Atlantic Ocean.

Genus HYPERERYTHROPS Holt and Tattersall

Hypererythrops HOLT and TATTERSALL, 1905, p. 119.

HYPERERYTHROPS CARIBBAEA Tattersall

FIGURE 39

Hypererythrops caribbaea TATTERSALL, 1937, p. 13, fig. 8.

Occurrence.—EAST COAST OF THE UNITED STATES: *Fish Hawk* stations 1035, latitude 39°57′ N., longitude 69°28′ W., 120 fathoms, September 14, 1881, 3 males, 5 females, 13 mm.; 1038, latitude 39°58′ N., longitude 70°6′ W., 146 fathoms, September 21, 1881, 3 males, 3 females; *Albatross* stations, 2091, 1 immature male, 6 mm.; 2229, 1 immature female,[11] 5.5 mm. CARIBBEAN SEA: Johnson-Smithsonian expedition, serial number 573, station 99, latitude 18°40′ N., longitude 64°51′ W., 200 fathoms, March 3, 1933, 1 male, 8 mm. (type); Frederiksted, Santa Cruz, 200 to 300 fathoms, February 6, 1906, 1 female,[11] collected by Dr. Th. Mortensen.

Distribution.—All the known occurrences of this species are here listed. It extends from the coast of Maine to the Caribbean Sea, in 117 to 220 fathoms, and it is not known as yet from any other part of the world.

Remarks.—The material is somewhat defective, but there is no difficulty in referring it to the species described from the Caribbean

---

[11] Doubtfully referred to this species.

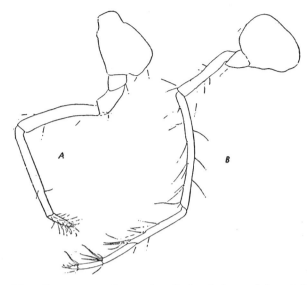

FIGURE 38.—*Metamblyops macrops* Tattersall: *a*, Endopod of second thoracic limb, × 33⅓; *b*, endopod of third thoracic limb, × 33⅓.

Sea. The northern specimens are somewhat larger than the type, 13 mm. as against 8 mm. The eyes in the preserved material are a light golden-brown, and there is a small papilla formed by the raised edge of the eyestalk projecting as a blunt process over the cornea

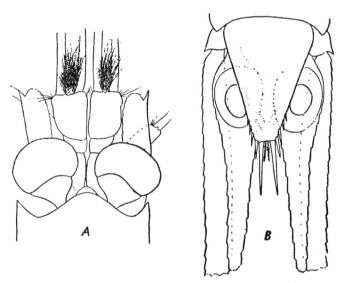

FIGURE 39.—*Hypererythrops caribbaea* Tattersall: *a*, Dorsal view of anterior end of male specimen to show rostral plate, eyes, antennular peduncle, and antennal scale, × 22½; *b*, telson and uropods, × 50.

on the inner upper face. I overlooked this point in the description of the type but on reexamination I find a similar process is present. The mouth parts and thoracic limbs do not show any special differences from those of the genus *Erythrops*. I have not been able to see any sternal processes in male specimens such as are characteristic of the type species of the genus.

Genus LONGITHORAX Illig

Longithorax ILLIG, 1906a, p. 200.

LONGITHORAX CAPENSIS Zimmer

FIGURE 40

Longithorax capensis ZIMMER, 1914, p. 392, pl. 24, figs. 20–24.
Longithorax sp. nov. TATTERSALL, 1936a, p. 96.

Occurrence.—Bermuda Oceanographical Expedition of the New York Zoological Society, under the direction of Dr. William Beebe: Net 900, surface; net 976, surface.

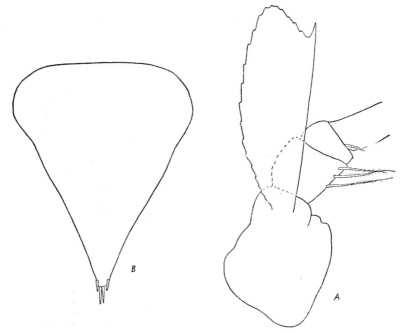

FIGURE 40.—*Longithorax capensis* Zimmer: *a*, Antennal scale and peduncle, × 70; *b*, telson, × 70.

Distribution.—*L. capensis* has been recorded previously only once. Zimmer (1914) reported it from the south Atlantic, latitude 35°39′ S., longitude 8°16′ W., from 3,000 meters. It seems likely that it is a bathypelagic species, widely distributed in the tropical regions of the Atlantic. The occurrence of young specimens in surface nets is interesting, but such occurrence is probably connected with special conditions existing near the Bermudas, where there is an upwelling of water from the depths, which would have the result of bringing up with it its contained organisms.

Remarks.—The specimens caught in the surface nets comprise all immature specimens, 12 young females and 8 young males, 6 to 9 mm. The specimens from the deep water net include 2 adult females, 13 mm., and 2 immature males, 10 mm. The specimens agree with Zimmer's account very closely except that the rostral plate is not bluntly pointed. The rostral plate has straight sides set at an angle of about 120° with the apex bluntly rounded. This difference at first led me to think that these specimens represented a new species, but further examination suggests that the difference in the rostral plate may be a sexual one, since Zimmer's specimen was an adult male. There are no adult males in the above specimens, but all the females and young males have the rostral plate as I have described it above. The difference, if sexual, does not become apparent until just before sexual maturity is reached.

One or two additional points seem worthy of note. All the specimens of both sexes have a tuft of long setae at the base of the outer and stouter flagellum of the antennule. In addition the male has the usual setose lobe on the antennule. The eye papilla is much more developed in the adult than in the young stage and appears to become longer with age. In the adult specimens, as Zimmer shows, it is a long slender fingerlike process, but in the young stages it is much shorter and therefore much blunter.

The third to the eighth thoracic limbs have a very long and slender endopod, and in this respect they agree closely with those figured by Hansen (1908a, pl. 5, figs. 1a–1o), in *L. fuscus*. The telson (fig. 40, *b*) agrees closely with that described by Zimmer. In all the specimens there are four short spinules at the apex but curiously enough in none of them are the spines symmetrically arranged. There are no other spines or armature on the telson.

L. capensis may be distinguished from the other two described species of the genus, *L. fuscus* and *L. similerythrops*, by the shape and armature of the telson and the shape of the antennal scale (fig. 40, *a*). All the specimens in this collection are strikingly black in color, but whether this is due to some special method of preservation or whether it is the natural color I am unable to say. I mention the fact, however, because *L. fuscus* is suffused with a dark grayish-brown pigment, in life, and it is quite likely that *L. capensis* is also suffused with a similar but darker color.

Genus GIBBERYTHROPS Illig

Gibberythrops ILLIG, 1930, p. 431.

GIBBERYTHROPS ACANTHURA (Illig)

Parerythrops acanthura ILLIG, 1906a, p. 197, fig. 4.
Gibberythrops acanthura ILLIG, 1930, p. 431, figs. 51–54.—TATTERSALL, 1939a,
    p. 244.
Erythrops acanthura COIFMANN, 1936, p. 32, pl. 15, figs. 21a–b; pl. 16, figs. 21c–f.

Occurrence.—PHILIPPINE ISLANDS: *Albatross* stations 5288, 3 females, 5 to 7 mm.; 5500, 2 females, 6 mm.

Distribution.—Hitherto this species has been recorded only from the Indian Ocean, Ceylon, and at the entrance to the Red Sea (Illig), Red Sea (Coifmann), and the Arabian Sea and Gulf of Aden (Tattersall). The Philippine records therefore mark a considerable extension of its known geographical range. It is probably widely distributed in the deeper waters of the Pacific and Indian Oceans.

Remarks.—All the specimens are females and appear to agree very closely with Illig's description and figures. The material is not in very good condition. Most of the thoracic limbs have been broken off and I am unable to add anything to Illig's account.

GIBBERYTHROPS PHILIPPINENSIS, new species

FIGURE 41

Description.—Thorax (fig. 41, *a*) in front of the cervical groove moderately vaulted in shape in lateral view (fig. 41, *b*) as in the type species, *G. acanthura;* front margin of the carapace (fig. 41, *a*) broadly and evenly rounded forming a narrow somewhat upturned rim to the thoracic region and leaving the eyes and eyestalks wholly uncovered.

Eyes (fig. 41, *a*) somewhat larger than in *G. acanthura*, more or less globular in shape, cornea as wide as the stalk, no ocular papilla.

Antennal scale (fig. 41, *c*) three times as long as broad at its widest part, shorter than the antennular peduncle, proximal three-quarters of the outer margin entire and terminating in a strong spine, beyond which the scale is produced as a terminal lobe, slightly longer than broad at its base; antennal peduncle about three-quarters of the length of the scale, its three joints more or less subequal in size; the setae fringing the scale are very long, as long as or longer than the scale.

Sixth somite of the abdomen more than twice as long as the fifth.

Telson (fig. 41, *d*) three-fifths as long as the sixth somite of the abdomen, narrowly triangular in shape, twice as long as broad at the base, narrowing evenly to a narrow apex armed by a pair of long spines equal in length to one-tenth the length of the telson; lateral margins of the telson armed along the distal half by 11 to 12 short spines regularly arranged; no plumose setae at the apex.

Inner uropod one and two-thirds as long as the telson, without spines on its inner margin; outer uropod about twice as long as the telson.

The third to the eighth thoracic limbs have the endopods long and slender, the carpus distinct, and the propodus divided into two subjoints.

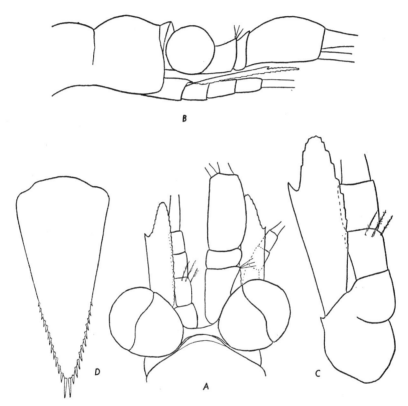

FIGURE 41.—*Gibberythrops philippinensis*, new species: *a*, Dorsal view of anterior end to show eye, rostral plate, antennular peduncle, and antennal scale, $\times$ 47½; *b*, lateral view of anterior end to show vaulted carapace and slightly upturned rostral plate, $\times$ 47½; *c*, antennal scale and peduncle, $\times$ 70; *d*, telson, $\times$ 70.

Length of an adult male 6 mm.

Type lot.—Four males, one female, U.S.N.M. No. 81260, *Albatross* station 5456, Legaspi Lighthouse, Philippine Islands.

Occurrence.—Philippine Islands: *Albatross* station 5456, 4 males, 1 female, 6 mm. (type lot).

Distribution.—Known only from these specimens taken near the Philippine Islands.

Remarks.—It is somewhat difficult to decide to which genus this species should be referred. It seems to be most closely allied to *Gibberythrops*, especially in the vaulted character of the thorax, the rounded anterior margin of the carapace, and the shape of the antennal scale. There are, however, no plumose setae at the apex of the telson and the latter is longer and more narrowly triangular and almost pointed at the apex, whereas in *G. acanthura* the telson is shorter and the apex broader and distinctly truncate. *G. acanthura* has only five spines on the lateral margins of the telson and the long spines on the truncate apex are widely separated and have a pair of plumose setae between them. In the present species there are 11 to 13 spines on the lateral margins of the telson, the two terminal spines are close together, and there are no plumose setae.

The mouth appendages show no very distinctive features. The maxilla has a well-developed exopod and is quite normal in form. The first thoracic limbs have a well-developed gnathobase on the second joint but not on the third and fourth. The remaining thoracic limbs are very slender in build with the propodal joint divided into two subjoints.

For the moment I refer these specimens to the genus *Gibberythrops* and hope that the species will be recognized by the combination of characters afforded by the vaulted thorax, the broadly rounded rostral plate, the shape of the antennal scale, and the shape and armature of the telson.

Genus SYNERYTHROPS Hansen

Synerythrops HANSEN, 1910, p. 64.

SYNERYTHROPS CRUCIATA, new species

FIGURE 42

Description.—Carapace produced in front into a rather long triangular rostral plate (fig. 42, *a*) with a bluntly pointed apex, extending some little distance in front of the eyes and covering the eyestalks.

Eyes (fig. 42, *a*) rather small, partially covered by the carapace, with a slender fingerlike process on the inner upper surface of the eyestalk, pigment light golden brown.

Antennal scale (fig. 42, *a*) four times as long as broad, outer margin entire, terminating in moderately strong spine, beyond which the antennal scale does not project, so there is no terminal lobe.

Sixth somite of the abdomen twice as long as the fifth.

Telson (fig. 42, *b*) half as long as the sixth somite of the abdomen, equilaterally triangular in shape with a broadly rounded apex, as long as broad at its base, distal quarter of each lateral margin armed with eight spines, graded in size, the terminal spine equal in length to one-third the length of the telson, a pair of plumose setae on the apex between the terminal pair of long spines.

Inner uropod (fig. 42, *b*) twice as long as the telson, with three spines on the inner lower margin near the statocyst.

Outer uropod (fig. 42, *b*) three times as long as the telson.

Length of adult female 13 mm.

Type.—One adult female, U.S.N.M. No. 81261, off Frederiksted, Santa Cruz, West Indies.

Occurrence.—Off Frederiksted, Santa Cruz, West Indies, 200 to 300 fathoms, February 6, 1906, 1 adult female, 13 mm. (type), collected by Dr. Th. Mortensen.

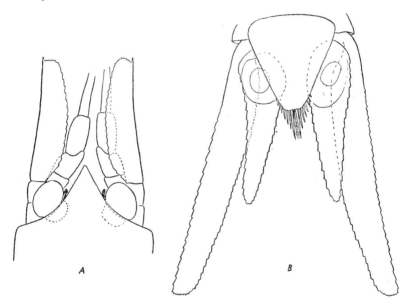

FIGURE 42.—*Synerythrops cruciata*, new species: *a*, Dorsal view of anterior end to show rostral plate, eye, antennal scale and its peduncle, × 25; *b*, telson and uropods, × 25.

Distribution.—Known only from the type specimen collected in deep water off the West Indies. The type species is found in the tropical Pacific and Indian Oceans. Both species appear to be bathypelagic in habit.

Remarks.—The single specimen is not in good condition, the antennular peduncles are both broken away, and most of the thoracic limbs are missing. Moreover, what remains of the specimen is rather crushed, so that it is not easy to make out the exact relations of the eyes and rostral plate. The figure I give of the anterior end represents what I believe to be the relations of these parts but better preserved material may necessitate modifications. Having only the one defective specimen I have not attempted to dissect it and therefore cannot say whether the mouth parts and thoracic limbs conform to Hansen's definition of the genus *Synerythrops*, to which the species otherwise seems to belong, or at least to approach most nearly. It has the same type of antennal scale, and the telson and uropods are closely similar in form and relative proportions to those of the type species, *S. intermedia*. *S. cruciata* differs from *S. intermedia* in the somewhat larger and longer rostral plate, which partially covers the eyes, in the rather smaller eyes with an ocular papilla, and in the larger number of spines on the lateral margins of the telson. It is also somewhat larger, though Hansen's specimen was immature.

Genus DACTYLERYTHROPS Holt and Tattersall

Dactylerythrops HOLT and TATTERSALL, 1905, p. 121.

DACTYLERYTHROPS BIDIGITATA Tattersall

FIGURE 43

Dactylerythrops bidigitata TATTERSALL, 1907, p. 109; 1911b, p. 34, pl. 3, figs. 7–10; pl. 4, fig. 1.—ZIMMER, 1909, p. 97.

Occurrence.—EAST COAST OF UNITED STATES: *Fish Hawk* station 1093, latitude 39°56′ N., longitude 69°45′ W., 349 fathoms, August 11, 1882, 1 immature male; *Albatross* station 2046, 2 males, 2 females, 16 mm.; 2172, 1 immature female; 2180, 1 immature male; 2187, 1 female; 2213, 6 females, 18 mm.; 2215, 1 male, 2 females, immature.

Distribution.—New to the American fauna. Hitherto known only from the type locality off the west coast of Ireland. Its range extended now to the east coast of the United States, it is another example of a probably widely spread boreal species penetrating southward wherever conditions are suitable.

Remarks.—The material is defective, but the peculiar form of the eye and the character of the telson are quite sufficient to recognize the species. The salient characters of this species are given in figure 43.

Genus DACTYLAMBLYOPS Holt and Tattersall

Dactylamblyops HOLT and TATTERSALL, 1906a, p. 8.

DACTYLAMBLYOPS sp. ?

Occurrence.—CALIFORNIA: *Albatross* station 4536, 1 male, 25 mm.

Remarks.—This specimen is much too damaged to describe adequately, though it appears to belong to an undescribed species. The antennal scales are both broken. The eye is pyriform in shape, with a blunt fingerlike process on the upper inner surface of the eyestalk. The visual elements of the eye appear to be imperfectly developed but the eye is too damaged to be sure on this point. The telson is very massive, almost quadrangular in shape, as long as the sixth somite of the abdomen, one and two-thirds as long as broad at the base. The apex is truncate, even slightly emarginate and equal in width to one-quarter of the length of the telson. The spines of the telson are all broken off save one on the apex, but from examination of the

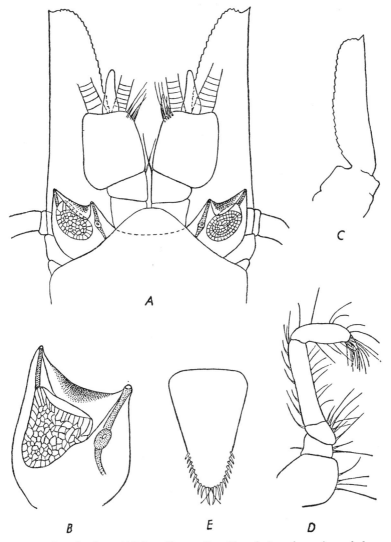

FIGURE 43.—*Dactylerythrops bidigitata* Tattersall: *a*, Dorsal view of anterior end; *b*, eye; *c*, antennal scale; *d*, endopod of second thoracic limb; *e*, telson.

sockets there would appear to have been about 26 on each lateral margin, occupying rather more than the distal half of the margin, and four on each side of the apex, with a pair of plumose setae in the center of the apex.

Genus AMBLYOPS G. O. Sars

Amblyops G. O. SARS, 1869, p. 328; 1872b, p. 3.

AMBLYOPS ABBREVIATA (G. O. Sars)

FIGURE 44

Pseudomma abbreviatum G. O. SARS, *in* M. Sars, 1869, p. 262 (*nomen nudum*).
Amblyopsis abbreviata G. O. SARS, 1869, p. 328.
Amblyops abbreviata G. O. SARS, 1872b, p. 5, pl. 6.

Occurrence.—EAST COAST OF UNITED STATES: U. S. Fish Commission locality 344, off Cape Cod, 130 fathoms, September 10, 1879, 1 male; *Fish Hawk* stations 952, latitude 39°55′ N., longitude 70°28′ W., 396 fathoms, August 23, 1881, 1 female; 997, latitude 39°42′ N., longitude 71°32′ W., 335 fathoms, September 8, 1881, 2 females; 998, latitude 39°43′ N., longitude 71°32′ W., 302 fathoms, September 8, 1881, 17 females, 10 males; 1029, latitude 39°57′6″ N., longitude 69°16′ W., 458 fathoms, September 14, 1881, 1 male; *Albatross* station 2046, 3 males, 2 females; 2192, 1 male. WEST COAST OF UNITED STATES: *Albatross* station 4753, 1 male, 1 female, 13 mm. JAPAN: *Albatross* stations 4781, 1 female, 17 mm.; 4800, 1 male, 14 mm.

Distribution.—The present series of records represent the first from the American coasts and the first of the species from the Pacific Ocean. Inasmuch as former collections were from the Irish and Norwegian coasts of the North Atlantic, the present series provides a further example of an Arctic-boreal species, which is circumpolar in distribution and has penetrated into the boreal area of both the Atlantic and Pacific Oceans.

Remarks.—The last three records listed above are from stations in the Pacific Ocean. The specimens from these stations agree with the typical form in the proportions of the body, the antennal scale, and the telson. The antennal scale (fig. 44, *d*) even has the accessory spine at the inner base of the terminal spine of the outer border. The telson (fig. 44, *e*) has a slightly greater number of spines on the lateral margins, 28 to 32 as against about 25 in the typical form, but this small difference is well within the limits of individual variation. They differ in that the process on the anterior median border of the eye is longer and more acute in lateral view (fig. 44, *b*) especially in the male. The anterior border of the ocular plate is also microscopically spinulose especially at the outer corner (fig. 44, *a-b*), but examination of Atlantic specimens reveals the fact that they also are microscopically spinulose, though the spinules are very much smaller and finer than in the Pacific specimens. I give figures (fig. 44, *a-f*) of the Pacific specimens to illustrate these small differences. I do not consider the

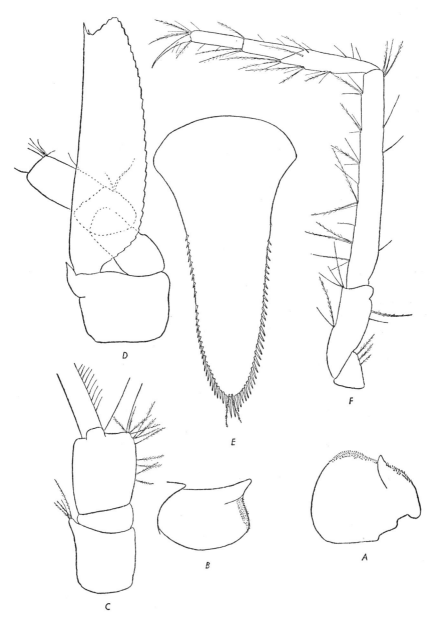

FIGURE 44.—*Amblyops abbreviata* (G. O. Sars) (from *Albatross* station 4753): *a*, Eye from dorsal aspect, × 42½; *b*, eye from lateral aspect, × 42½; *c*, antennular peduncle, × 42½; *d*, antennal scale and peduncle, × 42½; *e*, telson, × 42½; *f*, endopod of third thoracic limb, × 42½.

differences constitute characters of specific significance and record the specimens as *A. abbreviata*.

AMBLYOPS sp. ?

Occurrence.—EAST COAST OF UNITED STATES: *Albatross* station 2215, 3 mutilated specimens.

Remarks.—Identification is impossible because of the damaged condition of the specimens.

AMBLYOPS sp. ?

Occurrence.—CALIFORNIA: *Albatross* station 4537, 1 adult female, 20 mm.

Remarks.—The specimen is badly damaged, both antennal scales and telson being broken. Identification is therefore impossible.

AMBLYOPS OHLINII, new species

FIGURE 45

Amblyops crozetii OHLIN, 1901a, p. 371; 1901b, p. 9.—ZIMMER, 1904, p. 451, figs. 114–116.—STEPHENSEN, 1913, p. 73.
Amblyops crozeti ZIMMER, 1909, p. 114, figs. 229–231.
Amblyops new species HANSEN, 1908a, p. 108.

Description.—This species is very closely allied to *A. crozetii* (Willemoes-Suhm) G. O. Sars, but as far as can be seen from the rather defective material in this collection it may be distinguished by the following characters:

(1) The telson (fig. 45, *c*), while of the same shape and proportions as in *A. crozetii*, has only 6 spines arming the broad truncate or slightly emarginate apex of the telson. In *A. crozetii* there are 14 spines on the apex, and to judge from Sars' figures these spines are more slender than those in the present species. Unfortunately, the material is very defective, and I have shown only those spines that are actually still present on the specimens. There appear to be 18 to 20 spines on each lateral margin.

(2) The anterolateral angle of the ocular plate (fig. 45, *a*) is microscopically spinulose or denticulate. In *A. crozetii* the eye is described as smooth.

Type lot.—Two adult females, U.S.N.M. No. 81262, *Albatross* station 2550, east coast of the United States.

Occurrence.—EAST COAST OF UNITED STATES: *Albatross* stations 2192, 1 immature female, 11 mm.; 2550, 2 adult females, 25 mm. (type lot).

Distribution.—New to the American fauna. Known previously only from the specimens recorded from east Greenland by Ohlin at depths of 2,000 meters. It is a very deep-water form, the American records being from 1,060 to 1,081 fathoms.

Remarks.—The differences pointed out between *A. ohlinii* and *A. crozetii* are admittedly small, but taken in conjunction with the geographical distribution they warrant the institution of a new species. The form of the antennal scale (fig. 45, *b*) and its proportions are almost exactly the same in both species, as are also the shape and proportions of the telson. The spine on the outer corner of the basal joint

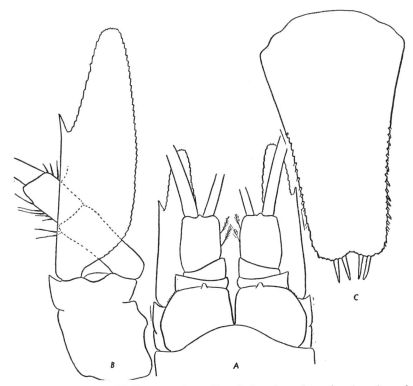

FIGURE 45.—*Amblyops ohlinii*, new species: *a*, Dorsal view of anterior end to show the ocular plate; *b*, antennal scale and peduncle, × 20; *c*, telson, × 20.

of the antennal scale is almost obsolete in *A. ohlinii* and there is a single spine on the inner margin of the inner uropod near the statocyst.

It is obvious that these specimens belong to the same species as those recorded as *A. crozetii* by Ohlin (1901a, 1901b). The other papers quoted in the synonymy are all references to Ohlin's record and are not based on specimens actually examined. Zimmer's two papers quote the description of the real *A. crozetii* from the *Challenger* report and reproduce Sars' figures of that species, but the recorded distribution refers to Ohlin's paper. Hansen expressed the opinion that Ohlin's specimens really belonged to a new species, but as he had no material at hand he refrained from naming it. With Hansen's opinion, after examining actual specimens, I am in agreement, and I therefore name the species after its discoverer. The species may be recognized by the characters of the telson, the ocular plate, and the antennal scale.

Genus PARAMBLYOPS Holt and Tattersall

Paramblyops HOLT and TATTERSALL, 1905, p. 124.

PARAMBLYOPS ROSTRATA Holt and Tattersall

Paramblyops rostrata HOLT and TATTERSALL, 1905, p. 125, pl. 21; 1906b, p. 26.—HANSEN, 1908a, p. 108; 1927, p. 25, pl. 1, figs. 7a-c.

Occurrence.—EAST COAST OF UNITED STATES: *Albatross* station 2180, 2 males.

Distribution.—This is the first record of this species from the American side of the Atlantic slope. First described from the west coast of Ireland, this species has since been recorded from the eastern Atlantic slope from the Bay of Biscay to the Faroe Islands and Iceland, and from the Mediterranean. It forms part of the boreal fauna of the North Atlantic, which extends southward on both eastern and western sides wherever suitable conditions of depth and temperature are available.

Remarks.—The two specimens are in a very poor state of preservation, but they clearly belong to this species.

Genus PSEUDOMMA G. O. Sars

Pseudomma G. O. SARS, 1870a, p. 154.

PSEUDOMMA AFFINE G. O. Sars

Pseudomma affine G. O. SARS, 1870a, p. 156.—HOLT and TATTERSALL, 1906b, p. 27.—HANSEN, 1908a, p. 110.

Occurrence.—EAST COAST OF UNITED STATES: *Fish Hawk* station 999, 1 adult male, 14 mm.

Distribution.—Now recorded from the American coast for the first time. It is known from the eastern Atlantic slope from Norway to the Bay of Biscay, Iceland, and Greenland, in depths of 65 to 500 fathoms.

PSEUDOMMA ROSEUM G. O. Sars

FIGURE 46

Pseudomma roseum G. O. SARS, 1870a, p. 154.—WHITEAVES, 1874a, p. 4; 1874b, p. 191; 1901, p. 247.—S. I. SMITH, 1879, p. 98; 1881, p. 445.—VERRILL, 1885, p. 558.—M. RATHBUN, 1905, p. 29.—FOWLER, 1912, p. 541.—KINDLE and WHITTAKER, 1918, p. 253.—TATTERSALL, 1939b, p. 283.

Occurrence.—EAST COAST OF UNITED STATES: *Fish Hawk* stations 998, latitude 39°43′ N., longitude 71°32′ W., 302 fathoms, September

8, 1881, 3 males, 1 female, 17 mm.; 1093, latitude 39°56′ N., longitude 69°45′ W., 349 fathoms, August 11, 1882, 1 female, 15 mm.; 891*, off southern New England; *Albatross* stations 2046*, 2213*; *Bache* station 13* (all specimens from stations marked * were identified by S. I. Smith).

Distribution.—Smith (1879) has summarized the then-known American records of this species and his summary includes the records

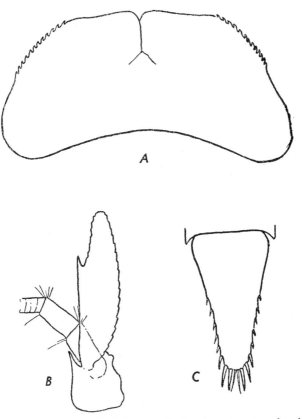

FIGURE 46.—*Pseudomma roseum* G. O. Sars: *a*, Ocular plate; *b*, antennal scale; *c*, telson. (After G. O. Sars.)

by Whiteaves (1874a, 1874b, 1875). Smith's records (1881) and Verrill (1885) probably refer to the specimens from *Fish Hawk* station 891. The remaining records enumerated contain no new localities for this species but are merely references to the earlier papers of Smith, Verrill, and Whiteaves. The additional specimens here recorded merely confirm the earlier ones but add nothing new as to its geographical range or bathymetric distribution. Outside America it has a wide distribution in the boreal waters of the Atlantic from Norway to

Iceland. It does not appear to extend as far southward as does *P. affine.*

PSEUDOMMA TRUNCATUM S. I. Smith

FIGURE 47

Pseudomma, new species WHITEAVES, 1874a, p. 5; 1874b, p. 191.
Pseudomma truncatum S. I. SMITH, 1879, p. 99, pl. 12, figs. 3, 4.—RICHTERS, 1884, p. 406.—KINDLE and WHITTAKER, 1918, p. 253.—TATTERSALL, 1933, p. 6; 1939b, p. 283.

Occurrence.—EAST COAST OF UNITED STATES: *Albatross* station 2046, 3 young specimens. WEST COAST OF UNITED STATES: Explorations in Alaska, 1884, Lieut. G. M. Stoney, U. S. N., tag 27, latitude 62°15′

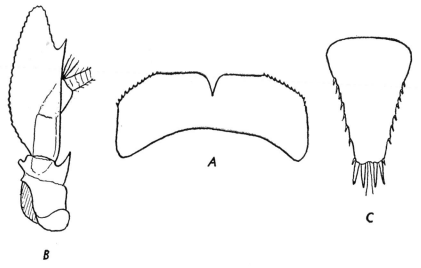

FIGURE 47.—*Pseudomma truncatum* S. I. Smith: *a,* Ocular plate; *b,* antennal scale; *c,* telson. (After G. O. Sars.)

N., longitude 167°48′ W., 20½ fathoms, June 13, 1884, 4 females, 13–15 mm.; tag 28, latitude 62°54′ N., longitude 166°38′ W., 22 fathoms, June 14, 1884, 4 females; *Albatross* station 2861, 1 immature male, 10 mm.

Distribution.—This species was described by Smith from specimens collected by Whiteaves in the Gulf of St. Lawrence. In 1884 Richters recorded it from the Bering Sea. In 1933 I recorded it from British Columbia, and in 1939 I added several new records from Canada. As a matter of fact the specimens from *Albatross* station 2046 are actually the first record from the coasts of the United States and the most southerly record in the Atlantic Ocean. The species is a circumpolar boreal species extending southward in appropriate depths on both sides of the American continent and the west coasts of Europe.

Remarks.—The specimen from *Albatross* station 2861 is attributed to *P. truncatum* with some hesitation. It is not in good condition and differs from typical specimens of the species in having three spines on each side of the apex of the telson, the outermost spine only half as long as the two inner pairs. This outer spine may be regarded as belonging to the lateral margins of the telson, but it is longer than the remainder and distinctly apical in position. Figure 47, *a-c*, shows the salient characters of this species.

PSEUDOMMA BERKELEYI Tattersall

FIGURE 48

This species is described on page 243.

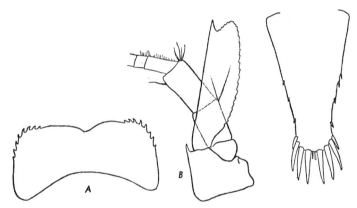

FIGURE 48.—*Pseudomma berkeleyi* Tattersall: *a*, Ocular plate, × 37½; *b*, antennal scale, × 37½; *c*, telson, × 37½.

PSEUDOMMA sp. ?

Reference is made to this species on page 244.

PSEUDOMMA OCULOSPINUM, new species

FIGURE 49

Description.—A species of *Pseudomma* characterized by the following special features:

(1) The ocular plate (fig. 49, *a*) has the median furrow separating the two halves about half as deep as the median length of the plate; the outer distal corner of the plate drawn out into a long sharp spinous process; inner distal corner of each plate somewhat produced and bluntly rounded; margins of the ocular plate smooth, without teeth or denticles.

(2) The antennal scale (fig. 49, *b*) extends beyond the distal end of the antennular peduncle by one-third of its length; four times

as long as broad, outer margin terminating in a strong spine, which projects slightly beyond the remainder of the scale so that there is virtually no terminal lobe to the scale; spine on the outer distal corner of the basal joint of the scale very long and strong.

(3) The telson (fig. 49, *c*) is very long and comparatively narrow, equal to the inner uropod in length, two and a half times as long as broad at the base; apex narrow and truncate, two-fifths of the breadth of the telson at its base, armed with four pairs of spines, the inner pair the shortest and the outer pair the longest, equal in length to one-eighth of the length of the telson; lateral margins

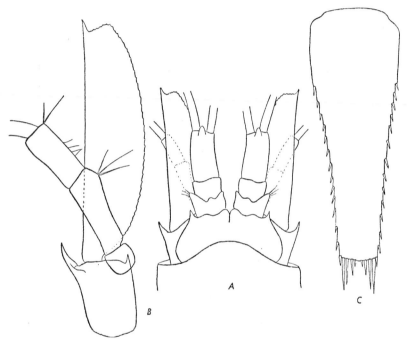

Figure 49.—*Pseudomma oculospinum*, new species: *a*, Dorsal view of anterior end to show ocular plate; *b*, antennal scale and peduncle, × 25; *c*, telson, × 25.

armed with 14 short spines, which occupy the distal three-fourths of the margins, the most distal spine situated at the lateral corners of the apex so that they almost appear to be part of the apical armature. I could not detect any median plumose setae at the apex but they may have been broken off.

(4) Inner uropod has a single long sharp spine on the inner margin near the statocyst.

Type lot.—One male, 2 females, and the anterior ends of 2 additional females, U.S.N.M. No. 81263, *Albatross* station 4400, off the coast of California.

Occurrence.—CALIFORNIA: *Albatross* station 4400, 1 male, 2 females, and the anterior ends of 2 additional females, 18 mm. (type lot).

Distribution.—Known only from the type-lot specimens collected off the coast of California in 500 to 507 fathoms.

Remarks.—This species is distinguished from all other known species of the genus by the combination of characters given above. The ocular plate with its smooth margins and long spiniform process at each anterolateral angle is unique. In the absence of a terminal lobe to the antennal scale projecting beyond the terminal spine of the outer margin, this species differs from all other northern species of the genus except *P. calloplura, P. nanum,* and *P. berkeleyi,* and from these species the form and armature of the telson will form a ready means of distinction. The antennal scale and the telson recall those of the genus *Michthyops,* but *P. oculospinum* has fully developed biramous pleopods in the male and the ocular plate is strongly dissimilar to that found in the genus *Michthyops.*

Genus CAESAROMYSIDES Colosi

Caesaromysides COLOSI, 1916, p. 136.

CAESAROMYSIDES LIGURIAE Colosi

The records of this species are given on page 244.

Genus MICHTHYOPS Tattersall

Michthyops TATTERSALL, 1911b, p. 60.

MICHTHYOPS PARVA (Vanhöffen)

Pseudomma parvum VANHÖFFEN, 1897, p. 199; 1907, p. 508, pl. 20, figs. 1–3.—
    ZIMMER, 1904, p. 439; 1909, p. 104, figs. 208–210.—HANSEN, 1908a, p. 111, pl. 5,
    figs. 4a–h.
Michthyops parva TATTERSALL, 1911b, p. 60.—STEPHENSEN, 1913, p. 76.

Occurrence.—EAST COAST OF UNITED STATES: *Albatross* station 2095, 1 male; 2195, 2 males; 2215, 1 male; 2229, 1 male; 2230, 1 male.

Distribution.—Known hitherto from Greenland and from the west coast of Ireland, this species is now recorded for the first time from the western Atlantic slope off the east coast of the United States. Here again we have a member of the boreal fauna that penetrates southward into the Atlantic on both sides where suitable conditions prevail. Its bathymetric distribution is interesting. Off the west coast of Greenland it occurs in 100 fathoms. Off the west coast of Ireland it was found in 880 fathoms, and the above records from eastern America range from 578 to 1,438 fathoms. The species appears to seek deeper water as it extends southward. It is an interesting addition to the American fauna, though its occurrence there was to be expected.

Remarks.—The material is very much damaged, but the salient features of the species can be made out with no doubt of its identity.   All the specimens taken are males.

Tribe LEPTOMYSINI

Endopods of the third to the eighth thoracic limbs with the carpus and propodus fused and the combined joints divided into a small number of subjoints by vertical articulations; four posterior pairs of pleopods of the male generally well developed (rudimentary in *Mysidetes*); exopod of the fourth pair of pleopods of the male either elongated or terminating in a thickened spine, while the endopod is always normal; antennal scale lanceolate and setose all around except in *Paramysidetes*.

Remarks.—Fourteen genera have been referred to this tribe, of which *Metamysidopsis* is described as new in this report.   Eight of the genera are represented in the material of this collection.

Genus LEPTOMYSIS G. O. Sars

Leptomysis G. O. SARS, 1869, p. 333.

LEPTOMYSIS GRACILIS G. O. Sars

Leptomysis gracilis G. O. SARS, 1869, p. 333.

Occurrence.—Bristol Channel, England, identified by G. E. Bullen.

LEPTOMYSIS MEDITERRANEA G. O. Sars

Leptomysis mediterranea G. O. SARS, 1877, p. 45, pls. 14–16.

Occurrence.—Naples, identified by A. M. Norman.

Genus MYSIDOPSIS G. O. Sars

Mysidopsis G. O. SARS, 1864, p. 249.

KEY TO THE AMERICAN SPECIES OF MYSIDOPSIS

a^1. Antennal scale with an acutely pointed apex_____acuta (p. 139)
a^2. Antennal scale with apex more or less rounded.
   b^1. Apex of the telson armed with 3 pairs of long strong spines, much longer than spines arming lateral margins_____bigelowi (p. 139)
   b^2. Spines at apex of telson not specially longer than those arming margin.
      c^1. Inner uropods without spines_____inermis (p. 245)
      c^2. Inner uropods with a row of spines on inner margin extending from statocyst almost to apex.
         d^1. Antennal scale narrowly lanceolate in shape, 9 times as long as broad; lateral margins of telson armed with 25 small, acute spines.
            californica (p. 142)
         d^2. Antennal scale oval in shape, $3\frac{1}{2}$ times as long as broad; lateral margins of telson armed with 15 to 20 short, stout, blunt spines.
            mortenseni (p. 145)

MYSIDOPSIS ANGUSTA G. O. Sars

Mysidopsis angusta G. O. SARS, 1864, p. 254.

Occurrence.—Off Start Point, Devonshire, England, identified by G. E. Bullen.

Distribution.—Coasts of England and Norway and the Mediterranean Sea.

MYSIDOPSIS GIBBOSA G. O. Sars

Mysidopsis gibbosa G. O. SARS, 1864, p. 252.

Occurrence.—Off Start Point, Devonshire, England, identified by G. E. Bullen.

Distribution.—Coasts of Norway, Denmark, England, and the Mediterranean Sea.

MYSIDOPSIS ACUTA Hansen

Reference to this species may be found on page 244.

MYSIDOPSIS BIGELOWI Tattersall

FIGURE 50

Mysidopsis bigelowi TATTERSALL, 1926, p. 10, pl. 1, figs. 1–8.

Description.—Carapace (fig. 50, *a*) produced between the eyes into a short low triangular rostral plate with a bluntly pointed apex; anterolateral corners rounded.

Eyes (fig. 50, *a*) of moderate size, cornea occupying less than half of the whole eye in dorsal view; no fingerlike process on the outer dorsal portion of the eyestalk.

Antennal scale (fig. 50, *b*) five times as long as broad, narrowly lanceolate, setose all around, without a distal joint, apex bluntly rounded, extending beyond the peduncle of the antennule by about one-quarter to one-third of its length, a prominent spine on the outer distal corner of the joint from which the scale springs; the distal joint of the antennal peduncle only slightly more than half as long as the preceding joint, the whole peduncle extending to about two-thirds of the antennal scale.

Maxillules (fig. 50, *c*) with a definite shoulder on the outer margin of the outer plate proximal to which are a few spinules; inner plate with two setae.

Maxillae (fig. 50, *d*) with the proximal lobe narrow; distal lobe divided into two parts by a short furrow; palp long, distal joint narrowly oval, nearly twice as long as broad and twice as long as the proximal joint; exopod long and narrow, setae present only on its outer margin and the distal setae much longer than the proximal.

First thoracic limbs (fig. 50, *e*) of the normal form characteristic of the genus with the second and third joints of the endopod fused; the limbs are shorter and stouter than in European species of the genus especially with regard to the sixth joint; seventh joint not longer than broad; dactylus stout and straight.

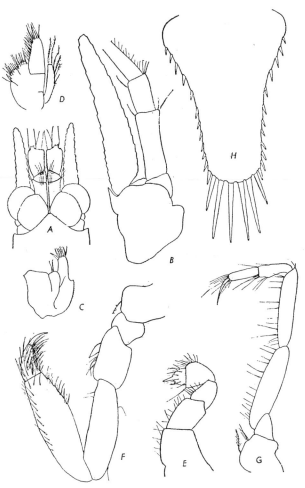

FIGURE 50.—*Mysidopsis bigelowi* Tattersall: *a*, Anterior end, dorsal view, × 22; *b*, antennal scale and peduncle, × 43⅓; *c*, maxillula, × 43⅓; *d*, maxilla, × 43⅓; *e*, endopod of first thoracic limb, × 43⅓; *f*, endopod of second thoracic limb, × 43⅓; *g*, endopod of third thoracic limb, × 43⅓; *h*, telson, × 66⅔.

Second thoracic limbs (fig. 50, *f*) with the endopod relatively enormously developed, much more robust than in any known species of the genus and as far as the present material goes, more robust in the female than in the male; this relative development of the limbs is attained mainly by the large size of the sixth joint which is one-quarter longer than the fifth and four times as long as broad; it is widest just distal to the middle and from this point the joint narrows considerably, the distal portion of the inner margin being slightly concave and armed with numerous spiniform setae; the outer distal margins are also armed with numerous setae; the seventh joint is about one-fourth of the length of the sixth and terminates in a strong somewhat curved nail; the outer margin is convex and the inner margin concave and fringed also with spiniform setae; the inner face of this joint is armed with numerous very strong setae, which are barbed on one side only; the concave inner margin of the seventh joint folds down against the distal portion of the inner margin of the sixth joint to form a kind of subchela to the limb; in the male specimens, which are immature, the second thoracic limbs have the same general form as in the female here described, but they appear to be less robust and the subchelate appearance of the limbs is less well marked.

Remaining thoracic limbs with the carpopropodus of the endopod (fig. 50, *g*) divided into two subjoints by a transverse suture; seventh joint very short and terminating in a long slender nail.

Sixth abdominal somite one and two-thirds as long as the fifth.

Telson (fig. 50, *h*) as long as the sixth abdominal somite, one and a third times as long as broad at the base and three times as long as the breadth at the apex, entire and broadly linguiform in shape with the apex broadly rounded; lateral margins with about 12 short stout spines distributed along the whole length; apex armed with 3 pairs of long strong spines, the inner pair equal in length to one-third of the telson, the next pair slightly shorter and the outer pair only one-fifth of the telson in length; no plumose setae on the apex.

Inner uropods 1½ times as long as the telson, with five spines on the inner lower margin in the region of the statocyst; outer uropods slightly longer than the inner.

Length of adult specimens 7.5 mm.

Occurrence.—EAST COAST OF UNITED STATES: Woods Hole region, 1 male, 1 female; Calcasieu Pass, La., W. H. Spaulding collector, No. 19, 7 : 30 p. m., September 19, 1907, 4 males, 4 females; *Bache* station 10157, latitude 36°46′ N., longitude 75°38′ W., January 20, 1914, 2 specimens; Bureau of Fisheries Survey of Chesapeake Bay, 1920, stations 8888, bell buoy No. 1, SE. ½ E. 1 mile, buoy 10C, NW. by W. ⅛ W., off Sandy Point, 8 fathoms, gray sand, October 20, 1920, 1 adult female, 7 mm., 1 immature male, 4.5 mm.; 8895, lightship S. ⅜ E., Cape Henry Light S. ¼ W., whistling buoy SW. by W. ¼ W., 16½ fathoms, mud and sand, October 21, 1920, 1 adult male, 7.5 mm.; 8896, Cape Henry Light SW. by S. ¾ S., lightship N. ¾ W., 23 fathoms, sand and mud, October 21, 1920, 2 males, 5 to 6 mm.; 8890,

Cape Henry Light SW. by S. ¾ S., lightship N. ¾ W., 23 fathoms, black mud and sand, December 4, 1920, 1 adult female, 7 mm., and 27 immature specimens.

Distribution.—The above records extend the distribution of this species from the coasts of New England to Louisiana. It is probably distributed all along the coasts of the Atlantic shores of America in shallow water. It appears to be found in association with *M. munda*, at any rate in Chesapeake Bay and off Louisiana, and probably everywhere where it occurs.

Remarks.—This species may be recognized by the combination of characters afforded by the unjointed antennal scale, the powerfully developed endopod of the second thoracic limbs, and the form and armature of the telson. It is very distinct from all the other species of the genus from American waters.

MYSIDOPSIS INERMIS Coifmann

This species is diagnosed on page 245.

MYSIDOPSIS CALIFORNICA Tattersall

FIGURES 51, 52

Mysidopsis californica TATTERSALL, 1932a, p. 307, figs. 14–25.

Description.—Carapace produced in front into a very short, bluntly rounded, triangular plate not covering any part of the eyestalks; anterolateral angles rounded.

Sixth segment of the pleon 1½ times as long as the fifth.

Antennular peduncle in the male shorter and stouter than in the female, with the last joint relatively shorter and having a well developed setose lobe. Antennal scale (fig. 51, *f*) extending for one-third of its length beyond the antennular peduncle, narrowly lanceolate in shape and setose all around, nine times as long as broad, distal joint equal to about one-quarter of the scale, apex rather acute; antennal peduncle (fig. 51, *f*) about half as long as the scale and slightly shorter than the antennular peduncle; third joint two-thirds of the length of the second.

Eyes large, about 1⅗ as long as broad; cornea occupying nearly half of the whole eye in dorsal view; pigment black.

Mandibles (fig. 51, *a-c*) with a molar process. Maxillulae (fig. 51, *d*) with the inner lobe small and armed with two setae. Maxillae (fig. 51, *e*) with a well-developed exopod but with the setiferous expansion from the second joint.

Third to the eighth thoracic limbs (fig. 52, *c*) long and slender; carpo-propodus divided by a transverse articulation into two subjoints; dactylus long and slender, longer than the distal subjoint of

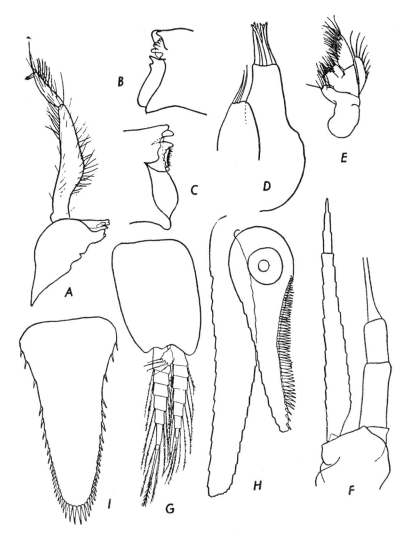

FIGURE 51.—*Mysidopsis californica* Tattersall: *a*, Mandible and palp, × 100; *b*, cutting edge of right mandible, × 330; *c*, cutting edge of left mandible, × 330; *d*, maxillule, × 330; *e*, maxilla, × 100; *f*, antennal scale and peduncle, × 100; *g*, fourth pleopod of male, × 100; *h*, uropod, × 100; *i*, telson, × 100.

the sixth joint; a small curved fingerlike process (gill?) on the outer margin of the basal joint; basal plate of the exopod with the outer distal corner rounded.

Telson (fig. 51, *i*) as long as the sixth abdominal somite, 1¾ times as long as broad at the base, linguiform in shape, apex entire and rounded; lateral margins armed with about 25 spines extending throughout the entire margin; the proximal two-fifths of the margins with 3 or 4 distantly placed spines; the distal three-fifths of the margins with the spines crowded together; apical pair of spines about one-tenth of the telson in length; no plumose setae.

Inner uropod (fig. 51, *h*) about 1⅓ as long as the telson; inner margin armed with a dense row of large blunt spines, about 50, ex-

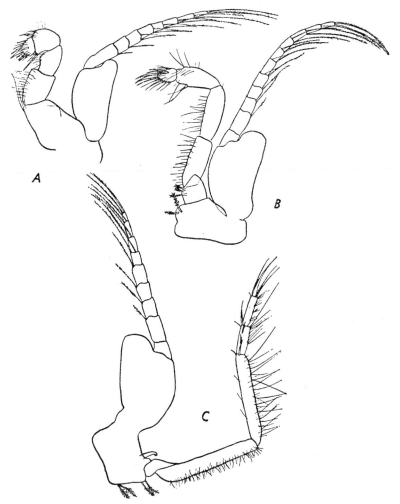

FIGURE 52.—*Mysidopsis californica* Tattersall: *a*, First thoracic limb, × 100; *b*, second thoracic limb, × 100; *c*, third thoracic limb, × 100.

tending from the level of the statocyst to the apex. Outer uropod nearly twice as long as the telson.

Pleopods in the male typical for the genus; fourth pair (fig. 51, *g*) with the exopod slightly longer than the endopod and terminating in a long powerful plumose seta.

Length of adult specimens of both sexes 8 mm.

Occurrence.—CALIFORNIA: Mission Bay (False Bay), summer of 1924, collected by the Scripps Institution, many specimens.

Distribution.—Known only from the coast of California.

MYSIDOPSIS MORTENSENI, new species

FIGURE 53

Description.—Carapace produced into a short, pointed, triangular rostral plate, not extending forward to the distal end of the eyestalks.

Eyes moderately large, kidney-shaped, and slightly depressed, pigment brown.

Antennal scale (fig. 53, *a*) extending forward slightly beyond the antennular peduncle and considerably longer than its own peduncle,

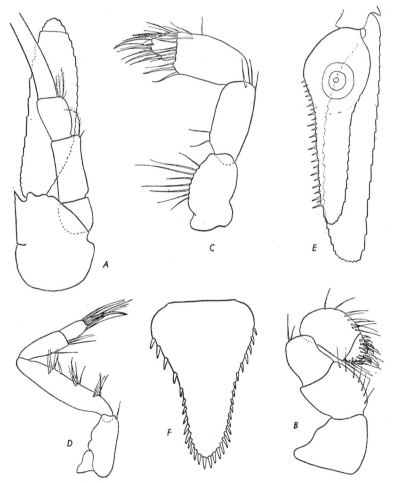

FIGURE 53.—*Mysidopsis mortenseni*, new species: *a*, Antennal scale and peduncle, × 90; *b*, endopod of first thoracic limb, × 90; *c*, endopod of second thoracic limb, × 90; *d*, endopod of third thoracic limb, × 90; *e*, uropods, × 90; *f*, telson, × 90.

oval in shape, 3½ times as long as broad, setose all around, distal part marked off by a distinct suture.

Maxilla with an exopod but lacking the setiferous expansion on the lobe from the second joint.

First thoracic limb very stout, endopod (fig. 53, *b*) as usual in the genus, 6-jointed, last two joints very broad, nail well developed.

Third to the eighth thoracic limbs (fig. 53, *d*) with the carpopropodus of the endopod divided into two or three subjoints by transverse sutures, nail very long and slender, longer than the distal subjoint of the carpopropodus.

Telson (fig. 53, *f*) shorter than the sixth abdominal somite and about five-eighths of the length of the outer uropod, triangular, nearly twice as long as broad at the base, without apical cleft, lateral margins armed throughout their entire length with about 15 to 20 short, stout, blunt spines, more crowded distally. In the specimen figured there are 15 spines on one side and 19 on the other.

Inner uropod (fig. 53, *e*) extending about halfway between the apex of the telson and the distal end of the outer uropods, with a row of about 24 spines on the inner margin extending from the statocyst almost to the distal end.

Length of adult specimens of both sexes 3 mm.

Type.—A male, U.S.N.M. No. 81264, St. Croix.

Occurrence.—CARIBBEAN SEA: St. Croix, 4 fathoms, collected by Dr. T. Mortensen, February 19, 1906, 2 females, 3 males, 3 mm. (type).

Remarks.—The specimen described is defective, but the species may be recognized by the combination of characters afforded by the antennal scale, uropods, and particularly by the telson with its armature of short blunt spines.

METAMYSIDOPSIS, new genus

Similar to *Mysidopsis* G. O. Sars, except that the maxilla is without an exopod and without the setiferous expansion of the lobe from the second joint.

Type species.—*Mysidopsis munda* Zimmer, 1918.

The establishment of this genus seems justified on the characters mentioned. Zimmer (1918) in the original description of *M. munda* noted the special characters of the maxilla given above, but while suggesting that they may be of more than specific value he did not actually found a new genus for his species. Two further species referred to *Mysidopsis*, *M. elongata* Holmes and *M. pacifica* Zimmer, show the same type of maxilla, and in my view the absence of the exopod should be regarded as of generic significance.

Fifteen species of the genus *Mysidopsis* have been described and of these it may be definitely stated that the following have an exopod to the maxilla: *M. didelphys* (Norman), *M. gibbosa* G. O. Sars, *M. angusta* G. O. Sars, *M. bigelowi* Tattersall, *M. acuta* Hansen, *M. inermis* Coifmann, *M. californica* Tattersall, *M. major* (Zimmer), *M. similis* (Zimmer), and *M. schultzei* (Zimmer). The form of the maxilla in *M. indica* Tattersall, and *M. kempii* Tattersall is not known, but in all probability in both species an exopod is present.

Other characters which are common to the three species of this new genus and may prove of generic significance, are: (1) The narrowly lanceolate form of the antennal scale; (2) the fact that the spines arming the lateral margins of the telson are confined to the distal portion only, the proximal part of the margins being smooth.

METAMYSIDOPSIS MUNDA (Zimmer)

FIGURE 54

Mysidopsis munda ZIMMER, 1918, p. 17, figs. 8–15.

Description.—General form of the body slender; carapace somewhat produced in the middorsal line into a broadly rounded rostral plate.

Eyes large, cylindrical, extending forward beyond the distal end of the second joint of the antennular peduncle, cornea shorter than the eyestalk.

Antennular peduncle rather long and slender, first joint longer than the third.

Antennal scale (fig. 54, *a*) about as long as the antennular peduncle, rather narrowly lanceolate, outer margin somewhat concave, 5 to 6 times as long as broad, distal joint marked off by a distinct suture.

Antennal peduncle (fig. 54, *a*) extending forward as far as the suture of the scale.

Maxilla (fig. 54, *c*) without exopod and without the setiferous expansion of the lobe from the second joint.

Carpopropodus of the endopods (fig. 54, *f*) of the third to the eighth thoracic limbs divided into two subjoints by a transverse suture.

Telson (fig. 54, *i*) broadly triangular, one and a third times as long as broad at the base, proximal two-thirds of the lateral margins smooth and without spines, distal third of the lateral margins armed with about 18 short acute spines, the terminal pair at the apex somewhat longer than those on either side of them; apex entire, without cleft.

Inner uropod (fig. 54, *h*) one and a half times as long as the telson with a row of about 46 spines extending from the statocyst almost to the distal end of the lower inner margin.

Outer uropod twice as long as the telson.

Length of adults of both sexes 6 mm.

Occurrence.—GULF OF MEXICO: Calcasieu Pass., La., W. H. Spaulding, collector, No. 19, 7:30 p. m., September 19, 1907, 4 males. EAST COAST OF UNITED STATES: Fort Macon, Beaufort, N. C., August 2, 1915.

4 specimens from the stomach of *Menticirrhus littoralis* caught at the surface; Bureau of Fisheries biological survey of Chesapeake Bay, 1920, stations 8895, lightship S. ⅜ E., Cape Henry Light, S. ¼ W.,

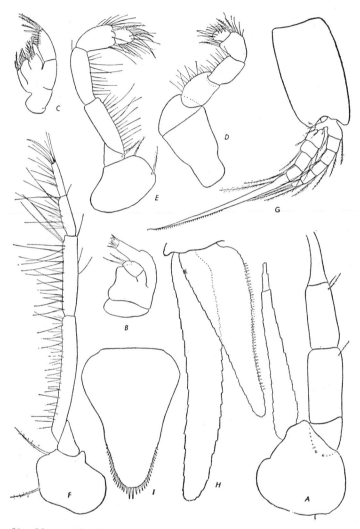

FIGURE 54.—*Metamysidopsis munda* (Zimmer): *a*, Antennal scale and peduncle, × 72; *b*, maxillule, × 72; *c*, maxilla, × 72; *d*, endopod of first thoracic limb, × 72; *e*, endopod of second thoracic limb, × 72; *f*, endopod of third thoracic limb, × 72; *g*, fourth pleopod of male, × 72; *h*, uropods, × 72; *i*, telson, × 72.

whistling buoy SW. by W. ¼ W., 16½ fathoms, October 21, 1920, 2 males; 8896, Cape Henry Light, SW. by S. ¾ S., lightship N. ¾ W., 23 fathoms, October 21, 1920, 10 males, 1 female.

Distribution.—Atlantic: Coast of Brazil. The present records add the Gulf of Mexico and the east coast of the United States.

Remarks.—Figure 54 is taken from a specimen from Chesapeake Bay and a comparison with the figures given by Zimmer reveals the closest agreement and leaves no doubt of the identity of the specimens. The species can be distinguished by the combination of characters afforded by the rostral plate, antennal scale, and telson. It is most closely allied to *M. pacifica* and to *M. elongata.*

METAMYSIDOPSIS ELONGATA (Holmes)

FIGURE 55

Mysidopsis elongata HOLMES, 1900, p. 226, pl. 4, figs. 77–80.—TATTERSALL, 1932a, p. 310, figs. 26–38.

Description.—Body slender; carapace very slightly produced in front into a short, wide-angled, bluntly pointed rostral plate which does not cover any part of the eyestalks.

Eyes large, (fig. 55, *e*) cylindrical; cornea occupying rather less than half of the whole eye.

Antennular peduncle (fig. 55, *f*) in the female rather long and slender, first joint longer than the third but shorter than the second and third combined. In the male the antennular peduncle is shorter and stouter than in the female and the setose lobe at the distal end is short and densely fringed with long setae.

Antennal scale (fig. 55, *g*) about as long as the antennular peduncle, rather slender and narrow, setose all around, about seven times as long as broad; the distal joint equal to about one-fifth of the whole scale and marked off by a distinct articulation; antennal peduncle (fig. 55, *g*) shorter than the scale, the terminal joint three-quarters the length of the preceding joint. In the male the antennal scale is somewhat shorter than in the female with the result that the antennal peduncle appears relatively longer, extending beyond the articulation of the distal joint of the scale.

Labrum forming a rather prominent conical papilla.

Mandibles (figs. 55, *a–b*) with a distinct molar process; on the anterior outer angle of the body of the mandible, outside the articulation of the palp, is a prominent, sharp, forwardly directed spine. Maxillulae (fig. 55, *c*) with a very short inner lobe armed with two long setae. Maxillae (fig. 55, *d*) without exopod and without the setiferous expansion of the lobe from the second joint; palp two-jointed. Maxillipeds (first thoracic limbs) (fig. 55, *h*) of the true *Mysidopsis* type, with the second and third joints of the endopod fused.

Third to the eighth thoracic limbs (fig. 55, *j*) rather slender, the carpopropodus divided into two by a transverse articulation; dactylus long and slender, longer than the distal division of the sixth joint.

Basal plate of the exopod with the outer distal corner rounded and without spine.

Pleopods in the male of the type characteristic of the genus; fourth pair (fig. 55, *k*) with the exopod rather longer than the endopod and terminating in a single long and rather stout plumose seta.

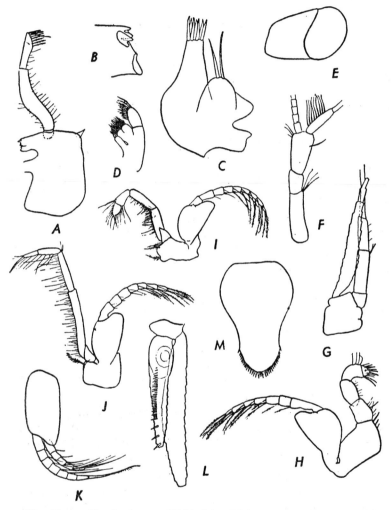

FIGURE 55.—*Metamysidopsis elongata* (Holmes): *a*, Right mandible with palp, × 100; *b*, cutting edge of left mandible, × 330; *c*, maxillule, × 330; *d*, maxilla, × 100; *e*, eye, × 100; *f*, peduncle of antennule, × 78; *g*, antennal scale and peduncle, × 78; *h*, first thoracic limb, × 100; *i*, second thoracic limb, × 78; *j*, third thoracic limb, × 78; *k*, fourth pleopod of male, × 100; *l*, uropod, × 78; *m*, telson, × 100.

Telson (fig. 55, *m*) short, two-thirds as long as the sixth abdominal somite, one and a half times as long as broad, linguiform in shape with the distal half much narrower than the proximal half; apex rounded and convex and armed with about 30 to 34 short spines; lateral margins terminating in a spine but otherwise unarmed.

Inner uropod (fig. 55, *l*) one and a third times as long as the telson, inner margins armed with a row of spines from the statocyst to the apex, the spines arranged in series of smaller spines between larger ones in the proximal three-quarters of the row, distal three spines large, widely separated, and without smaller ones between them. Outer uropod twice as long as the telson.

Length.—Adult specimens of both sexes 6 to 7 mm.

Occurrence.—CALIFORNIA: La Jolla, Scripps Institution, haul 87, August 19, 1916, 12 specimens; haul 377, September 21, 1916, 3 specimens; haul 432, October 3, 1916, 7 specimens; haul 586, October 17, 1916, 5 specimens; haul 1237, January 13, 1917, 4 specimens; haul 1789, May 10, 1917, 1 specimen; haul 1846, May 23, 1917, 1 specimen; haul 1966, June 6, 1917, 6 specimens; haul 2301, June 29, 1917, 3 specimens; haul 2308, August 23, 1917, 1 specimen. San Pedro* identified by M. J. Rathbun.

Distribution.—Known only from the coast of California, where it appears to be an abundant planktonic species during the hours of darkness.

Remarks.—This species is most closely related to *M. pacifica* (Zimmer), and in 1932 I suggested that the two species were synonymous in spite of small differences to be noted between California specimens and the description and figures given by Zimmer of *M. pacifica*. Coifmann (1937) considers the two species distinct and finds that the differences I pointed out are constant in numerous examples of *M. pacifica* she has examined. Under the latter species I give a summary of these differences. I have not seen any specimens of *M. pacifica*. *M. elongata* is also closely related to *M. munda* and differs mainly in the form of the telson. Both species have the same type of maxilla, without exopod and inner setiferous expansion.

METAMYSIDOPSIS PACIFICA (Zimmer)

Diagnosis of this species may be found on page 245.

Genus PROMYSIS Dana

Promysis DANA, 1850, p. 130.
Uromysis HANSEN, 1910, p. 71.

PROMYSIS ORIENTALIS Dana

Promysis orientalis DANA, 1852b, p. 651; 1855, pl. 43, fig. 4a–c.—CZERNIAVSKY, 1887, p. 40.—TATTERSALL, 1936b, p. 154, fig. 5.
Uromysis armata HANSEN, 1910, p. 72, pl. 11, figs. 2a–n.—ZIMMER, 1915b, p. 170.— COLOSI, 1919, p. 9; 1920, p. 243.

Occurrence.—PHILIPPINE ISLANDS: *Albatross* stations 5596, 1 male, 1 female; 5669, 10 males, 3 females.

Distribution.—A common species in the waters of the Dutch East Indies, the eastern Pacific, and the coasts of Queensland. Known also from the Philippine Islands. It appears to be a planktonic species especially at night.

PROMYSIS ATLANTICA Tattersall

FIGURE 56

Diagnosis of this species may be found on page 245.

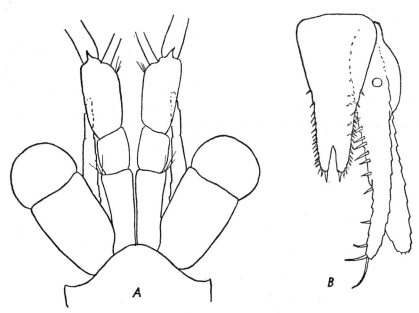

FIGURE 56.—*Promysis atlantica* Tattersall: *a*, Anterior end to show rostral plate, eye, antennular peduncle, and antennal scale, × 100; *b*, telson and uropods, × 100.

Genus DOXOMYSIS Hansen

Doxomysis HANSEN, 1912, p. 205.

DOXOMYSIS QUADRISPINOSA (Illig)

Mysis quadrispinosa ILLIG, 1906a, p. 207, fig. 14.—TATTERSALL, 1911a, p. 127, pl. 6, figs. 6, 7.
Doxomysis pelagica HANSEN, 1912, p. 205, pl. 8, figs. 3a–g.
Doxomysis quadrispinosa ZIMMER, 1915a, p. 216.—ILLIG, 1930, p. 480, figs. 163–166.
Doxomysis Zimmeri COLOSI, 1920, p. 247, pl. 19, figs. 7a–d.
Doxomysis Tattersallii COLOSI, 1920, p. 248, pl. 19, figs. 8a–e.

Occurrence.—PHILIPPINE ISLANDS: *Albatross* station 5422, 1 male, 1 female. WEST COAST OF SOUTH AMERICA: *Albatross* station 4640*, identified by H. J. Hansen as *D. pelagica* (1912) (type).

Distribution.—This species is widely distributed in the tropical waters of the Indian and Pacific Oceans and is apparently a surface form, or at any rate it is found in the upper strata of water.

Remarks.—I am still of the opinion that *D. zimmeri* and *D. tattersallii* are not separable from *D. pelagica* and *D. quadrispinosa* by any characters that can be regarded as of specific value.

DOXOMYSIS MICROPS Colosi

Synonymy and distribution records are given on page 246.

Genus BATHYMYSIS Tattersall

Bathymysis TATTERSALL, 1907, p. 116.

The discovery of a new species of this genus necessitates a modification of the original description of the eyes. The new species has large well-developed eyes with normal visual functional elements, correlated with the fact that it is found in much shallower water than the type, *B. helgae*. The diagnosis of the genus should therefore be amended to read: "Eyes large and normally developed with definite eyestalks and normal visual elements, or small, set close together, apparently without definite eyestalks, somewhat flattened and subquadrangular in shape, visual elements imperfectly developed and unpigmented in preserved specimens." The new species also has a rostral projection absent in the type species.

BATHYMYSIS RENOCULATA, new species

FIGURES 57, 58

Description.—Carapace covering all but the last thoracic somite; produced in front into a well-developed, broadly triangular, bluntly pointed rostral plate (fig. 57, *a*), extending not quite halfway along the first joint of the antennular peduncle; anterolateral corners rounded.

Eyes (fig. 57, *a*) very large, reniform, and somewhat compressed dorsoventrally, as long as the first joint of the antennular peduncle, in dorsal view one and a half times as long as broad, visual area very extensive both dorsally and ventrally, pigment golden brown.

Antennular peduncle (fig. 57, *a*) with the first joint longer than the combined length of the remaining two.

Antennal scale (figs. 57, *a*, *b*) extending forward slightly beyond the distal end of the antennular peduncle, in the male as far forward as the distal end of the setose lobe, narrowly lanceolate, seven and a half times as long as broad, with a small well-marked distal joint, two spines on the basal joint from which the scale arises, one at the base of the scale and the other at the base of the peduncle; peduncle about half as long as the scale, second joint longer than the third.

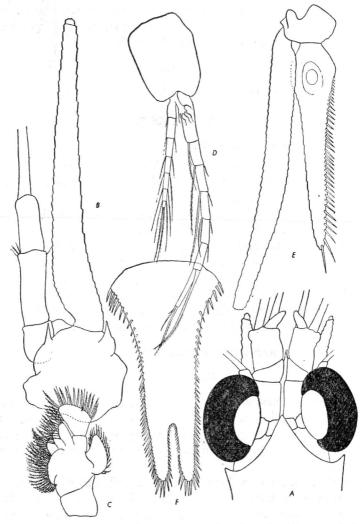

FIGURE 57.—*Bathymysis renoculata*, new species: *a*, Anterior end to show rostral plate and eyes, × 12; *b*, antennal scale and peduncle, × 26⅔; *c*, maxilla, × 26⅔; *d*, fourth pleopod of male, × 26⅔; *e*, uropods, × 26⅔; *f*, telson, × 26⅔.

Mandibles with the lacinia mobilis and spine row well developed and more or less typical; molar process strong; cutting incisor edge well developed.

Maxillule normally developed and without any special features.

Maxilla (fig. 57, *c*) with the distal joint of the endopod broadly expanded at the apex and bearing about twelve long strong plumose setae. They are, in fact, in every way similar to those of the type species.

First thoracic limbs (fig. 58, *a*) with strong gnathobasic lobes from the second, third, and fourth joints of the endopod; nail well developed, as long as the sixth joint, rather long and slender.

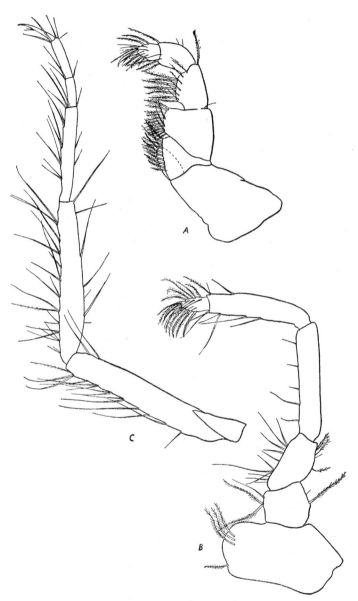

FIGURE 58.—*Bathymysis renoculata*, new species: *a*, Endopod of first thoracic limb, × 25; *b*, endopod of second thoracic limb, × 25; *c*, endopod of third thoracic limb, × 25.

Third to the eighth thoracic limbs (fig. 58, *c*) with the carpo-propodus of the endopod divided into three subjoints by transverse sutures, the first subjoint longer than the combined length of the second and third subjoints; third subjoint longer than the second; nail well developed and long, as long as the last subjoint of the carpopropodus.

Female with three pairs of incubatory lamellae.

Fourth pleopod of the male (fig. 57, *d*) with the endopod of seven joints; exopod nearly twice as long as the endopod, 8-jointed, sixth joint with a very long strong plumose seta on its outer distal corner, as long as the combined length of the fourth, fifth, and sixth joints, seventh joint long and narrow, about half as long as the long seta on the sixth joint, with a delicate plumose seta on the outer distal corner as long as the joint; eighth joint very short with a long and a short seta at the apex.

Sixth abdominal somite one and a quarter times as long as the fifth.

Telson (fig. 57, *f*) 1¼ times as long as the sixth abdominal somite and nearly twice as long as broad at the base; cleft for one-quarter of its length, sides of the cleft armed with about 20 spines, mostly short but the distal 3 or 4 longer and merging into the spines arming the lobes at the apex, lateral margins armed with about 40 to 45 long sharp spines extending throughout the entire margin; the apical lobes of the telson armed with 3 or 4 spines, rather longer than those on the lateral margins but grading into the lateral spines on the one hand and into those arming the cleft on the other.

Inner uropod (fig. 57, *e*) 1¼ times as long as the telson, inner margin armed with a continuous row of long spines extending from the statocyst to the apex and gradually increasing in size distally.

Outer uropod 1⅓ times as long as the inner.

Length of adult specimens of both sexes 18 mm.

Type lot.—Two males, 8 females, U.S.N.M. No. 81265, *Fish Hawk* station 939, east coast of the United States.

Occurrence.—EAST COAST OF UNITED STATES: *Fish Hawk* stations 869, 4 adult females, 18 mm.; 878, 1 male, 15 mm.; 939, 2 males, 8 females, 18 mm. (type lot); 1026, 3 females, 17 mm.; 1033, 1 female, 16 mm.; 1035, 19 males, 20 females, 13 to 14 mm., immature; 1038, 1 adult female, 17 mm., 1 immature specimen; *Albatross* stations 2091, 1 immature specimen, 4 mm.; 2642, 1 female.

Distribution.—The species is known only from the above records, which show that it is distributed in the deep water off the east coast of the United States from New England to Florida in 120 to 264 fathoms. In suitable conditions it is apparently not rare.

Remarks.—This species is one of the most interesting species in the collection, and it belongs to a genus of which hitherto only the type species, *B. helgae*, from very deep water off the west of Ireland was known. It differs from the type species in the following characters: (1) In the possession of very large eyes with normal functional visual elements; (2) in the presence of a rostral plate; (3) in the longer and more slender antennal scale; (4) in the form of the first and second thoracic limbs and the more slender endopods of the third to the eighth thoracic limbs; (5) in minor details of the telson and remaining appendages. It agrees closely with the type in the structure of the mouth parts, especially in the form of the maxilla. It is a typical member of the genus, the greatest difference, the form, structure, and size of the eye, being obviously correlated with the shallower water in which it lives, 120 to 264 fathoms, as against 447 to 720 fathoms for *B. helgae*.

Genus PSEUDOMYSIS G. O. Sars

Pseudomysis G. O. SARS, 1879b, p. 430.

PSEUDOMYSIS DACTYLOPS, new species

FIGURE 59

Description.—The types are two adult females, not in very good condition but sufficiently well preserved to make out the salient characters.

The species is very closely allied to *P. abyssi* G. O. Sars (1879b, p. 430), and it will be sufficient to point out the differences between the two. *P. dactylops* differs from *P. abyssi* in the following characters:

(1) The rostrum (fig. 59, *a*) is considerably longer and more pointed. It extends forward as far as the distal end of the first joint of the antennular peduncle and is very acutely pointed. It far outreaches the eye. In *P. abyssi* the rostrum is shorter and extends forward only about halfway along the first joint of the antennular peduncle and to about the level of the eye.

(2) The eyes (fig. 59, *a*) are pyriform and possess a long fingerlike process on the inner upper margin, which projects slightly beyond the eye. The eyes are considerably larger than in *P. abyssi*, and the visual elements, though reduced, are distinctly present and form a corneal region to the eye. There is no pigment in preserved specimens. In *P. abyssi* the eyes appear as a pair of small obtuse conical organs with an acute conical projection at the distal end, but no fingerlike process.

(3) The telson (fig. 59, *b*) is relatively longer than in *P. abyssi* though essentially of the same form and shape. It is almost twice as long as broad at the base and is cleft for about one-third its length, the cleft wide and triangular with diverging margins. Each margin of the cleft is armed with about 30 sawlike teeth. Each lobe of the

apex terminates in a single stout spine and each lateral margin has
from 10 to 12 small regularly arranged spines along the distal half
of the margin, the proximal part of the margin being smooth. There
is a pair of plumose setae at the base of the cleft. In *P. abyssi* the
telson is much shorter, only about one-third longer than broad at the
base, and there are no plumose setae at the base of the cleft. Otherwise
it has the same general structure as in *P. dactylops*.

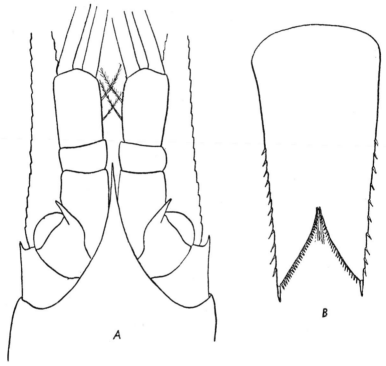

FIGURE 59.—*Pseudomysis dactylops*, new species: *a*, Anterior end to show rostral plate and
eyes, × 20; *b*, telson.

(4) It appears to be a smaller species than *P. abyssi*. Both the
type specimens measure about 30 mm. but have the incubatory lamellae
fully developed and are thus adult. Sars' types of *P. abyssi* measured
35 mm., but the incubatory lamellae were still very small and undeveloped. Hansen gives 45 mm. as the length of an adult female with
fully developed marsupial plates and 42 mm. for an adult male.

It is unfortunate that the antennal scale and uropods in both specimens are so broken that I am unable to give comparative measurements. What remains of them is, however, sufficient to show that
they are essentially of the same form as in *P. abyssi*. The inner
uropod has a row of spines extending along the inner margin from
the statocyst almost to the apex.

Type lot.—Two adult females, U.S.N.M. No. 81266, *Albatross* station 3697, Japan.

Occurrence.—JAPAN : *Albatross* station 3697, 2 adult females (type lot).

Distribution.—This species was collected off the coasts of Japan in 120 to 264 fathoms. *P. abyssi* is known only from the Arctic Ocean in 781 to 1,309 fathoms in water with the temperature below zero. The discovery of a new species of this rare and interesting genus in a new and isolated geographical area is a matter of great interest. It may be noted that *P. dactylops* occurs in much shallower water than does *P. abyssi*, and in correlation with this habit the eyes, while much reduced, are larger and better developed than in the latter species.

Genus MYSIDETES Holt and Tattersall

Mysidetes HOLT and TATTERSALL, 1906b, p. 39.

MYSIDETES CRASSA Hansen

This species is recorded on page 247.

Tribe MYSINI

Endopods of the third to the eighth thoracic limbs with the carpus and propodus fused and the combined joint subdivided by vertical articulations into a number of subjoints; first and second pleopods of the male rudimentary, exopod of the fourth pair always very elongated, antennal scale and telson very variable.

Remarks.—This is the largest tribe of the Mysinae. About 31 genera have been referred to it, and 15 of these are represented in the collections of the United States National Museum, though not all are found off the American coasts. In general, the members of this tribe are littoral and coastal in habit and dominate the shallow water mysidacean fauna.

Genus INUSITATOMYSIS Ii [12]

Inusitatomysis II, 1940, p. 162.

Antennal scale with the outer margin devoid of setae, serrate, and terminating in a strong spine.

---

[12] At the time the manuscript for the present publication was prepared Dr. Tattersall was apparently unaware of Ii's paper in which the genus *Inusitatomysis* was established. He therefore proposed a new genus for the species described below. Although this species is obviously distinct from the genotype of *Inusitatomysis*, it appears to be congeneric with it. Tattersall was inclined to assign the genus to the tribe Leptomysini near the genus *Mysidetes*, stating that the "antennal scale is, however, quite unlike that of any other genus of the tribe, in having the outer margin devoid of setae and serrated. The telson is of a form not uncommon in other genera of this tribe and the mouth parts and thoracic limbs seem to me to be more like those of the Leptomysini in general than of the Mysini." These circumstances have been brought to our attention by Dr. A. H. Banner, of the University of Hawaii.—F. A. CHACE, Jr.

Telson cleft, the cleft armed with teeth and a pair of plumose setae, lateral margins armed with spines along the whole length.

First, second, third, and fifth pleopods of the male simple unjointed plates as in the female; fourth pleopod of the male consisting of sympod and endopod only, the exopod absent; endopod fused with the second joint of the sympod, elongate and multiarticulate, terminal joint armed with two spines (or modified setae).

Remarks.—The systematic position of this genus is obscure. Unfortunately the single specimen is immature, and the full elucidation of its systematic position must await the advent of fully grown specimens. The fourth pleopod of the male is unique if my interpretation of the immature appendage is correct. The exopod appears to be completely absent and the endopod to be fused with the second joint of the sympod. I have interpreted the single ramus as the endopod because it bears at its base the usual side lobe, which is more or less characteristic of the endopods of the male pleopods in Mysidae. In this genus the endopod is elongated and composed of 14 joints altogether including the fused basal joint and sympod. I know of no other mysid that has the fourth pleopod of the male of this type. In those Mysidae in which the fourth pleopod of the male is modified it is usually the exopod which is the elongate and modified ramus.

INUSITATOMYSIS SERRATA, new species

FIGURE 60

Description.—Carapace leaving the last thoracic somite completely uncovered and the penultimate somite uncovered in the middorsal line; produced in front into a short triangular rostral plate, obtusely rounded at the apex and leaving the eyes and eyestalks completely uncovered; the front margin is also slightly produced into a small spine on each side to the outside of the eyestalks; anterolateral corners rounded.

Eyes very large, reniform, depressed dorsoventrally, extending forward almost to the end of the second joint of the antennular peduncle, cornea occupying more than half the entire eye in dorsal view, a small blunt tubercle on the dorsal side of the eyestalk, pigment golden-brown.

Antennal scale (fig. 60, *a*) extending forward beyond the distal end of the antennular peduncle by about one-fifth its length, three and a half times as long as broad, outer margin not setose but terminating in a strong spine and provided with five strong teeth in addition to the terminal spine; apex of the scale produced beyond the terminal spine of the outer margin into a lobe which is as broad as long; no distal suture.

Maxilla (fig. 60, *c*) of normal structure, exopod present, lobe from the second joint with a well-marked setiferous expansion, terminal joint of the endopod about twice as long as broad and the distal end not expanded.

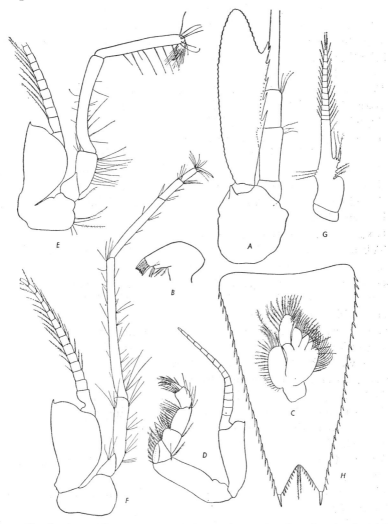

FIGURE 60.—*Inusitatomysis serrata*, new species: *a*, Antennal scale and peduncle, × 18; *b*, maxillule, × 18; *c*, maxilla, × 18; *d*, first thoracic limb, × 18; *e*, second thoracic limb, × 18; *f*, third thoracic limb, × 18; *g*, fourth pleopod of male, × 22; *h*, telson.

Endopod (fig. 60, *d*) of the first thoracic limbs with a well developed gnathobasic lobe from the second joint, the third and fourth joints somewhat expanded but without specially marked lobes, nail well developed.

Endopod (fig. 60, *e*) of the second thoracic limbs somewhat long and slender, fourth and fifth joints subequal, long and narrow, about ten times as long as broad, sixth joint short, nail distinct.

Third to the eighth thoracic limbs (fig. 60, *f*) long and slender; carpopropodus of the endopod divided into three subjoints, the first much longer than the combined length of the remaining two, second longer than the third, dactylus about as long as the third; exopods of all the thoracic limbs with an acute spine on the outer distal corner of the expanded basal plate.

Fourth pleopod of the male (fig. 60, *g*) (in an immature specimen) apparently consisting of one branch only (? the sympod plus the endopod), longer than the fifth abdominal somite; exopod absent; endopod apparently fused with the second joint of the sympod but the setose side lobe, which is usually found at the base of the first joint of the endopod, is clearly distinguishable and has four setae on the inside margin and 7 or 8 on the outer margin, remaining part of the endopod composed of 13 short equal joints, last joint terminated by 2 spines or setae.

Sixth segment of the pleon about one-third longer than the fifth.

Telson (fig. 60, *h*) slightly longer than the sixth segment of the pleon; slightly more than one and a half times as long as broad at the base, narrowing to an apex, which is about one-third of the breadth of the base; apex cleft, cleft about one-eighth of the length of the telson, wide and triangular in outline, margins of the cleft armed with about 10 teeth and a pair of plumose setae is situated at the base of the cleft; apical lobes armed with a single strong spine; lateral margins armed with about 25 spines, short, acute, and more or less equally spaced, extending throughout their entire length.

Outer uropod about 1½ times as long as the telson.

Inner uropod shorter than the outer, with a single spine on the inner margin near to the statocyst.

Length of an immature male 18 mm.

Type.—One immature male, U.S.N.M. No. 81267, from *Albatross* station 4788, Bering Sea.

Occurrence.—BERING SEA: *Albatross* station 4788, 1 immature male, 18 mm. (type).

Distribution.—Known only from the type specimen collected in the Bering Sea, off Bering Island, in 56 to 57 fathoms.

Remarks.—This species may be distinguished by the combination of characters afforded by the large reniform eyes, serrated outer margin of the antennal scale, and the form and armature of the telson.

Genus ANTARCTOMYSIS Coutière

Antarctomysis COUTIÈRE, 1906, pp. 1, 6.

ANTARCTOMYSIS MAXIMA (Hansen)

Mysis maxima HANSEN, *in* Holt and Tattersall, 1906a, p. 11.
Antarctomysis maxima COUTIÈRE, 1906, p. 1, pl. 1; pl. 2, figs. 13–20.—HANSEN,
1908b, p. 13, pl. 2, figs. 3a–m.—TATTERSALL, 1908, p. 36, pl. 8, fig. 1.

Occurrence.—ANTARCTIC: Bay of Islands, January 1913, collected
by R. C. Murphy, 2 specimens from the stomach of *Pygoscelis papua.*

Distribution.—Circumpolar in the Antarctic and sub-Antarctic
regions.

Remarks.—With reference to what is written under the genus *Mysis*
as to the presence of a pair of vestigial oöstegites on each of the fifth
and sixth thoracic limbs, it is interesting to note that Coutière (1906)
in his original description of this species notes that the marsupium
is composed of three pairs of brood lamellae and that there is a rudimentary pair on the fifth thoracic limbs, which takes no part in the
formation of the marsupium.

The present record is the first one to indicate that this species forms
part of the food of another animal, in this case one of the penguins.

Genus ARTHROMYSIS Colosi

Macromysis CUNNINGHAM, 1871, p. 497.
Arthromysis COLOSI, 1924, p. 3.

ARTHROMYSIS MAGELLANICA (Cunningham)

Synonymy and locality record may be found on page 246.

Genus HEMIMYSIS G. O. Sars

Hemimysis G. O. SARS, 1869, p. 336.

HEMIMYSIS LAMORNAE (Couch)

Mysis lamornae COUCH, 1856, p. 5286, figs. 1–5.

Distribution.—Naples*, identified by A. M. Norman.

Genus MYSIS Latreille

Mysis LATREILLE, 1803, p. 282.
Megalophthalmus LEACH, 1830, p. 176.
Onychomysis CZERNIAVSKY, 1882a, p. 138, pars; 1887, p. 79.
Michtheimysis NORMAN, 1902, p. 477.
Mesomysis NORMAN, 1905, p. 11 (nec Czerniavsky, 1882a, p. 59; 1882b, p. 41).

The genus *Mysis* was established by Latreille with *Mysis oculata*
(Fabricius) as the type. *M. mixta*, described by Lilljeborg in 1853,

was referred to the same genus. In 1882 Czerniavsky established the genus *Onychomysis* for the species *O. mingrelica*, and without the examination of specimens he referred *Mysis latitans* Krøyer to the same genus. *Mysis latitans* is, however, synonymous with the earlier species *Mysis mixta* Lilljeborg and has no obvious affinity with Czerniavsky's species.

In 1902 Norman separated *Mysis mixta* from the genus *Mysis* and made it the type of the new genus *Michtheimysis* because of the unjointed and acutely pointed antennal scale and the form of the male pleopods as figured by Sars. Zimmer (1915a) pointed out that Sars' figures of the male pleopods of *Mysis oculata* were drawn from immature specimens, and that in the completely adult male they were almost identical with those of *M. mixta*. He regarded the character of the scale of *M. mixta* to be insufficient as a generic character alone and canceled the genus *Michtheimysis* as a synonym of *Mysis*. Later authors have used either generic name indiscriminately. In this paper I follow Zimmer's lead and retain *M. mixta* and *M. stenolepis* in the genus *Mysis* with *M. oculata* and *M. relicta*. I would point out, however, that a precisely parallel state of affairs occurs in the genus *Neomysis* where there are two groups of species separable on the character of the antennal scale. One group has the scale produced into an acute apex, the other group has the scale jointed, with the apex rounded. The former group is the genus *Neomysis* (*sensu stricto*) and the second group the genus *Acanthomysis*. Zimmer unites these two groups of species under the genus *Neomysis* on the grounds that the form of the male pleopods in each is identical. In 1933 I pointed out that the genus *Neomysis* (*sensu lato*) was becoming too unwieldy and that as a matter of convenience it might be perhaps desirable to reinstate the genus *Acanthomysis*. This has since been done by Ii (1937). The plea of expediency can hardly be raised in the genus *Mysis*, and for the present at least I am content to accept Zimmer's conclusions.

In 1905 Norman, I believe inadvertently, used the generic name *Mesomysis* for the species *M. mixta* and *M. stenolepis*, without giving any reasons. Czerniavsky's genus *Mesomysis* is, however, quite distinct in the characters of the antennal scale, having the outer margin entire and not setose.

Dr. Mary J. Rathbun called my attention to a paper by Leach (1830, p. 177) in which he describes a crustacean under the name of *Megalophthalmus fabricianus*. The description is very imperfect, but I strongly suspect it refers to *Mysis oculata*. *Cancer pedatus* Fabricius is given by Leach as a synonym of his species. The species is said to be abundant off the coasts of Greenland, especially in Baffin Bay. From the meager description the species is almost certainly a mysid and in all probability *Mysis oculata*.

A point of morphological interest, first observed by Zimmer (1927), may be referred to here. The brood pouch is composed of two pairs of brood lamellae attached to the seventh and eighth thoracic limbs as outgrowths from the coxal joints of the endopods. On the inner margins of the coxal joints of the endopods of the fifth and sixth thoracic limbs (fig. 65) of the female there is a small expanded setose lobe projecting inward and lying against the sternum of the thorax. The position of these lobes and their morphological relationships suggest that they represent vestigial brood lamellae, which no longer function in that capacity. Their relatively strong setose furnishings likewise suggest that they have taken on a new function, which is probably that of baling organs to help to maintain a steady flow of water through the marsupium. This current probably flows from behind forward through the marsupial pouch and helps to supplement the aeration of the water in the pouch by the pulsating movements of the large brood lamellae. There is no trace of the median sternal processes which I recorded as present in the marsupium of *Neomysis rayii* and allied species (Tattersall, 1932b), or of the baling lobe on the anterior pair of brood lamellae present in the latter species.

I counted the embryos in the marsupium of a large breeding female of *M. stenolepis* measuring 28 mm. in length and found that they numbered 190. This fact will emphasize the remarkable potential breeding capacity of this species. I am unable to give corresponding figures for *M. mixta* because of the absence of large breeding females in the material examined by me.

MYSIS OCULATA (Fabricius)

FIGURE 61

Cancer oculatus FABRICIUS, 1780, p. 245.
Mysis flexuosus ADAMS, 1852, p. ccv.—WALKER, 1862, p. 68.
Mysis fabricii BELL, 1855, p. 404.
Mysis spinulosus PACKARD, 1863, p. 419.
Mysis oculata STIMPSON, 1863, p. 2.—PACKARD, 1867, p. 301.—SMITH, 1883, p. 221; 1885, p. 57.—DAWSON, 1886, p. 202.—FEWKES, 1888, p. 49, pl. 2, figs. 5, 6.—OHLIN, 1895b, p. 8.—AURIVILLIUS, 1896, p. 212.—ORTMANN, 1901, p. 160.—STAFFORD, 1912, p. 60.—KINDLE and WHITTAKER, 1918, p. 252.—W. L. SCHMITT, 1919, p. 4b.

Occurrence.—NORTH ATLANTIC: U. S. Fish Commission *Grampus* station 42, September 21, 1 male, 5 females; 9 miles off Webster Point, N. Y., Oct. 14, 1894, C. H. Stronger collector, 12 specimens from stomach of bloater from deep water; Indian Harbor, Labrador, August 12, 1908, Owen Bryant collector, 16 immature specimens.[13]

---

[13] These specimens were sent to me in exchange as *M. relicta,* but I believe them to be young specimens of *M. oculata*. They were identified by Dr. Mary J. Rathbun, and they are probably those recorded in 1909 in Grenfell, "Labrador: The Country and Its People."

ARCTIC OCEAN: January 6, 1881, 1 female; Aberdare Channel, east of Alger Island, Franz Josef Land, June 1901, Baldwin-Ziegler Polar expedition, 1 male, 1 female, 1 immature. GREENLAND: Upernavik, 1883, Greely relief party, H. G. Dresel collector, 1 immature; latitude 59°31′ N., longitude 63°50′ W., July 12, 1927, 29 females, 8 males; Pendulum Island, July 20, 1930, 4 fathoms, 1 male, 2 females, 2 immature, one infested with an epicarid; 8 lots were collected by Capt.

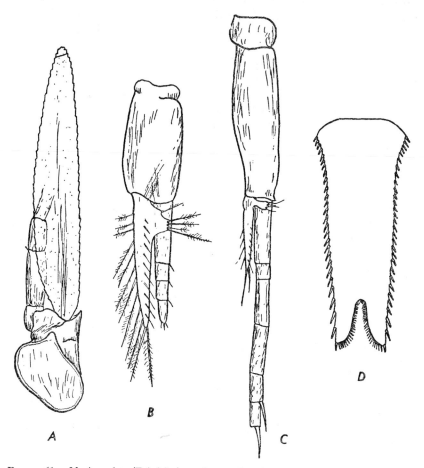

FIGURE 61.—*Mysis oculata* (Fabricius): *a*, Antennal scale; *b*, third pleopod of male (immature); *c*, fourth pleopod of male (immature); *d*, telson. (After G. O. Sars.)

R. A. Bartlett: Upernavik Fiord, May 4, 1926, anchored near shore, several hundred half-grown specimens; off Karnah, Inglefield Gulf, August 14–15, 1926, net down 5 minutes in 5 to 20 fathoms, 3 adult females, 27 young; off Northumberland Island, Whale Sound, August 15, 1926, dredge, 30 fathoms, 2 immature; Cape York, July 21, 1926, in dredge off village between glacier and bill of cape, 7 to 15 fathoms,

6 females; Cape York, July 21, 1926, dredge at edge of talus from glacier, 20 fathoms, 3 females; off Dalrymple Rock, Wolstenholme Sound, July 22, 1926, 1 female; off east end of Herbert Island, Whale Sound, July 25, 1926, dredge, 4 to 25 fathoms, 1 male, 3 females; Murchison Sound, August 19-20, 1926, 17 to 20 fathoms, 1 female; dredge, August 20, 1926, 3 females, 1 male. ALASKA: Latitude 66°45′ N., longitude 166°35′ W., 10 fathoms, W. H. Dall collector, 1 female; Kiska Harbor, Alaska, W. H. Dall collector, 1 damaged specimen; Plover Bay, Alaska, 10 to 25 fathoms, W. H. Dall collector, 1 damaged specimen; U. S. R. S. *Corwin*, Capt. M. A. Healy collector, 3 females; Coal Islands, July 8, 1886, H. D. Woolfe collector, gull feed, caught in dip net in holes between ice, 13 specimens; 2 badly damaged specimens collected by Lieut. G. M. Stoney, 1884. NORTHERN CANADA: The Norcross-Bartlett expedition collected at several localities: Nos. 23-26, Ducketts Cove, Hurd Channel, Melville Peninsula, Foxe Channel, Frozen Strait, August 11, 1933; Nos. 73-74, village of Pingitkalik, northeastern end of Melville Peninsula, September 5, 1933, 29 females, 13 males; No. 2, Harvard Islands, Inglefield Gulf, latitude 77°32′ N., longitude 67°00′ W., July 26-28, 1935, caught in fine mesh along rocky shore, several hundred young specimens; No. 10, southeast end of Cobourg Island, Baffin Bay, latitude 75°40′ N., longitude 78°55′ W., August 4, 1935, 50 to 100 feet of water, 2 males, 1 female; No. 11, southeast end of Cobourg Island, August 4, 1935, 15 to 30 feet of water, 8 females, 6 males. LABRADOR: Specimens identified by S. I. Smith and M. J. Rathbun*; Granville Bay, identified by A. E. Ortmann* (1901).

Distribution.—Circumpolar in the Arctic regions; in the Atlantic Ocean it is found as far south as the coasts of Labrador; in the Pacific it extends to the coasts of Alaska.

MYSIS RELICTA Lovén

FIGURE 62

Mysis relicta LOVÉN, 1861, p. 285.—SMITH, 1871, p. 3; 1874a, p. 642, pl. 1, fig. 2; 1874b, p. 694.—SMITH and VERRILL, 1871, p. 452.—FORBES, 1876, p. 20.—UNDERWOOD, 1886, p. 364.—MARSH, 1891, p. 275.—WARD, 1896, p. 15.—M. J. RATHBUN, 1909, p. 484.—PEARSE, 1910, p. 73.—HUNTSMAN, 1913, p. 273; 1915, p. 153, figs. 5, 6.—PRATT, 1916, p. 383, fig. 614.—ORTMANN, 1918, p. 844.—JUDAY and BIRGE, 1927, p. 449.—CLEMENS and BIGELOW, 1922, p. 90.—JOHANSEN, 1922, p. N 17.—CLEMENS et al., 1923, p. 188.—BAJKOV, 1930, p. 197, tables 19, 21, 24.—TATTERSALL, 1939b, p. 285 (summary of Canadian records).

Mysis diluvianus HOY, 1872, p. 100.

Mysis sp. MARSH, 1900, p. 375.

Occurrence.—Waterworks water of Duluth, Minn., received at the United States Fish Commission May 1, 1895, from A. J. Woolman,

1 male, 3 females. Stockholm*, identified by S. I. Smith; Lake Michigan* and Lake Superior*, identified by S. I. Smith.

Distribution.—This species has been recorded from Green Lake, Wis., by Marsh (1891) and from Green and Trout Lakes, Wis., by Juday and Birge (1927). These are the only records I can trace for the fresh waters of the United States except for those from the Great Lakes. Its occurrence in the water supply of Duluth is interesting.

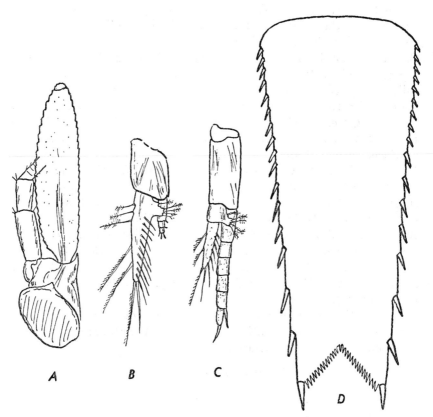

FIGURE 62.—*Mysis relicta* Lovén: *a*, Antennal scale; *b*, third pleopod of male; *c*, fourth pleopod of male; *d*, telson. (After G. O. Sars.)

MYSIS MIXTA Lilljeborg

FIGURE 63

Mysis mixta LILLJEBORG, 1852, p. 6.—S. I. SMITH, 1879, p. 102.—R. RATHBUN, 1880, p. 228; 1883, p. 212.—AURIVILLIUS, 1896, p. 198.—M. RATHBUN, 1905, p. 27; 1909, p. 484.—TATTERSALL, 1939b, p. 284.
Michtheimysis mixta ALLEE, 1923a, p. 180.—PROCTOR, 1933, p. 243.

Occurrence.—EAST COAST OF NORTH AMERICA: United States Fish Commission locations 10, off Salem, Mass., 20 fathoms, August 6, 1877, 23 specimens; 24, off Salem, 33 fathoms, August 13, 1877, 1 damaged specimen; 25, off Salem, 40 fathoms, August 13, 1877, 1 immature specimen; 25 to 31, off Salem, 48 fathoms, August 13, 1877, 1 specimen; 33, August 14, 1877, 1 female; 148, off Cape Ann, Mass., August 3, 1878, 1 immature specimen; 154, off Cape Ann, 38 fathoms, August 15, 1878, 1 female; 162, Gulf of Maine, August 16, 1878, 13 specimens; 184, Massachusetts Bay, August 29, 1878, 16 specimens; 206, Massachusetts Bay, 42 fathoms, September 16, 1878, 10 speci-

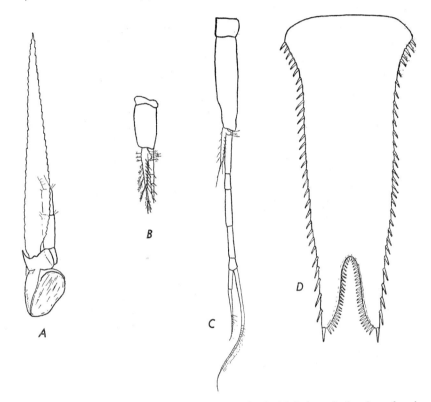

FIGURE 63.—*Mysis mixta* Lilljeborg: *a*, Antennal scale; *b*, third pleopod of male; *c*, fourth pleopod of male; *d*, telson. (After G. O. Sars.)

mens; 216, Massachusetts Bay, 35 fathoms, September 18, 1878, 13 specimens, and 1878, Gulf of Maine, 13 specimens; 232, 234, 238, Massachusetts Bay, September 24 and 26, 1878, 14 specimens; 237, Massachusetts Bay, September 26, 1878, 8 specimens; 306, off Cape Cod, Mass., August 25, 1879, 1 specimen; 309, off Cape Cod, August 25, 1879, 3 specimens; 319, off Cape Cod, August 30, 1879, 2 specimens; 321, off Cape Cod, 29½ fathoms, August 30, 1879, 2 specimens; 324, off Cape Cod, September 1, 1879, 1 specimen; 338, off Cape Cod, September 9, 1879, 11 specimens; 341, off Cape Cod, September 9, 1879, 1 specimen; 351, off Cape Cod, September 13, 1879, 1 specimen;

other material came from Eastport, Maine, summer, 1893, 2 specimens; Treats Island, Eastport, Maine, seine on gravel beach, collected by H. F. Moore, July 28, 1893, about 150 specimens; Long Beach, Grand Manan, New Brunswick, collected by M. J. Rathbun, August 16, 1898, 10 immature specimens; *Speedwell* stations 1–5*, 23–30*, 32*, 154*, 156*, 161*, 165*, 167*, 181*, 203–207*, 216*, 218*; *Bache* stations 29*, 63–65*; Labrador; *Albatross* station 2437*; Cape Cod Bay, Mass.,* 27 fathoms. All the material marked * was identified by S. I. Smith and is probably included in his records (1879).

Distribution.—Smith (1879) gave a full list of the localities at which this species was collected on the east coast of the United States. References to records subsequent to Smith's paper are given in the synonymy. These later records and the material here recorded add very little to Smith's account and merely serve to emphasize the fact that this species is common off the east coast of the United States between Woods Hole and the northern border in depths down to 100 fathoms where the bottom is suitable, that is, where algae and zostera are not present. The species does not appear to extend farther south than Woods Hole; at least I can trace no more southerly records. In the northerly direction it extends to Canada, Greenland, Iceland, and across to Scandinavia.

MYSIS STENOLEPIS S. I. Smith

FIGURES 64, 65

Mysis stenolepis S. I. SMITH, 1873, p. 551; 1879, p. 103.—VERRILL, 1874b, p. 135.— R. RATHBUN, 1881, p. 120.—PARKER, 1891, p. 99.—J. SCHMITT, 1904, p. 256.— PAULMIER, 1905, p. 128, fig. 2.—M. RATHBUN, 1905, p. 27.—PRATT, 1916, p. 383, fig. 613.—ALLEE, 1923a, p. 188.—KROPP and PERKINS, 1933, pp. 28, 31.— TATTERSALL, 1939b, p. 284.

Mysis spinulosus GOULD, 1841, p. 333.—DE KAY, 1844, p. 31, pl. 7, fig. 20.

Michtheimysis stenolepis SUMNER, OSBORN, and COLE, 1913, p. 663.—PRATT, 1935, p. 423, figs. 5–7.

Mesomysis stenolepis NORMAN, 1905, p. 11.

Occurrence.—EAST COAST OF NORTH AMERICA: United States Fish Commission, Casco Bay, Maine, 1873, 2 immature; Woods Hole, Mass., 1874, V. N. Edwards collector, 12 adult females (5 breeding, 7 shedding), 1 adult male; no locality, from sides of the fins of a pollack, V. N. Edwards collector, April 1876, embryos from brood pouch; Woods Hole, V. N. Edwards collector, November 11, 1876, several specimens; off Cape Ann, Mass., 6 immature specimens; Vineyard Sound, Mass., V. N. Edwards collector, April 1, 1878, 20 females, all full of embryos; U. S. Fish Commission locations 311, 2 immature specimens, and 314, Cape Cod, Mass., 6 fathoms, August 29, 1879, 2 immature; 3 lots were collected at Woods Hole by V. N. Edwards;

294 specimens, without locality data; no locality, 4 adult females, breeding; Woods Hole, 122 specimens; Woods Hole, V. N. Edwards collector, location 898, November 20, 1881, 75 adults; Woods Hole, V. N. Edwards collector, location 978, 100 specimens; Woods Hole,

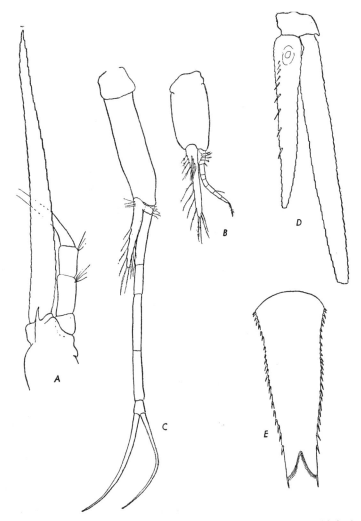

FIGURE 64.—*Mysis stenolepis* S. I. Smith: *a,* Antennal scale, × 13; *b,* third pleopod of male, × 13; *c,* fourth pleopod of male, × 13; *d,* uropods, × 13; *e,* telson, × 13.

V. N. Edwards collector, January 3, 1882, 2 females, breeding; Hadley Harbor, Mass., inside and outside Naushon, August 18, 1892, 30 immature; Great Egg Harbor, N. J., W. J. Stimpson collector, No. 46, 4 immature; Bathurst, New Brunswick, stomach of the smelt *Osmerus mordax,* S. E. Meek collector, No. 12230, 3 males; Woods Hole, August

12, 1882, 3 specimens; Woods Hole, V. N. Edwards collector, surface, evening, May 2, 1888, 1 adult female; Woods Hole, 1 adult female, 2 adult males, 16 immature; ? Puerto Rico, S. T. Danforth collector, 2 adult females, badly damaged and dry at some time; the following material was identified by S. I. Smith: Provincetown*; Woods Hole*; Casco Bay*; Noank*; Vineyard Sound*; *Speedwell* stations 56–58*, 65–66*, 994*; Dr. Mary J. Rathbun identified material from Anticosti*, St. Pierre Harbor, Newfoundland*; Casco Bay*; A. E. Verrill identified material from Casco Bay*; Vineyard Sound*.

Distribution.—The known distribution of this species extends from the littoral waters of the Gulf of St. Lawrence to the coast of New Jersey. Records from farther south are lacking, probably because very little collecting has been done on the more southerly coasts of eastern North America. It is therefore all the more regrettable that the specimens from Puerto Rico here doubtfully recorded as belonging to this species are in such a poor state of preservation that certain identification is precluded. If correct they represent the most southerly record for the species and suggest that it is probably to be found all along the eastern coast of North America. It would be interesting to have the southern limits of its distribution determined.

Remarks.—This species is very closely allied to *M. mixta*, and young specimens of both species are very difficult to separate. I am not sure that I have successfully accomplished this separation in the records of both species I have given here. Adult specimens are more easily distinguished. Smith (1879) summarized the distinguishing features of the two species as follows:

ANTENNAL SCALE: *M. mixta* (fig. 63, *a*), nine times as long as broad; outer margin nearly straight. *M. stenolepis* (fig. 64, *a*) 12 times as long as broad; outer margin concave in outline.

ANTENNULAR PEDUNCLE: *M. mixta*, penultimate joint one-third longer than the ultimate. *M. stenolepis*, penultimate and ultimate joints subequal.

TELSON: *M. mixta* (fig. 63, *d*), cleft much deeper than in *M. stenolepis;* spines of the lateral margins more than 30 extending almost to the distal end, at least three or four on the margin posterior to the base of the cleft. *M. stenolepis* (fig. 64, *d*), spines on the lateral margins about 25, the posteriormost spine at about the level of the base of the cleft, so that there is a considerable unarmed posterior portion of the lateral margins.

Smith also points out differences in color between the two species, *M. stenolepis* possessing many more chromatophores than *M. mixta*.

Of the differences pointed out by Smith, the telson is the most readily observed in preserved material. I give here figures of the telson and antennal scale for comparison with those of *M. mixta* as given in Sars' monograph. I have also figured the third and fourth pleopods of the male (fig. 64, *b–c*) and it will be seen that they closely resemble the same appendages in *M. mixta* (fig. 63, *b–c*).

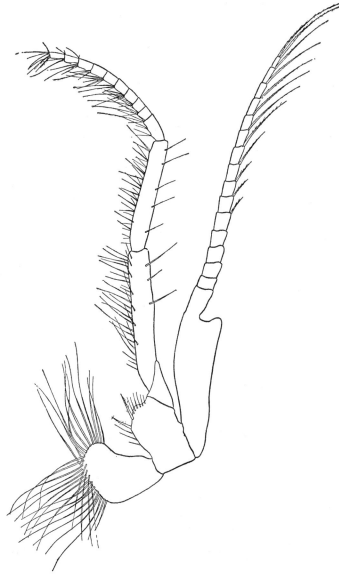

FIGURE 65.—*Mysis stenolepis* S. I. Smith: Fifth thoracic limb to show the reduced oöstegite on the coxal joint, × 24.

The differences between *M. mixta* and *M. stenolepis* in the form of the telson are closely paralleled by the related species *M. oculata* and *M. relicta.* A study of the figures of the telsons of these species (Sars,

1879a) will show that in *M. oculata* the cleft is much deeper than in *M. relicta* and there are four spines on the lateral margins of the telson of *M. oculata* behind the level of the base of the cleft, whereas in *M. relicta* the last spine of the lateral margin is at the level of the base of the cleft, and, between it and the terminal spine at the apex there is a considerable unarmed area.

It is generally accepted that *M. relicta* has been derived from *M. oculata* and has become adapted to life in waters of low salinity or to fresh water. It may be suggested, therefore, that *M. stenolepis* has been derived from *M. mixta* and become adapted to life in shallow water among weeds near land. *M. stenolepis* is a much more strictly littoral species than *M. mixta* and Smith has suggested that the more intense distribution of its chromatophores can be correlated with its association with zostera and algae.

These two cases provide a striking example of parallelism in evolution and one is tempted to speculate on the factors which have been at work in producing these more or less identical results. A lowering of the salinity of the water may be one factor for it is common to the two cases. *M. relicta* has actually penetrated to fresh water and *M. stenolepis* inhabits an area of the coast line in which the water must have an average salinity that is lower than that of the deeper water outside in which *M. mixta* lives. Salinity, however, cannot be the whole story for *M. mixta* penetrates the Baltic Sea, and I am not aware that anyone has observed or noted any indications of parallel changes in *M. mixta* living there. Other factors possibly involved include depth of water, intensity of light, amount of water disturbance and quantity of food, some or all of which may have been contributing factors. The whole forms a natural experiment on such a grand scale that it would be hopeless to repeat or to analyze it in the laboratory.

Genus PARAMYSIS Czerniavsky 1882

Paramysis CZERNIAVSKY, 1882a, pp. 59, 65; 1882b, p. 55.

PARAMYSIS ORNATA (G. O. Sars)

Mysis ornata G. O. SARS, 1864, p. 242.
Synmysis ornata CZERNIAVSKY, 1882b, p. 27.

Occurrence.—Kiel* (identified by Mobius); Seaham, Northumberland, England* (identified by A. M. Norman); Helgoland*; Plymouth* (identified by G. E. Bullen).

PARAMYSIS SPIRITUS (Norman)

Mysis spiritus NORMAN, 1860, p. 431, pl. 8, figs. 1, 1a.
Synmysis spiritus CZERNIAVSKY, 1882b, p. 28.

Occurrence.—Helgoland*; Plymouth* (identified by G. E. Bullen).
Distribution.—Atlantic coasts of southern Europe.

PARAMYSIS PARKERI (Norman)

Schistomysis parkeri NORMAN, 1892, p. 256, pl. 10, figs. 1–7.

Occurrence.—Plymouth* (identified by G. E. Bullen).
Distribution.—Coast of England.

Genus PRAUNUS Leach

Praunus LEACH, 1814, p. 401.

PRAUNUS FLEXUOSUS (O. F. Müller)

Synonymy and locality record may be found on page 247.

PRAUNUS INERMIS (Rathke)

Mysis inermis RATHKE, 1843, p. 20.

Occurrence.—Helgoland*.
Distribution.—Boreal European coasts, White Sea, Faroës, and Spitsbergen.

Genus MESOPODOPSIS Czerniavsky

Mesopodopsis CZERNIAVSKY, 1882a, p. 148.

MESOPODOPSIS SLABBERI (van Beneden)

Podopsis slabberi VAN BENEDEN, 1861, pp. 18, 142, pl. 7.

Occurrence.—Helgoland*.
Distribution.—Atlantic coasts of Europe and off western and south western Africa.

Genus STILOMYSIS Norman

Stilomysis NORMAN, 1892, p. 148.

Two described species have been referred to this genus. The type species is the well-known *S. grandis* (Goës), well described and figured by Sars (1879a). It has a wide distribution, circumpolar in the Arctic regions. The second species is *S. camtschatica*, described by Marukawa (1928). The description of this species is very inadequate and it is impossible to form any idea as to its affinities. The type specimens measured only 6 mm., in contrast with the large size to which *S. grandis* attains, namely 33 mm., and it is doubtful whether it is really a species of *Stilomysis* at all. It seems much more likely that it is a species of the genus *Acanthomysis*. A third species, described below, reaches an even greater size than *S. grandis*.

STILOMYSIS GRANDIS (Goës)

FIGURE 66

Mysis grandis GOËS, 1863, p. 176.
Mysideis grandis G. O. SARS, 1879a, p. 106, pls. 41–42.—RICHTERS, 1884, p. 406.—RODGER, 1895, p. 157.
Stilomysis grandis CALMAN, 1901, p. 24.—TATTERSALL, 1933, p. 8; 1939b, p. 283.

Occurrence.—BERING SEA: *Albatross* stations 2842, 3 males, 2 females, the largest specimen 27 mm., none quite adult; 3325, 1 adult male, 33 mm.; 3486, 1 adult female, 30 mm.; 3488, 1 male, 1 female, 32 mm., not quite adult; 3548, 1 male, 32 mm., not quite adult, 1 adult female. Franz-Josef Land: Baldwin-Ziegler Polar Expedition of 1901, Aberdare Channel, Alger Island, 9 adult males, 30 adult females, 30 mm., breeding.

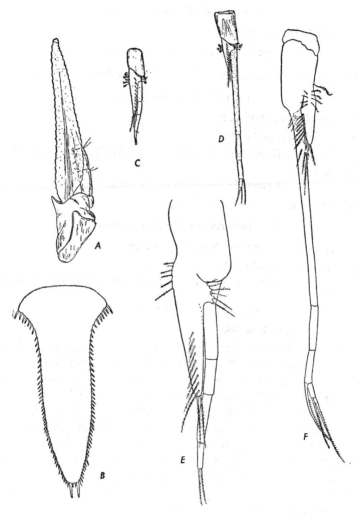

Figure 66.—*Stilomysis grandis* (Goës): *a*, Antennal scale; *b*, telson, *c*, third pleopod of male; *d*, fourth pleopod of male. (After G. O. Sars, 1879.) *e*, Third pleopod of a fully adult male, × 25; *f*, fourth pleopod of a fully adult male, × 14.

Distribution.—Most of the specimens in this collection were taken in the Bering Sea area, thereby confirming Richter's record of 1884 from this area. I have (1933) recorded a specimen from British Columbia and it is also known from off the coast of Labrador (Rodger, 1895) and from Franz Josef Land (now Fridtjof Nansen Land).

Outside American waters the species has a general Arctic distribution. The bathymetric range of the species has been increased by the above records, the specimens from *Albatross* station 3325 being taken in 284 fathoms, a greater depth than any previous record.

Remarks.—There is a small nodular papilla on the upper surface of the eyestalk and a well-developed spiniform subrostral process ventral to the rostral plate of the carapace. Fully adult males of this species have so far not been described. The specimen figured by Sars (1879a) on his plate 42 is not quite adult and shows no brush on the antennular lobe. I give herewith a figure of the third and fourth pleopods (figs. 66, *e*, *f*) of an adult male with the antennular brush of setae well developed. It will be seen that the general form of these appendages agreed with Sars' figures (figs. 66, *c*, *d*) but that in pleopod 4 the terminal joints are more elongate and the three setae at the distal end are very much longer and strongly plumose. The smallest adult male in the collection is 30 mm., but specimens measuring 32 mm. are not fully mature and the size of adults reaches 33 mm.

STILOMYSIS MAJOR, new species

FIGURE 67

Description.—This species is so similar to *S. grandis* (Goës) that the description and figures given by Sars (1879a) for that species will serve for the new one except for the following points:

(1) The antennal scale (fig. 67, *a*) is much longer and narrower than in *S. grandis.* It is at least 10 times as long as broad with the apical part very slender though not actually spiniform as in the genus *Neomysis.* In *S. grandis* the scale is only six times as long as broad with a rounded apex (fig. 66, *a*).

(2) The telson (fig. 67, *b*) is relatively more attenuated than in *S. grandis* though actually about the same length in proportion to the breadth at the base, i. e., twice as long as broad at the base. The distal end is, however, relatively narrower and more pointed and the truncate apex therefore smaller than in *S. grandis.* The lateral margins have about 84 spines distributed throughout their entire length, whereas in *S. grandis* there are about 55–60 spines (fig. 66, *b*).

(3) It is a larger species, attaining a length of 46 mm. as against 33 mm. for *S. grandis.*

In all its other characters this new species agrees with *S. grandis* so closely that detailed description is superfluous. It might legitimately be regarded as merely a giant and more attenuated variety of *S. grandis,* but its area of known distribution is separated from that of *S. grandis* by at least 20° of latitude, and it seems better for the moment to regard it as a separate species characterized by its larger size, longer and narrower antennal scale, and more slender telson with more numerous marginal spines. Since there are no adult males in the collection I am unable to compare the form of the male pleopods in the two species.

Two of the specimens are parasitized by an ellobiopsid that closely resembles *Amallocystis fasciatus* described by Fage (1936) from *Gnathophausia zoea*.

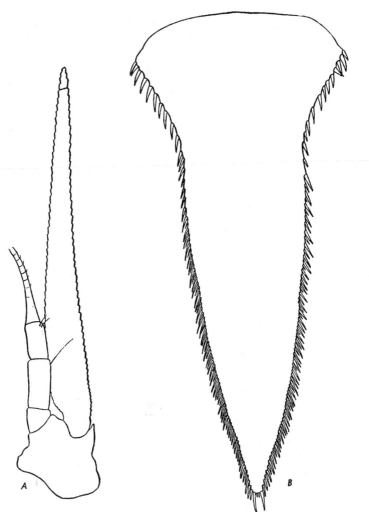

FIGURE 67.—*Stilomysis major*, new species: *a*, Antennal scale, × 10; *b*, telson, × 20.

Type lot.—Seven adult females, 1 immature female, 2 immature males, U.S.N.M. No. 81268, *Albatross* station 4862, Japan.

Occurrence.—JAPAN: *Albatross* stations 4861, 3 adult females, 42–46 mm.; 4862, 7 adult females, 1 immature female, largest specimen 46 mm., 2 immature males, 31 mm. (type lot); 4867, 1 adult female, 46 mm., 1 immature female, 31 mm.

Distribution.—All the specimens were caught in the Sea of Japan, off the coast of Korea.

Genus NEOMYSIS Czerniavsky

Neomysis Czerniavsky, 1882a, pp. 57, 63; 1882b, p. 23.
Heteromysis Czerniavsky (nec Smith) 1882a, pp. 57, 62; 1882b, p. 33.

In 1932, discussing the California species belonging to this genus in its widest interpretation, I suggested on the grounds of convenience that it would perhaps be desirable to separate those species with a spiniform apex to the antennal scale (*Neomysis, sensu stricto*) from those species in which the antennal scale has a rounded apex (*Acanthomysis* Czerniavsky). The genus *Neomysis* (*sensu lato*) is growing to unwieldy proportions, and the division into two groups of generic rank would be convenient. Ii (1936a) has now taken this definite step and reinstated the genus *Acanthomysis* for those species with the rounded antennal scale. Zimmer (1915) had previously canceled this genus as a synonym of *Neomysis* on the grounds of the close similarity of the two genera especially in the form of the fourth pleopod of the male. While recognizing the close morphological similarity of these genera, I accept Ii's conclusion, which I had myself suggested earlier as desirable on the grounds of convenience.

In 1932 I called attention to two morphological features of *N. mercedis, N. franciscorum,* and *N. kadiakensis* that had hitherto escaped notice, namely, the presence of a median sternal process on the last three thoracic sterna of the female and the presence of a baling lobe on the posterior border of the anterior pair of brood lamellae. Ii (1936a, p. 580) has called attention to an unfortunate misprint in my paper, the use of "posterior" instead of "anterior" in describing the lamellae on which the baling lobe is found. Ii states correctly that this lobe is on the posterior border of the anterior pair of oöstegites. Ii has found this lobe in other species of the genus, and it would seem to be a universal feature of this genus and probably also of *Acanthomysis.*

With regard to the sternal processes Ii could find them present only on the last two thoracic sterna in *N. japonica, N. intermedia, N. czerniawskii,* and *N. nakazawai,* and he failed to find them at all in *N. spinosa.* I can confirm Ii as regards *N. intermedia* and *N. czerniawskii,* but I have reexamined *N. rayii, N. mercedis,* and *N. kadiakensis* and have confirmed my original observation that there are three processes in these species. With regard to *N. nakazawai,* I believe this species to be synonymous with *N. mirabilis* (Czerniavsky), and in this species I have found two sternal processes in the female. I am also able to record the presence of two sternal processes in *N. americana* but have failed to detect them in any species of the genus *Acanthomysis*. These processes have now been found in nine species of the genus *Neomysis* (*sensu stricto*) and in no species of the genus *Acanthomysis*. Only one species of *Neomysis*, *N. spinosa*, has so far been found to be without them, but *N. patagona*, *N. monticelli*, and *N. meridionalis* still await examination from this point of view. Ii says that these processes are present in *N. japonica*, but in the material of this species at my disposal I failed to detect them.

There is a small rudimentary oöstegite on the sixth thoracic limb in several species of this genus, similar to those on the fifth and sixth limbs in the genus *Mysis*. I have found such oöstegites in *N. rayii*, *N. kadiakensis*, *N. mercedis*, *N. mirabilis*, *N. czerniawskii*, *N. americana*, and in one species of the genus *Acanthomysis*, *A. dybowskii*. It seems likely that they are present in all species of these two genera.

In 1932, I attempted a provisional grouping of the species of the genus *Neomysis* (*sensu lato*) based on the antennal scale, spines on the inner uropod and the form of the telson. As stated above those species with a rounded apex to the antennal scale have since been separated off under the genus *Acanthomysis*. The remaining species, 14 in number, now form the genus *Neomysis* (*sensu stricto*). The following key will serve as some guide to their identification. It is a modification of the key suggested in 1932, based on a more extended knowledge of the species.

KEY TO THE SPECIES OF NEOMYSIS

a^1. Free thoracic somites and all abdominal somites smooth, without furrows or ridges.
 b^1. Inner uropod with a dense row of spines on lower surface near statocyst, at least 10 in number and often as many as 80 to 90.
  c^1. Telson short, apex broadly truncate, spines on lateral margins few and widely spaced without small spines between them_awatschensis (p. 190)
                   intermedia (p. 188)
                   mercedis (p. 187)
  c^2. Telson long and narrow, triangular in shape, apex narrowly truncate, spines on lateral margins numerous and rather widely spaced without small spines between them_ _rayii (p. 181)
                   integer (p. 247)
  c^3. Telson long and narrow, triangular in shape, apex narrowly truncate, almost rounded, spines on lateral margins numerous, rather crowded, without small spines between them_ _ _ _ _ _ _ _ _ _ _ _kadiakensis (p. 192)
                   japonica (p. 194)
  c^4. Telson long and narrow, triangular in shape, apex rounded, lateral spines numerous, crowded and on part of margin at least, arranged in groups of larger spines with smaller spines between them_ _americana (p. 195)
                 spinosa Nakazawa, 1910

b^2. Inner uropod with only 1 or 2 spines on lower margin near statocyst; telson long and narrow, apex narrowly truncate, lateral spines numerous, crowded and not grouped_____patagona (p. 247)

meridionalis (p. 247)

monticelli (p. 248)

a^2. Last thoracic somite and first 5 abdominal somites ornamented with furrows and ridges developed to a greater or lesser extent_____mirabilis (p. 198)

czerniawskii (p. 200)

Of the 14 species of the genus the following are known from the coasts of America: *N. americana* from the east coast; *N. mercedis, N. rayii,* and *N. kadiakensis* from the west coast from Alaska to California; *N. patagona, N. meridionalis,* and *N. monticelli* from the southern part of the coasts of South America; and *N. intermedia, N. mirabilis,* and *N. czerniawskii* from the Arctic coast of Alaska and the Bering Islands. I have not seen specimens of any of the South American species, but I give figures of the antennal scale, telson, and fourth pleopod of the male of all the other American species, and such Asiatic ones as I have seen, in the hope that they may serve as a guide to the identification of the species.

NEOMYSIS RAYII (Murdoch)

FIGURES 68–71

Mysis rayii MURDOCH, 1885a, p. 519; 1885b, p. 141, pl. 1, fig. 3.

Neomysis franciscorum HOLMES, 1900, p. 223.—HANSEN, 1913b, p. 178, pl. 9, figs. 3a–b.—TATTERSALL, 1932b, p. 322, figs. 42–44; 1933, p. 8, figs. 3b, 4.

Neomysis rayi ZIMMER, 1904, p. 470.—ORTMANN, 1908, p. 9.

Neomysis toion DERSHAVIN, 1913, p. 198, figs. 1–4.

Neomysis franciscana W. L. SCHMITT, 1919, p. 6 B (*lapsus calami*).

Neomysis rayii TATTERSALL, 1932b, p. 323.

Occurrence.—ARCTIC AND BERING SEA REGIONS: Cape Lisburne, Arctic Ocean, August 21, 1880, W. H. Dall collector, 1 female; latitude 60°10′ N., longitude 168°45′ W., tag 15, Lieut. G. M. Stoney collector, 1 immature female, 20 mm.; latitude 61°3′ N., longitude 167°55′ W., tag 26, Lt. G. M. Stoney collector, 1 immature female, 13 mm.; latitude 62°15′ N., longitude 167°48′ W., tag 27, Lieut. G. M. Stoney collector, 2 adult males, 30 mm., and 2 immature females; latitude 56°30′ N., longitude 132°59′ W., Horn Cliff, near Petersburg, Alaska, August 18, 1927, H. C. McMillan collector, 1 female; Point Barrow Expedition*, Cape Smythe and Point Barrow, Alaska, cotypes, identified by Murdoch (1885); *Albatross* stations 2863, 7 females; 3235, 21 males, 6 females up to 40 mm.; 3236, 2 adult males, 35 mm.; 3240, 2 females, 35 mm.; 3241, 6 females, 30 to 35 mm.; 3243, 6 males, 3 females, 30 mm.; 3514, 1 male, 28 mm.; OFF WASHINGTON: *Albatross* stations 3444, 5 females; 3459, 1 female; 4756, 1 female. BRITISH COLUMBIA: Fulford Harbor, Salt Spring Isle, Gulf of Georgia, B. C., August 11, 1928, G. H. Wailes collector, 10 specimens; Berry Point, Vancouver Harbor, B. C., October 26, 1926, G. H. Wailes collector, 6 specimens. CALIFORNIA: Chinese shrimp nets, San Pablo Bay, November 8, 1890, C. H. Townsend, 10 females, 3 males, 25 mm. During the survey of SAN FRANCISCO BAY, 1912–13, the *Albatross* collected

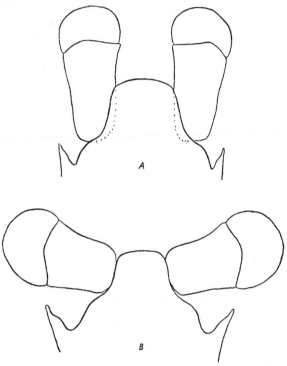

FIGURE 68.—*Neomysis rayii* (Murdoch): *a*, Anterior end showing eye and rostal plate from one of Murdoch's cotypes, × 12½; *b*, anterior end showing eye and rostral plate from a British Columbia specimen, × 12½.

at the following stations: H4989, 10 specimens; H4991, 9 specimens; H4992, 10+ specimens; H5007, 50+ specimens; H5011, 2 specimens; H5013, 50+ specimens; H5091, 50+ specimens; H5097, ? specimens; H5100, 3 specimens; H5101, 25+ specimens; H5107, 25+ specimens; H5122, ? specimens; H5123, 30+ specimens; H5128, 9 specimens; H5130, ? specimens; H5136, 35+ specimens; H5137, 50+ specimens; H5140, 2 specimens; H5147, 3 specimens; H5151, 3 specimens; H5154, 1 specimen; H5155, 20+ specimens; H5159, 50+ specimens; H5168, 10 specimens; H5177, 2 specimens; H5188, 20+ specimens; H5190, ? specimens; H5193, 20+ specimens; H5198, 6 specimens; H5199,

20+ specimens; H5211, 1 specimen; H5216, ? specimens; H5219, 4 specimens; H5228, 3 specimens; H5249, 1 specimen; H5255, 25+ specimens; H5266, ? specimens; H5273, 35+ specimens; H5277, ? specimens; H5298, 30+ specimens; H5299, ? specimens; H5301, 4 specimens; H5302, 6 specimens; H5303, 3 specimens; H5304, 1 specimen; H5305, 1 specimen; H5307, 1 specimen; H5310, 50+ specimens; H5312, 10+ specimens; H5313, 10+ specimens; H5314, 25+ specimens; H5321, 1 specimen; H5322, 2 specimens; H5328, ? specimens; H5337, 6 specimens; H5338, 2 specimens; H5339, 1 specimen; H5341, 15 specimens; H5346, 4 specimens; H5347, 1 specimen; D5764B, 1 specimen; D5798, 8 specimens; D5803, 5 specimens; D5805, 2 specimens; D5822, 1 specimen.

Distribution.—Pacific rim from San Francisco north and west to northeastern Asia.

Remarks.—The separate specific identity of *Neomysis rayii* Murdoch and *N. franciscorum* Holmes has always been a matter of some doubt. Murdoch's original description was meager and made comparison with later material difficult. Holmes (1900) when describing *N. franciscorum* said that it differed from *N. rayii* in having the telson acute instead of truncate and in having more joints in the propodal joint of the thoracic limbs. Hansen (1913b) showed that Holmes' description of the telson of *N. franciscorum* as being acute was an error and that it was in fact truncate and very similar to the telson of *N. rayii*. An examination of the cotypes of *Mysis rayii* Murdoch, shows that the thoracic limbs have about 20 joints in the propodus of the endopod. The number of these joints increases with age, and as Murdoch's specimens were as large as 65 mm. length the difference between Holmes' specimens and his can be explained as due to age, and the difference is negligible from a specific point of view. Hansen (1913b) was inclined to regard *N. rayii* and *N. franciscorum* as distinct species, differing in the length of the frontal plate, the proportions of the eye, and the telson. The differences pointed out by Hansen are small and such as may be accounted for by age and size. Nevertheless, in 1932 I agreed with Hansen's opinion and pointed out a further difference between the species in the form of the fourth pleopod of the male. In 1933, when recording *N. franciscorum* from British Columbia, I remarked that the specimens from the latter locality were rather puzzling and appeared to be intermediate between *N. rayii* and *N. franciscorum*, agreeing with the former in the character of the telson and with the latter in the form of the fourth pleopod of the male.

The material here recorded provides a more or less continuous series of specimens from the point of view of geographical distribution, extending from 69° N. to 29° N., the biggest gap between 48° N. and

29° N. having been filled by the collection from San Francisco reported on by me in 1932, which came from approximately 38° N. Apart from the original material of *Neomysis rayii* described by Murdoch from Alaska in latitude N. 72°, and the single original specimen of *Neomysis franciscorum* described by Holmes from San Francisco, all other known specimens of these two species have been examined by

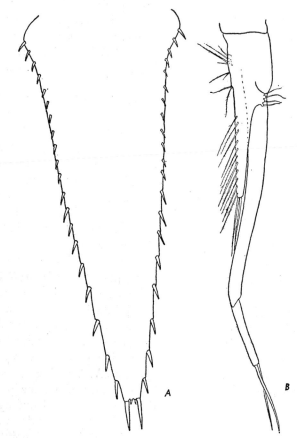

FIGURE 69.—*Neomysis rayii* (Murdoch): *a*, Telson, × 17½; *b*, fourth pleopod of male, × 17½. (From one of Murdoch's cotypes.)

me, and the results are given in the two papers already referred to (1932b and 1933) and in the present paper.

As a whole the material falls into three groups:

(1) Material from latitude N. 56° to 72°. Shallow water, 4 to 21 fathoms. Rostral plate more than half as long as broad; eye 2½ times as long as broad; terminal portion of the telson between the last pair of spines on the lateral margin and the apex shorter than broad; distal joint of the exopod of the fourth pleopod of the male

one-third of the proximal (figs. 68, *a;* 69, *a, b*). This group represents the true *Neomysis rayii* of Murdoch.

(2) Material from San Francisco and San Pablo, between latitude
N. 28° to 38°. Shallow water, 4 to 16 fathoms. Rostral plate less
than half as long as broad; eye twice as long as broad; terminal portion of the telson between the last pair of spines on the lateral margin

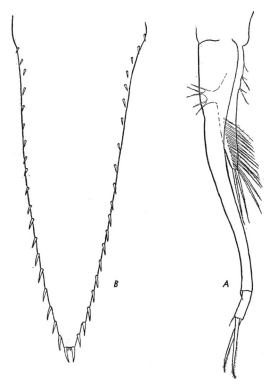

Figure 70.—*Neomysis rayii* (Murdoch): *a,* Fourth pleopod of male, × 17½; *b,* telson,
× 17½. (From a British Columbia specimen.)

and the apex longer than broad; distal joint of the exopod of the
fourth pleopod of the male one-sixth of the proximal (fig. 71, *a–c*).
This group represents the true *Neomysis franciscorum* of Holmes.

(3) Material from the deeper water off the coasts of British Columbia, about latitude N. 48°, 15 to 123 fathoms. Intermediate in character between groups 1 and 2, having the telson of *rayii* and the male
pleopods of *franciscorum* (figs. 68, *b,* 70, *a–b*).

Two interpretations of this material are possible: (1) That the two
species *N. rayii* and *N. franciscorum* are distinct and that the British
Columbia form represents an intermediate deep-water species, or (2)
that there is a single widely distributed species showing minor variations with geographical and bathymetrical range.

In 1932, when I had only the San Francisco material before me, I adopted the first interpretation and agreed with Hansen's view. In 1933 the examination of the material from British Columbia showed that the two species were linked up geographically by intermediate forms, and this is further supplemented by the examination of the present extensive material. I have come to the conclusion that it is

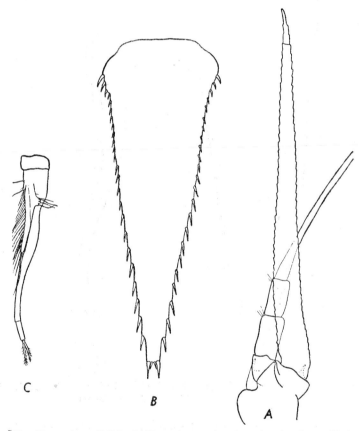

FIGURE 71.—*Neomysis rayii* (Murdoch): *a*, Antennal scale and peduncle, × 25; *b*, telson, × 37; *c*, fourth pleopod of male, × 25. (From California specimens.)

no longer possible to maintain the specific separation of *N. rayii* and *N. franciscorum* in the light of all the material examined. I have therefore united the two species under the earlier name, *N. rayii*, and adopted the second interpretation of the facts.

NEOMYSIS INTEGER (Leach)

Synonymy and locality record may be found on page 247.

NEOMYSIS MERCEDIS Holmes

FIGURE 72

Neomysis mercedis HOLMES, 1897, p. 199, pl. 19; 1900, p. 222.—TATTERSALL, 1932b, p. 318, figs. 39–41; 1933, p. 11.

Occurrence.—WEST COAST OF THE UNITED STATES: Waddell Creek Lagoon, Calif., tide out and water fresh at the time, November 4, 1932, 2 immature; South Channel, Grays Harbor, Wash., 1 male, 10 females, all immature; Carr Inlet, Puget Sound, Wash., 4 adult males, 1 immature, up to 15 mm. During the survey of SAN FRANCISCO BAY, by the *Albatross*, 1912–13, specimens were collected at the following stations: H4991 and H5106, 3 specimens; H5084, 6 specimens; H5085, 15+ specimens; H5090, 30+ specimens; H5110, 300+ specimens; H5113, 1 specimen; H5136, 1 specimen; H5137, 1 specimen; H5147, 1 specimen; H5151, 1 specimen; H5166, 15+ specimens; H5172, 1 specimen; H5177, 9 specimens; H5184, 1 specimen; H5288, 6 specimens; H5291, 6 specimens; H5292, 6 specimens; H5302, 1 specimen; H5304, 1 specimen; D5761B, 1 specimen; off Red Rock, San Francisco Bay, March 22, 1912, 1 specimen.

Distribution.—*N. mercedis* has been recorded from Lake Merced, a fresh-water lake on the San Francisco Peninsula, Calif. (Holmes, 1897); San Francisco Harbor (Tattersall, 1932b); Vancouver Island (Tattersall, 1933); Washington; Oregon.

Remarks.—*N. mercedis* is very closely related to *N. intermedia* (Czerniavsky), and to *N. awatschensis* (Brandt). It differs from the former in the following points:

(1) The antennal scale (fig. 72, *a*) is relatively shorter and broader, 8 times as long as broad, whereas in *N. intermedia* it is 10 times as long as broad.

(2) In the proportions of the joints of the outer branch of the fourth pleopod of the male (fig. 72, *c*). In *N. mercedis* the terminal joint is less than one-quarter of the length of the proximal joint and is shorter than the terminal setae. In *N. intermedia* the terminal joint is half as long as the proximal and is longer than the terminal setae. In all other particulars the two species agree very closely.

N. mercedis differs from *N. awatschensis* in the following points:

(1) In size. *N. awatschensis* is 10 mm. when adult and *N. mercedis* reaches 15 mm.

(2) In color. *N. awatschensis* is black and *N. mercedis* is certainly not black.

(3) In the rostral plate. That of *N. awatschensis* is pointed, while that of *N. mercedis* is broadly quadrangular in shape.

(4) In the sixth joint of the thoracic endopods, which in *N. awatschensis* has only 3 to 6 subsidiary joints, in *N. mercedis* 8 to 10.

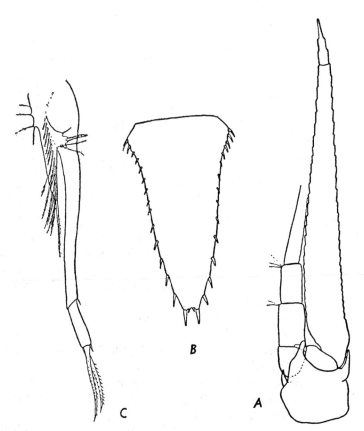

FIGURE 72.—*Neomysis mercedis* Holmes: *a*, Antennal scale and peduncle, × 78; *b*, telson, × 62; *c*, fourth pleopod of male, × 78.

It will be seen from this summary that *N. mercedis* is closely allied to *N. awatschensis* and to *N. intermedia*, but it is sufficiently different from both to be regarded as a distinct species.

NEOMYSIS INTERMEDIA (Czerniavsky)

FIGURE 73

Heteromysis intermedia CZERNIAVSKY, 1882b, p. 35; 1887, pl. 30, figs. 25–27.
Neomysis intermedia ZIMMER, 1904, p. 469, fig. 164.—UENO, 1933a, p. 109, fig. 1; 1936a, p. 242; 1936b, p. 248.—MIYADI, 1933a, p. 30; 1933b, p. 183; 1938a, p. 131; 1938b, p. 239.—BIRSTEIN, 1939, p. 56.
Neomysis awatschensis DERSHAVIN, 1913, p. 197; 1923, p. 181, pl. 7.—TATTERSALL, 1921, p. 412, pl. 15, figs. 1–4.—MIYADI, 1932a, p. 18; 1932b, p. 240; 1933b, p. 183.
Neomysis awachensis DERSHAVIN, 1930, p. 1.
Neomysis isaza MARUKAWA, 1928, p. 6, pl. 2, figs. 30, 31; pl. 3, figs. 32–37.

Occurrence.—ALASKA: Sanburn Harbor, Nagai Island, Shumagins, collected by the *Albatross*, June 24, 1893, large numbers of specimens of both sexes. JAPAN: Yatabe, No. 33, A. S. Pearse collector, June 22, 1929, large numbers of specimens of both sexes.

Distribution.—This species is abundant in brackish water in Japan, the east coast of Asiatic Russia, and China, and is here recorded for the first time from American waters.

Remarks.—This species may be recognized by the following characters:

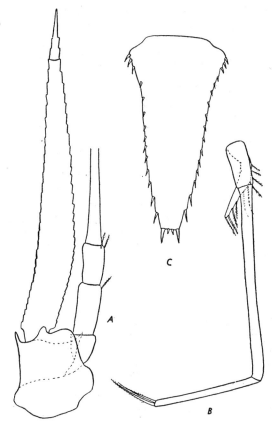

FIGURE 73.—*Neomysis intermedia* (Czerniavsky): *a*, Antennal scale and peduncle, × 33; *b*, fourth pleopod of male, × 33; *c*, telson, × 33.

(1) The carapace is produced into a broadly rounded rostral plate. (2) The eye is rather more than 1½ times as long as broad, the peduncle is only two-fifths as wide as the eye is long, and the cornea occupies less than one-half of the eye. (3) The antennal scale (fig. 73, *a*) is 10 times as long as·broad. (4) Sixth joint of the endopod of the third to the eighth thoracic limbs is divided into 7 to 11 joints. (5) Telson (fig. 73, *c*) triangular in shape, twice as long as broad at the base, apex truncate, one-fifth of the width of the telson

at the base, armed with two pairs of spines, the inner much shorter than the outer, lateral margins armed with from 13 to 21 spines not arranged in series but regularly spaced and increasing gradually in size, posterior to the three large spines at the base, from the anterior to the posterior end. (6) Fourth pleopod of the male (fig. 73, *b*) with the distal joint of the exopod slightly more than half as long as the proximal joint, terminal setae less than half as long as the distal joint.

This species is very closely related to *N. awatschensis* (Brandt), but it may be distinguished by the following characters:

(1) The rostral plate is broadly rounded whereas in *N. awatschensis* it is pointed and triangular. (2) The eye is relatively smaller. (3) The antennal scale is relatively longer. (4) The telson is slightly longer in proportion to the breadth at the base, the spines on the lateral margins are somewhat fewer and appear to be less crowded together. (5) The fourth pleopod of the male has the distal joint of the exopod much longer, about half of the proximal, whereas in *N. awatschensis* it is only about one-quarter of the proximal joint.

The specimens here referred to *N. intermedia* agree closely with the description and figures given by Czerniavsky, except for the fourth pleopod of the male. It is almost certain that Czerniavsky's male specimens were immature. Both Dershavin and I had previously recorded this species under the name *N. awatschensis* but examination of true specimens of the latter species enables me to correct the error.

NEOMYSIS AWATSCHENSIS (Brandt)

FIGURE 74

Mysis awatschensis BRANDT, 1851, p. 126.
Neomysis awatschensis ZIMMER, 1904, p. 468, fig. 163.—TATTERSALL, 1932b, p. 321.—UENO, 1933b, p. 188, fig. 8.—MIYADI, 1938b, p. 240.
Neomysis nigra NAKAZAWA, 1910, p. 248, pl. 8, figs. 3, 17, 30.—TATTERSALL, 1921, p. 410, pl. 15, figs. 5–6.—MIYADI, 1933a, p. 27.

Occurrence.—JAPAN: No specific collection data; large numbers of both sexes; Yatabe, No. 33, A. S. Pearse collector, June 22, 1929, many specimens of both sexes.

Distribution.—This species is abundant in brackish water in China and Japan, where it occurs in company with *N. intermedia*. It has not yet been recorded from eastern Asiatic Russia.

Remarks.—This species may be recognized by the following characters: (1) The carapace is produced into a broadly triangular rostral plate with a pointed apex. (2) The eye is slightly less than 1½ times as long as broad, the peduncle is half as wide as the eye is long, and the cornea occupies half the entire eye. (3) The antennal scale (fig. 74, *a*) is about eight times as long as broad. (4) The sixth joint of the endopod of the third to the eighth thoracic limbs is divided into from 3 to 6 subjoints. (5) The telson (fig. 74, c) is triangular, about 1¾ times as long as broad at the base; apex truncate, one-quarter of the width of the telson at its base, armed with two pairs of spines, the inner pair much shorter than the outer pair; lateral margins armed with about 17 to 21 spines, not arranged in series, and, after the three large spines at the base, gradually and regularly increasing in size toward the apex. (6) The fourth pleopod of the male (fig. 74, b) has the

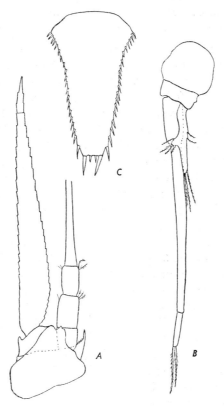

FIGURE 74.—*Neomysis awatschensis* (Brandt): *a*, Antennal scale and peduncle, × 33; *b*, fourth pleopod of male, × 33; *c*, telson, × 33.

distal joint of the exopod only about one-quarter of the proximal joint and the terminal setae are longer than the distal joint.

I have already pointed out the close resemblance of this species to *N. intermedia*. Because of the difference in the relative proportions of the telson the spines on the lateral margins appear to be more crowded than in *N. intermedia* (figs. 73, *c* and 74, *c*) though the actual number of spines present is not greatly different in the two species. The fourth pleopod of the male and the character of the rostral plate afford the most distinctive differences between the two species.

In recording this species under the name *N. nigra* in 1921 I called attention to the differences in the fourth pleopod of the male in my possession from that described by Nakazawa. It is now clear, as I suggested at the time, that my specimens were immature. The present specimens agree with Nakazawa's description.

NEOMYSIS KADIAKENSIS Ortmann

FIGURE 75

Neomysis kadiakensis ORTMANN, 1908, p. 8.—W. L. SCHMITT, 1919, p. 7B, fig. 3e.—
TATTERSALL, 1932b, p. 324, figs. 45–50; 1933, p. 10.

Occurrence.—WEST COAST OF NORTH AMERICA: Half Moon Bay, Calif., electric light, April 23, 1890, 1 adult male; San Pablo Bay, Calif., Chinese shrimp nets, November 11, 1890, C. H. Townsend collector, 1 female; Monterey Bay, Calif., 30 fathoms, Nov. 12, 1930, G. E. MacGinitie collector, 10 females, 15 males; *Albatross* stations: 2883, 2 females; 2884, 1 male; 4272*, types, identified by Ortmann (1908); 4440, 2 adult females; 4441, 6 females, 3 males; 4756, 1 adult male. During the survey of San Francisco Bay, 1912–13, the *Albatross* collected at the following stations: H4998, 15+ specimens; H5101, 2 specimens; H5114, 1 specimen; H5115, 1 specimen; H5120, 9 specimens; H5123, 1 specimen; H5128, 1 specimen; H5136, 12 specimens; H5137, 50+ specimens; H5140, 35+ specimens; H5193, 15 specimens; H5228, 8 specimens; H5242, 7 specimens; H5255, 25+ specimens; H5264, 7 specimens; H5274, 2 specimens; H5275, 2 specimens; H5298, 35+ specimens; H5301, 5 specimens; H5302, 3 specimens; H5303, 2 specimens; H5304, 1 specimen; H5305, 17 specimens; H5306, 15 specimens; H5307, 2 specimens; H5312, 1 specimen; H5313, 4 specimens; H5314, 6 specimens; H5316, 6 specimens; D5777A, 1 specimen; D5778B, 3 specimens; D5797, 2 specimens; D5798, 12 specimens; D5799, 7 specimens; D5828, 8+ specimens; D5830, 2 specimens.

Distribution.—This species is found along the whole of the west coast of America from Alaska to California in depths to 115 fathoms.

Remarks.—This species has the following distinguishing characters: (1) The front margin of the carapace (fig. 75, *d*) is produced into a wide subquadrangular plate, less than half as long as broad, with rounded angles. (2) The eyes, including the stalk, about 1½ times as long as broad, cornea occupying two-fifths of the eye in dorsal view. (3) The antennal scale (fig. 75, *a*) is 13 to 14 times as long as broad. (4) The sixth joint of the endopod of the third to the eighth thoracic limbs is divided into 10 to 12 subsidiary joints. (5) The telson (fig. 75, *b*) is triangular in shape, about 2½ times as long as broad at the base, narrowingly regularly to a slender truncate apex, which is about one-tenth of the width of the base; apex armed with two pairs of spines, the outer pair twice the length of the inner pair;

lateral margins armed throughout their whole length by 29–35 spines, not arranged in series but increasing regularly in length toward the apex and becoming more crowded together. (6) The fourth pleopod of the male (fig. 75, c) has the distal joint of the exopod about one-

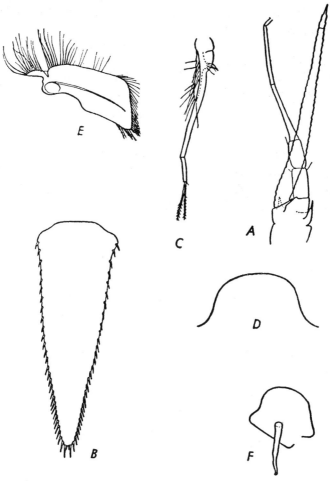

FIGURE 75.—*Neomysis kadiakensis* Ortmann: *a*, Antennal scale and peduncle, × 25; *b*, telson, × 37; *c*, fourth pleopod of male, × 25; *d*, rostral plate, × 78; *e*, one of anterior oöstegites to show posterior lobe or baler, × 78; *f*, finger-shaped process on thoracic sternum of sixth, seventh, and eighth somites, × 78.

half the length of the proximal joint and slightly longer than the terminal setae.

This species is very closely allied to *N. rayii*. It is, however, a smaller species and differs clearly in the form of the telson. The latter in *N. kadiakensis* is proportionately more slender and tapering than in *N. rayii*, the apex distinctly narrower and, though truncate, appearing almost pointed.   The spines arming the lateral margins are more numerous and distally much more crowded than in *N. rayii*. The two species also differ in the slightly different proportions of the joints of the exopod of the fourth pleopod of the male.   *N. kadiakensis* also shows some similarity to *N. mirabilis* and to *N. japonica* but may be distinguished by the characters of the telson and the fourth pleopod of the male.

The pleopods of the males in the present material agree with Ortmann's description, and it is now clear that the pleopods I figured from San Francisco specimens (1932b) were taken from a not quite fully grown specimen, as I suggested at the time.

NEOMYSIS JAPONICA Nakazawa

FIGURE 76

Neomysis japonica NAKAZAWA, 1910, p. 247, pl. 8, figs. 2, 25.—I1, 1936a, p. 580.

Occurrence.—Japan: Unknown locality, large numbers of specimens of both sexes; Yatabe, No. 33, June 22, 1929, A. S. Pearse collector, large numbers of both sexes.

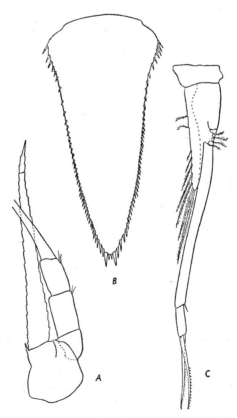

FIGURE 76.—*Neomysis japonica* Nakazawa: *a*, Antennal scale and peduncle, × 28; *b*, telson, × 40; *c*, fourth pleopod of male, × 40.

Distribution.—This species is known only from Japan. Nakazawa states that it is abundant in brackish water and forms the object of an important fishery at all times of the year. I have no information of the type of locality in which the present material was collected.

Remarks.—These specimens agree closely with the description and figures given by Nakazawa (1910). The only reference to the species subsequent to Nakazawa's paper is by Ii (1936a) who mentions the species without further description except to say that he had observed sternal processes on the seventh and eighth thoracic sterna of the female and the baling lobe on the anterior oöstegites. I have myself failed to find the sternal processes in the females of this species.

N. japonica may be recognized by the following characters: (1) The carapace is produced into a rostral plate, which is broadly rounded, almost semicircular in shape. (2) The eye is about twice as long as broad, and the cornea occupies the distal third. (3) The antennal scale (fig. 76, *a*) is 10 times as long as broad. (4) The sixth joint of the endopod of the third to the eighth thoracic limbs is divided into 8 to 12 subjoints. (5) The telson (fig. 76, *c*) is triangular in shape, twice as long as broad at the base, lateral margins armed with about 40 more or less uniform short spines, not arranged in series, but regularly spaced; apex armed with two pairs of spines, the outer pair twice as long as the inner. (6) The fourth pleopods of the male (fig. 76, *b*) have the proximal joint of the exopod nine times as long as the distal joint and the terminal setae are three times as long as the distal joint.

I counted 30 embryos in the brood pouch of a large adult female.

NEOMYSIS AMERICANA (S. I. Smith)

FIGURE 77

Mysis americana SMITH, 1873, p. 552; 1879, p. 106.—VERRILL, 1874a, p. 45.
Mysis americanus BENEDICT, 1885, p. 176.—M. J. RATHBUN, 1905, p. 27.—PAULMIER, 1905, p. 128.—FOWLER, 1912, p. 541.
Neomysis americana SUMNER, OSBURN, and COLE, 1913, p. 663.—FISH, 1925, p. 152.—TATTERSALL, 1926, p. 12; 1939b, p. 285.—PROCTOR, 1933, p. 243.—FISH AND JOHNSON, 1937, pp. 285, 298.

Occurrence.—EAST COAST OF NORTH AMERICA: Portland Harbor, Maine*, identified by Hansen; Vineyard Sound*, identified by S. I. Smith; Vineyard Sound, surface, evening, August 29, 1882, 1 breeding female; Vineyard Sound, surface, January 21, 1876, V. N. Edwards collector, 2 males, 2 females; Vineyard Sound, surface, January 12 to 14, 1880, V. N. Edwards collector, 1 male, 1 nearly adult female, 20 immature; U. S. Fish Commission locality 314, off Cape Cod, 6 fathoms, August 29, 1879, 5 specimens; numerous collections were made at Woods Hole: No specific data, several hundred specimens; 2 males, 1 female, identified by Verrill*; surface, March 7, 1888, about a hundred specimens; surface, March 12, 1888, 4 males, 4 females, 4 immature; surface, June 15, 1888, 44 immature; from weed on piles at Robinsons Hole, January 5, 1906, 1 male, 1 immature female; identified by S. I. Smith*; V. N. Edwards collected at several Woods Hole localities: No. 65, surface, February 29, 1876, 2 immature; 30 specimens; June 20, 1 male, 2 females, February 15, 16 specimens; April

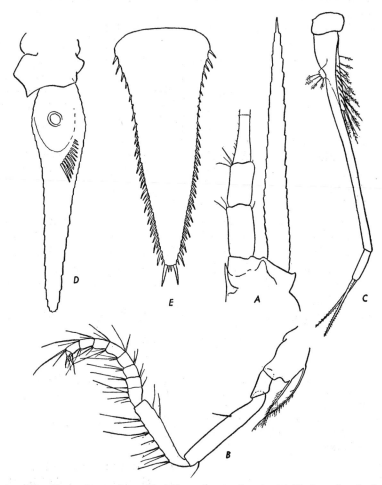

FIGURE 77.—*Neomysis americana* (Smith): *a*, Antennal scale, ✕ 38; *b*, endopod of third thoracic limb, ✕ 38; *c*, fourth pleopod of male, ✕ 38; *d*, inner uropod, ✕ 38; *e*, telson, ✕ 38.

6–12, 1883, 1 male, 3 males, 2 females; May 1, 1886, 2 specimens; surface, February 1888, 3 females, 1 male; surface, March 3, 1888, 2 males, 4 females; surface, March 7, 1888, 6 males, 3 females, 4 immature; surface, May 2, 1888, 17 specimens; surface, January 22, 1906, 5 males, 9 females; surface, April 1, 1905, 1 adult male, 5 immature; surface, April 14, 1906, 21 males, 9 females. *Fish Hawk* stations 824, off Newport, R. I., 13 fathoms, sand bottom, August 24, 1880, 2 specimens; 1058, Chesapeake Bay, south end of Barren Island, 3 to 25 fathoms, brown mud bottom, February 28, 1882, 1 male; 1059, Chesapeake Bay, south end of Barren Island, 2¾ to 25 fathoms, brown mud bottom, February 28, 1882, 1 male; 1077, Sandy Point Lighthouse, 11 to 12 fathoms, mud bottom, March 13, 1882, 1 male; 1239*, Block Island South, Mass., No Man's Land, August 30, 1887, 16 fathoms, identified by S. I. Smith. *Bache* station 10157, off Cape Henry, Va., latitude 36°46′ N., longitude 75°38′ W., surface, January 20, 1914, many specimens. Casco Bay and off Montauk Point*, identified by S. I. Smith.

Distribution.—This species is confined to the east coast of North America, where it ranges from the Gulf of St. Lawrence to the coast of Virginia in shallow water

Remarks.—*Neomysis americana* may be distinguished by the following characters: (1) The carapace is produced into a broadly rounded rostral plate. (2) The eye, including the stalk, is 1½ times as long as broad at the widest point, stalk narrower than the cornea, latter occupying at least half of the whole eye. (3) The antennal scale (fig. 77, *a*) is ten times as long as broad. (4) The sixth joint (fig. 77, *b*) of the endopod of the third to the eighth thoracic limbs divided into 8 to 9 joints. (5) The telson (fig. 77, *e*) is triangular in shape, 2½ times as long as broad at the base, with a narrowly truncate apex armed with two pairs of spines, the outer pair three times as long as the inner pair; lateral margins armed with about 40 spines which, on the distal two-thirds of the margins at least, are arranged in groups with one to three smaller spines between the larger spines. (6) The proximal joint of the exopod of the fourth pleopod of the male is seven times (fig. 77, *c*) as long as the distal; latter joint about half as long as the terminal pair of setae.

This species has never been adequately figured. W. L. Schmitt (1919) gave a figure of the distal part of the telson, but no other author has illustrated the species in anything but a general way. I therefore here give figures to illustrate the salient features of the species. Zimmer (1904 and 1909) was inclined to regard this species as merely a local variety of *Neomysis integer* (Leach), but the two species are in reality very distinct in the form of the telson. In *N. integer* there are only about 22 spines on the lateral margins of the telson, more or less evenly spaced and not in any way arranged in series of smaller and larger spines. In *N. americana* there are about 40 spines on the lateral margins, and at least distally these are grouped with one to three smaller spines between the larger ones. The proportions of the joints of the exopod of the fourth pleopod of the male also differ markedly in the two species.

NEOMYSIS MIRABILIS (Czerniavsky)

FIGURE 78

Heteromysis mirabilis CZERNIAVSKY, 1882b, p. 33; 1887, p. 84, pl. 20, figs. 1–17.
Neomysis mirabilis ZIMMER, 1904, p. 468, figs. 161, 162.—DERSHAVIN, 1913, p. 197.—
    BIRSTEIN, 1939, p. 56, figs. 1a–c.
?*Neomysis andersoni* W. L. SCHMITT (pars), 1919, p. 6 (juv. fig. 3a).
Neomysis nakazawai II, 1936a, p. 581, figs. 3–13.

Occurrence.—SIBERIA: Bering Island, from mouth of cod, N. Grebnitzky collector, 1 adult female; No. 2539, 1882–83, L. Stejneger collector. COMMANDER ISLANDS: No. 2462, 1882–83, L. Stejneger collector,
1 immature female; Petropavlovsk-Kamchatskii, 1883, N. Grebnitzky
collector, 1 adult breeding female, 20 mm., 100 mostly immature males
and females, 12 to 15 mm., but some of the females breeding at 15 mm.;
L. Stejneger, 1882–83, collection numbers 2624, 1 immature male; 2630,
5 adult females, 9 immature females and 8 males, 15–16 mm.; 2631,
6 adult females, 11 immature females and 24 immature males, 15 to 16
mm.; 2633, 2 immature specimens; *Albatross* collector, 1906, 77 breeding females, largest 30 mm., 5 males, largest 25 mm. JAPAN: Mororan,
shore, *Albatross* collector, July 6, 1906, 75 adult breeding females;
Albatross station 5003, 2 adult females. ALASKA: Grantley Harbor,
Port Clarence, August 3–4, 1913, at surface, 2 immature.

Distribution.—Gulf of Castries, Asiatic Russia (Czerniavsky,
1882b); (Dershavin, 1913); Kamchatka (Dershavin, 1913); Sagha-
lien, Japan (Ii, 1936a). The present material is mainly from Asiatic
Russia and Petropavlovsk, but it includes a large number of specimens
from Mororan, Japan, and two immature specimens from Alaska.

Remarks.—This species may be distinguished by the following characters: (1) The last thoracic somite is furnished with well-marked
furrows and ridges; these are much less marked on the first three
abdominal somites and quite incipient on the fourth and fifth abdominal somites. (2) The carapace is produced into a quadrangular
rostral plate with rounded angles, front margin somewhat concave;
rostral plate leaves the eye and antennules completely uncovered.
(3) The eye, including the eyestalk, is about 1½ times as long as
broad with the cornea occupying about one-third of the eye in dorsal
view. (4) The antennal scale (fig. 78, *a*) is 12 to 15 times as long as
broad. (5) The sixth joint of the endopods of the third to the eighth
thoracic limbs is divided into 9 to 15 subjoints. (6) The telson (figs.
78, *c*, *d*) is about 2½ times as long as broad at the base, linguiform in
shape with sinuous lateral margins and a narrowly rounded apex;
lateral margins armed with 40 to 50 stout blunt spines, which in the
proximal part of the margins are somewhat widely spaced, in the
central part of the margins arranged in groups of two to four smaller
spines between rather larger spines, and in the distal third of the

margin are not grouped, densely packed and of equal size. (7) The fourth pleopod of the male (fig. 78, *b*) has the proximal joint of the exopod six times as long as the distal joint; terminal setae one-quarter longer than the distal joint.

This species was described by Czerniavsky (1882b) from specimens taken in the North Pacific in the Gulf of Castries. It was later recorded by Dershavin (1913), without comment, from Kamchatka and

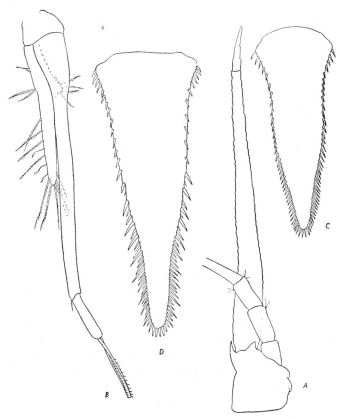

FIGURE 78.—*Neomysis mirabilis* (Czerniavksy): *a*, Antennal scale and peduncle, × 22⅔; *b*, fourth pleopod of male, × 26⅔; *c*, telson of typical form, × 22⅔; *d*, telson of a not uncommon variety, × 30⅔.

by Birstein (1939) from Asiatic Russia. Birstein gave a figure of the telson which agrees with that of the present material. Ii (1936a) has described a species, *N. nakazawai*, which appears to me to be indistinguishable from *N. mirabilis*. He makes no reference whatsoever to the latter species, and I can only suppose that he overlooked Czerniavsky's description, not perhaps recognizing that the genus *Heteromysis* of Czerniavsky, of which this species is the type, is only a synonym of *Neomysis*. Ii's description is very detailed and complete and agrees very closely with the specimens here recorded.

N. mirabilis has well-marked grooves and ridges on the last thoracic somites and incipient grooves and furrows on the first five abdominal somites. The furrows on the abdominal somites are sometimes very difficult to see and are much fainter in the young than in fully grown specimens.

The telson is very characteristic, linguiform in shape, with sinuous lateral margins and a rounded apex. The spines are coarse, rather blunt and closely set. In some specimens the spines in the center of the lateral margins show a tendency to be arranged in groups, but the smaller spines between the larger ones are only slightly smaller than the latter and the grouping is not nearly so well marked as in *N. czerniawskii*, wherein the smaller spines are much smaller than the long spines and more numerous (figs. 78, *c–d*, 79, *b*). In other specimens (fig. 78, *c*) the grouping of the spines is almost completely obscured. The apex has only one pair of spines, and there is no pair of small spines between them. The species grows to a large size, 30 mm. in the female and 25 mm. in the male, though females of 16 mm. occur in the collection with eggs in the brood pouch. I counted 40 embryos in the brood pouch of a large female. There are sternal processes on the seventh and eighth thoracic sterna of the female and a baling lobe on the anterior oöstegite.

N. mirabilis is most closely allied to *N. czerniawskii* but may be distinguished by the different arrangement of the spines on the telson and by the somewhat different proportions of the joints of the exopod of the fourth pleopod of the male. The two species often occur together, and I think that the young specimens attributed to *N. andersoni* (*N. czerniawskii*) by Schmitt are in reality *N. mirabilis*. Schmitt's figure 3a is remarkably like that of the telson of *N. mirabilis*. Schmitt noted the differences and attributed them to age, but in the present collection there are young specimens of *N. czerniawskii* that have the telson exactly as in the adult.

NEOMYSIS CZERNIAWSKII Dershavin

FIGURE 79

Neomysis, czerniawskii DERSHAVIN, 1913, p. 199, figs. 5–7.—TATTERSALL, 1933, p. 11.—II, 1936a, p. 585, figs. 14–21.
Neomysis andersoni (pars) W. L. SCHMITT, 1919, p. 6, figs. 1, 2, 3b.

Occurrence.—BERING SEA REGION: Chamisso Harbor, Eschscholtz Bay, Alaska, 5 to 8 fathoms, W. H. Dall collector, 3 adult males, 5 immature males, 2 not quite adult females, up to 20 mm.; Grantley Harbor, Port Clarence, Alaska, August 3–4, 1913, at surface, 1 female, *Neomysis andersoni* Schmitt cotype; Petropavlovsk, Kamchatka,

1882–83, L. Stejneger collector, 7 immature; Petropavlovsk, *Albatross* 1906 collection, 1 adult male, 1 adult female, breeding, 20 mm. Japan, Tomakomai, *Albatross* 1906 collection, 2 adult males, 20 mm.

Distribution.—Kamchatka (Dershavin); Alaska (Schmitt); Japan (Ii). The present material adds nothing to the known distribution

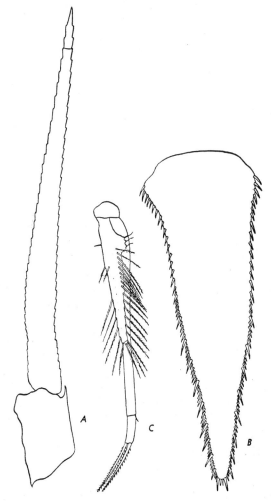

FIGURE 79.—*Neomysis czerniawskii* Dershavin: *a*, Antennal scale, × 25; *b*, telson, × 26; *c*, fourth pleopod of male, × 26.

of the species, which is evidently widely distributed in shallow water in the north Pacific both on the American and Asiatic shores.

Remarks.—This species may be recognized by the following characters: (1) The free thoracic somites and the first five abdominal somites are furnished with two or three furrows and ridges most marked dorsally and fading away laterally; they are much more prominent than in *N. mirabilis*. (2) The antennal (fig. 79, *a*) scale is 14 times as long as broad. (3) The sixth joint of the endopod of the third to the eighth thoracic limbs is divided into 9 to 12 subjoints. (4) The telson (fig. 79, *b*) is narrowly triangular in shape, nearly three times as long as broad at the base, apex narrowly truncate, almost rounded, armed with two pairs of spines, the inner of which is half the length of the outer; lateral margins armed with a continuous series of spines extending from the base to the apex; in the proximal third of the margin the spines, 17 in number, are more or less regularly spaced without small spines between them; on the distal two-thirds of the margin there are 11 large spines, increasing in length toward the apex, and between each pair of large spines there are 5 to 7 conspicuously smaller spines. (5) The fourth pleopod of the male (fig. 79, *c*) has the proximal joint of the exopod seven times as long as the distal; the terminal setae are strongly barbed and twice as long as the distal joint.

The specimens from Tokomai, Japan, agree with Ii's specimens in having the apical spines of the telson all of equal size, but the northern specimens have the inner pair only half as long as the outer. In spite of this difference I think that Ii's specimens and the present material belong to the same species. I have already expressed the opinion (1933) that *N. andersoni* Schmitt is synonymous with this species. His figure of the telson of the adult agrees closely with that of the present specimens. The young specimens, which Schmitt doubtfully referred to *N. andersoni*, I now think should be referred to *N. mirabilis*.

N. czerniawskii is closely related to *N. mirabilis* but differs in the arrangement of the spines on the lateral margins of the telson. In *N. mirabilis* the spines are stouter and blunter, those at the apex are all of equal size, and in the center of the margins where the spines tend to be arranged in groups the smaller spines between the larger ones are longer and fewer than in *N. czerniawskii*, so that the grouping arrangement is not so obvious as in the latter species. There are also differences in the fourth pleopod of the male. Both species have the free thoracic somites and the first five abdominal somites ornamented with grooves and ridges, but these are more pronounced in *N. czerniawskii* than in *N. mirabilis*. In this character these two species differ from all the other species of the genus but some species of the allied genus, *Acanthomysis*, *A. costata*, *A. sculpta*, and *A. stelleri*, are similarly ornamented.

NEOMYSIS PATAGONA Zimmer

Synonymy and distribution records may be found on page 247.

NEOMYSIS MERIDIONALIS Colosi

Recorded on page 247.

NEOMYSIS MONTICELLI Colosi

Records of this species are given on pages 248.

Genus ACANTHOMYSIS Czerniavsky

Acanthomysis CZERNIAVSKY, 1882a, pp. 58, 64, 134.—II, 1936a, p. 588.
Dasymysis HOLT and BEAUMONT, 1900, p. 245.
Metamysis NAKAZAWA, 1910, p. 250 (nec Sars, 1895).
Orientomysis DERSHAVIN, 1913, p. 200.

As stated above I accept Ii's restoration of this genus to include those species hitherto referred to *Neomysis* in which the antennal scale is rounded at the apex and not produced into a spine. It is significant that no species of this genus has yet been found to possess sternal processes on the last two or three thoracic sterna in the female. This may prove an additional generic character when all the species of the genus *Neomysis* (*sensu stricto*) have been examined for this point. The baling lobe on the anterior oöstegite is present but not so well developed as in *Neomysis*.

Seven species of this genus are known from American waters. They may be separated according to the key.

KEY TO THE AMERICAN SPECIES OF ACANTHOMYSIS

a[1]. Supraocular spine on carapace; incipient grooves on last thoracic and first three abdominal somites_ **columbiae** (p. 204)

a[2]. No supraocular spine on carapace.

  b[1]. Grooves well marked on all abdominal somites.

    c[1]. Fourth abdominal somite with a dorsal median posterior spine; fifth abdominal somite with a dorsal median posterior spine and a strong lateral spine on each side; sixth abdominal somite with an anterior median dorsal broad plate and a posterior pair of blunt spines, and a median dorsal spine on the posterior margin_ _ _ _ _ _ _ _**sculpta** (p. 208)

    c[2]. Fourth and fifth abdominal somites without dorsal median spines; sixth abdominal somite with an anterior dorsal triangular plate and a posterior area of peculiar sculpture, and a median posterior dorsal marginal spine_ **costata** (p. 208)

    c[3]. None of abdominal somites with posterior dorsal medial spines or with sculpture_ _**stelleri** (p. 210)

  b[2]. Thoracic and abdominal somites smooth, without grooves.

    c[1]. Eyes normal. Telson linguiform_ _ _ _ _ _ _ _ _ _ _ _ _ _ _ _ _**dybowskii** (p. 213)

    c[2]. Eyes elongate.

      d[1]. Eyes 3¼:1, no labral spine, one spine on inner margin of the inner uropod_ _**macropsis** (p. 215)

      d[2]. Eyes 2½:1, labral spine present, no spines on inner uropod.

          pseudomacropsis (p. 217)

ACANTHOMYSIS COLUMBIAE (Tattersall)

FIGURES 80-82

Neomysis columbiae TATTERSALL, 1933, p. 12, figs. 5, 6.

Occurrence.—Monterey Bay, Calif., 1928, 1 adult, 1 immature male, 1 nearly adult female, 14 mm.

Distribution.—The type specimens were collected in British Columbia. The occurrence of the species on the California coast is

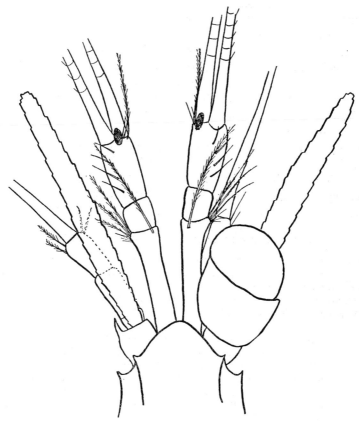

FIGURE 80.—*Acanthomysis columbiae* (Tattersall): Anterior end of male specimen from California to show rostral plate and spines, eye, antennular peduncle, and antennal scale, for comparison with specimens from British Columbia (Tattersall, 1933), × 44.

interesting and marks a considerable extension of its known geographical range.

Remarks.—This very distinct species may be recognized by the following characters:

(1) The last thoracic somite is furnished with two ridges and two furrows; there are similar grooves and ridges on the first abdominal

somite, three ridges and four grooves on the second abdominal somite, and three ridges and three grooves, barely perceptible, on the third abdominal somite; the grooves and ridges are most pronounced on the second abdominal somite, and are most marked dorsally, fading away laterally.

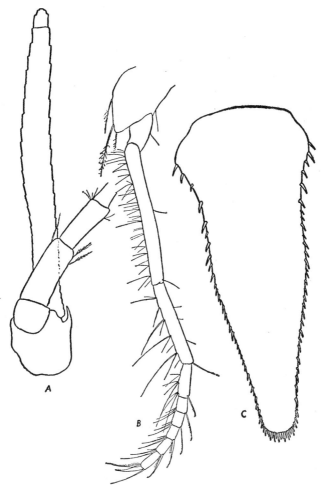

FIGURE 81.—*Acanthomysis columbiae* (Tattersall): *a*, Antennal scale and peduncle, × 40; *b*, endopod of fifth thoracic limb, × 40; *c*, telson, × 45. From a California specimen, for comparison with specimens from British Columbia (Tattersall, 1933).

(2) There is a well-marked sharp supraocular spine on the carapace (fig. 80).

(3) The carapace is produced in front into a short broadly triangular rostral plate with an obtuse apex; anterolateral angles acute (fig. 80).

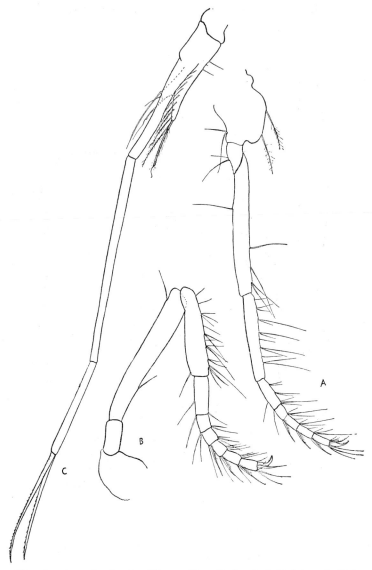

FIGURE 82.—*Acanthomysis columbiae* (Tattersall): *a*, Endopod of third thoracic limb, × 40; *b*, endopod of eighth thoracic limb, × 40; *c*, fourth pleopod of male, × 40. From a California specimen, for comparison with specimens from British Columbia (Tattersall, 1933).

(4) The eyes are large and prominent (fig. 80), pigment black, one and a half times as long as broad, the cornea occupying more than half the eye in dorsal view.

(5) The antennal scale (fig. 81, *a*) is very long and narrow, 12 to 15 times as long as broad.

(6) The endopods of the third to the eighth thoracic limbs (figs. 81, *b*; 82, *a*, *b*) have the sixth joint divided into 5 to 7 subjoints, nail well developed.

(7) The telson (fig. 81, *c*) is linguiform in shape, 2½ times as long as broad at the base, apex broadly rounded and armed with a row of 20 to 30 densely set sharp spines between the somewhat larger spines at each angle. The lateral margins are armed throughout their entire length with about 42 spines, rather widely spaced proximally, more crowded distally and with smaller spines between the larger ones.

(8) The fourth pleopod of the male (fig. 82, *c*) has the proximal joint of the exopod 2½ times as long as the distal joint, and the terminal setae are as long as the distal joint.

I overlooked the grooves and ridges on the thoracic and abdominal somites in my original description of the species. The specimens from California agree closely with those from British Columbia. This species is distinguished from all others known to me by the supra-ocular spines on the carapace. Otherwise it is perhaps most nearly allied to *A. macropsis* and to *A. pseudomacropsis*, differing in the more normal form of the eye and the details of the telson and fourth pleopod of the male.

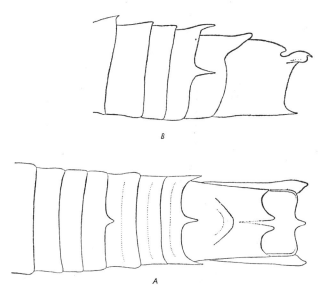

FIGURE 83.—*Acanthomysis sculpta* (Tattersall): *a*, Last three somites of abdomen, dorsal aspect, × 27½; *b*, last three somites of abdomen, lateral aspect, × 27½.

ACANTHOMYSIS SCULPTA (Tattersall)

FIGURES 83–85

For a full diagnosis of this species refer to page 248.

ACANTHOMYSIS COSTATA (Holmes)

FIGURES 86, 87

Mysis costata HOLMES, 1900, p. 221, pl. 4, figs. 70–72.—HANSEN, 1913b, p. 177, pl. 9, fig. 2a–d.—ESTERLY, 1914, p. 15.

Neomysis costata TATTERSALL, 1932b, p. 327, figs. 51–58.

Occurrence.—CALIFORNIA: Scorpion Harbor, Santa Cruz Island, 2 to 3 fathoms, June 29, 1939, 1 breeding female, 12 mm., 1 immature female, 8 mm.; during the survey of San Francisco Bay by the *Albatross*, 1912–13, collections were made at stations H5099, 30+specimens; H5101, 50+ specimens; H5128, 4 specimens; H5137, 2 specimens; H5138, 4 specimens; H5140, 10+ specimens; H5146, 2 specimens; H5147, 2 specimens; H5188, 15 specimens; H5228, 7 specimens; H5300, 2 specimens.

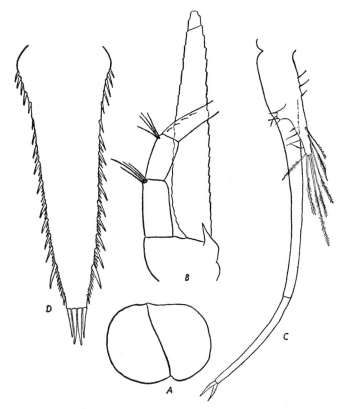

FIGURE 84.—*Acanthomysis sculpta* (Tattersall): *a*, Eye, × 40; *b*, antennal scale and peduncle, × 40; *c*, fourth pleopod of male, × 40; *d*, telson, × 40.

Distribution.—Known only from the coast of California.

Remarks.—This species is closely related to *A. sculpta* and it will suffice if the main differences are enumerated, as follows:

(1) The form of the body is more compact and robust.

(2) The somites of the pleon are furnished with folds and ridges, three on the first somite and two on the succeeding somites. There are, however, no spines on the fourth and fifth somites, and the sixth somite has an anterior median triangular plate and a posterior sculptured region but no pair of median blunt spines.

(3) The antennal scale (fig. 86, *d*) is five times as long as broad.

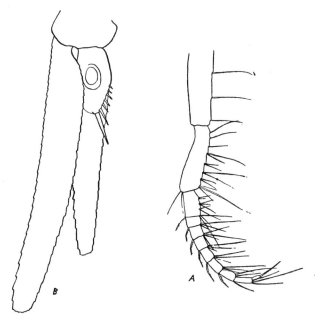

FIGURE 85.—*Acanthomysis sculpta* (Tattersall): *a*, Distal joints of endopod of one of posterior thoracic limbs, × 40; *b*, uropods, × 40.

(4) The endopods of the third to the eighth thoracic limbs (fig. 87, *a*) have the sixth joint divided into four or five subjoints.

(5) The telson (fig. 87, *c*) is narrowly triangular in shape, two and a half times as long as broad at the base. The apex is narrowly truncate and armed with two pairs of spines, the inner pair of which is less than half as long as the outer. The lateral are armed throughout their whole length with numerous large spines which increase considerably in length toward the apex. On the distal two-thirds of the margins the spaces between the large spines are occupied by two, three, or four smaller spines.

(6) The inner uropod (fig. 87, *b*) has four or five strong spines on its lower margin near the statocyst.

(7) The fourth pleopod of the male (fig. 86, *e*) is short and rather stout, with the proximal joint of the exopod five times as long as the distal and the terminal setae three times as long as the distal joint.

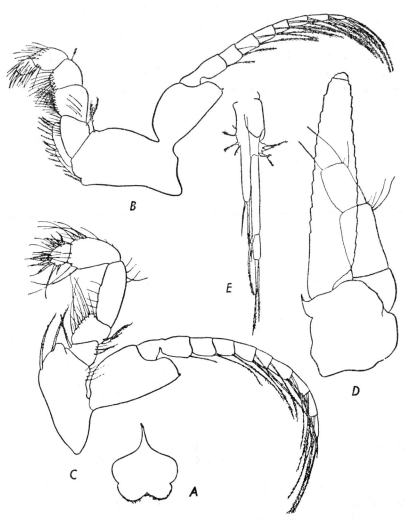

FIGURE 86.—*Acanthomysis costata* (Holmes): *a*, Labrum, × 78; *b*, first thoracic limb, × 100; *c*, second thoracic limb, × 100; *d*, antennal scale and peduncle, × 100; *e*, fourth pleopod of male, × 100.

ACANTHOMYSIS STELLERI (Dershavin)

FIGURE 88

Orientomysis stelleri DERSHAVIN, 1913, p. 202, figs. 8–10.

Occurrence.—BERING SEA REGION: Latitude 62°15′ N., longitude 167°45′ W., Lt. G. M. Stoney collector, 3 males, 1 female; latitude

62°54′ N., longitude 166°38′ W., 4 males, 1 female; Bering Island, L. Stejneger collector, 1 adult breeding female, 19 mm.; Kiska Harbor, Aleutian Islands, 9–12 fathoms, sandy mud, collected by W. H. Dall, 3 females; *Albatross* station 3600, 2 males.

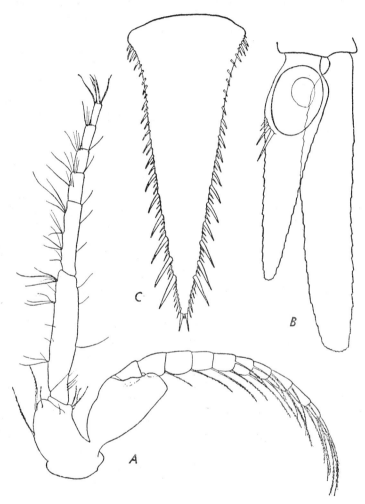

FIGURE 87.—*Acanthomysis costata* (Holmes): *a*, Third thoracic limb, × 100; *b*, uropod, × 100; *c*, telson, × 100.

Distribution.—Known previously only from Kamchatka (Dershavin, 1913). The present material is from Alaska, Bering Island, and the Aleutian Islands, and the species is probably not uncommon in shallow water north of latitude 50° on both sides of the Pacific.

Remarks.—This species may be distinguished by the following characters: (1) The last thoracic somite and all the abdominal somites have two or three grooves and ridges, but the sixth abdominal somite has otherwise no special ornamentation or sculpture. (2) The carapace is produced into an acute triangular rostral plate with a bluntly rounded apex. (3) The antennal scale is seven times as long as broad. (4) The endopod of the third to the eighth thoracic limbs has the sixth joint divided into four to six subjoints. (5) The inner uropod has a row of five spines on the lower margin near the statocyst. (6) The

telson (fig. 88) is narrowly triangular in shape, two and a half times as long as broad at the base, apex narrowly truncate, almost rounded, and armed by two pairs of spines, the outer pair twice as long as the inner pair and considerably stouter; the lateral margins are armed with about 27 large spines extending throughout the entire length of the margin and increasing very conspicuously in length toward the apex; on the distal three-quarters of the margins there are small spines between the large ones; proximally only two or three small spines between the large ones, but the number gradually increases so that distally there may be 10 to 12 small spines between the larger ones.

The present material is defective and much damaged but appears to agree very closely with Dershavin's description. The telson has many more small spines between the larger spines on the lateral margins, especially distally, than would appear from the figure given by Dershavin. Since no details are given in the description it is a little difficult to decide how much importance should be given to this point. In other characters, antennal scale, rostral plate, inner uropods, and the folds on the abdominal somites, these specimens agree

FIGURE 88.—*Acanthomysis stelleri* (Dershavin): Telson, × 22½.

very closely with *A. stelleri*, and provisionally at any rate I refer them to this species. The material is so badly damaged that the drawing of the telson here given had to be made from a telson that had evidently at one time been damaged and then the damaged part regenerated. I have had to guess the breadth distally and may possibly have drawn it too narrow in proportion to its length.

Unfortunately none of the males is complete, and I am unable to describe the form of the fourth pleopod in that sex. The species is most closely allied to *A. costata* and *A. sculpta* but differs from both in the absence of any special sculpturing on the sixth abdominal somite other than the simple furrows and ridges. The telson is more like that of *A. costata* than of *A. sculpta*.

ACANTHOMYSIS DYBOWSKII (Dershavin)

FIGURE 89

Orientomysis dybowskii DERSHAVIN, 1913, p. 203, figs. 11–15.
Acanthomysis dybowskii II, 1936b, p. 597, figs. 47–55.

Occurrence.—BERING SEA REGION : *Albatross* station 3239, 1 female; Petropavlovsk, Kamchatka, *Albatross* collection, 1906, 25 adult females, breeding; Chiachi Islands, northeast of the Shumagins, south shore of Alaska peninsula, No. 1159, W. H. Dall collector, 1 adult female; explorations in Alaska of Lt. George M. Stoney, 1884, tag Nos. 15, latitude 60°10′ N., longitude 160°18′ W., 1 adult female; 24, latitude 60°22′ N., longitude 168°45′ W., 8 adult breeding females; 26, latitude 61°3′ N., longitude 167°55′ W., 20 fathoms, June 7, 1884, 335 females, 16 males; 27, latitude 62°15′ N., longitude 167°48′ W., 20½ fathoms, June 13, 1884, 78 females, 14 males; 28, latitude 62°54′ N., longitude 166°38′ W., 22 fathoms, June 14, 1884, 4 females, 1 male. BRITISH COLUMBIA : Berry Point, north arm, Vancouver, 15 to 30 fathoms, June 14, 1928, 1 adult breeding female.

Distribution.—Kamchatka (Dershavin) ; Korea Straits (Ii). The above records show that this species is distributed all along the Pacific coasts of Asia and North America from the Korean Straits to Vancouver in water up to 22 fathoms in depth.

Remarks.—This species may be recognized by the following characters:

(1) There are no grooves or ridges on the thoracic and abdominal somites.

(2) The carapace is produced into a short triangular pointed rostral plate.

(3) The antennal scale (fig. 89, *a*) is seven times as long as broad.

(4) The endopod of the third to the eighth thoracic limbs has the sixth joint subdivided into five to eight subjoints.

(5) The telson (fig. 89, *b*) is broadly spatulate in shape, 2½ times as long as broad at the base, apex broadly rounded and armed with two pairs of spines, the inner only half as long as the outer; the lateral margins are armed with a continuous series of spines, rather short and extending throughout the whole margin; distally the spines tend to be arranged in series of two or three smaller spines between each pair of larger spines but the grouping is not nearly so obvious as it is in *A. costata* or *A. stelleri* because of the very much shorter larger spines.

(6) The fourth pleopod of the male (fig. 89, *c*) has the proximal joint of the exopod five times as long as the distal; the terminal setae are longer than the distal joint.

(7) The fifth pleopod of the male (fig. 89, *d*) is modified; it is considerably elongated, rather longer than the sixth somite of the pleon, stout and terminating in a single robust seta.

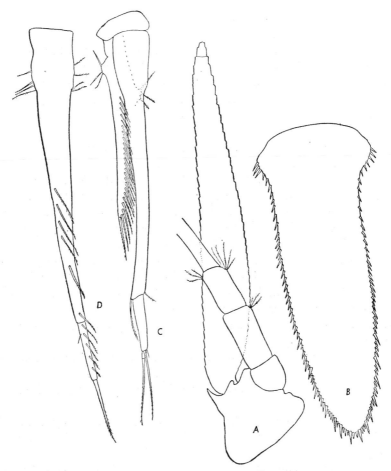

FIGURE 89.—*Acanthomysis dybowskii* (Dershavin): *a*, Antennal scale and peduncle, × 24; *b*, telson, × 24; *c*, fourth pleopod of male, × 24; *d*, fifth pleopod of male, × 24.

This is a very distinct species, particularly in the broadly spatulate form of the telson. Ii (1936b) referred specimens from the Korea Straits with some doubt to this species. They showed two characters not mentioned by Dershavin, a minute papilla on the eye, and the presence of groups of long setae on the carpal and propodal joints of the endopods of the third to the eighth thoracic limbs. In all the specimens I have examined these structures are present, and I have little doubt that Ii's specimens belong to the same species as those described by Dershavin as *Orientomysis dybowskii*. My specimens are in the closest agreement with Ii's description. The modification of the fifth pleopod of the male is not found in any other species of the genus and it escaped Ii's notice, though his largest specimens were as big as mine. The female appears to be completely adult at 19 mm. but it was only in the largest males, 25 mm., that I observed the fully modified condition of the fifth pleopod. In a large female I counted 24 embryos in the brood pouch. The striking disproportion of the sexes in the two large hauls of this species is interesting.

ACANTHOMYSIS MACROPSIS (Tattersall)

FIGURE 90

Neomysis macropsis TATTERSALL, 1932b, p. 330, figs. 59–65; 1933, p. 14.

Occurrence.—CALIFORNIA: During the survey of San Francisco Bay, 1912–13, the *Albatross* collected at stations H4988, 2 specimens; H4990, 500+ specimens; H4995, 20+ specimens; H4996, 30+ specimens; H4997, 200+ specimens; H5000, 25+ specimens; H5003, 50+ specimens; H5005, 250+ specimens; H5008, 60+ specimens; H5011, 300+ specimens; H5012, 200+ specimens; H5082, 200+ specimens; H5098, 500+ specimens; H5100, 6 specimens; H5106, 50+ specimens; H5123, 12 speciments; H5125 specimens?; H5126, 30+ specimens; H5127, 50+ specimens; H5128, 50+ specimens; H5133 specimens?; H5140, 25+ specimens; H5141, 1 specimen; H5147, 60+ specimens; H5149, 35+ specimens; H5151, 10+ specimens; H5152, 20+ specimens; H5154, 75+ specimens; H5177, 25+ specimens; H5186, 150+ specimens; H5196, 150+ specimens; H5198, 75+ specimens; H5211, 10 specimens; H5219 10+ specimens; H5228, 4 specimens; H5232, 25+ specimens; H5244, 200+ specimens; H5245, 35+ specimens; H5246, 10 specimens; H5247, 9 specimens; H5248, 15+ specimens; H5249, 10+ specimens; H5257, 100+ specimens; H5261, 200+ specimens; H5267, 500+ specimens; H5273, 500+specimens; H5282 specimens?; H5286, 250+specimens; H5287, 300+ specimens; H5300, 25+ specimens; H5302, 100+ specimens; H5310, 250+ specimens; H5316, 500+ specimens; H5319, 300+ specimens; H5321, 75+ specimens; H5322, 100+ specimens; H5323, 60+ specimens; H5324, 15+ specimens; H5325, 60+ specimens; H5326, 50+ specimens; H5337, 15+ specimens; H5338, 8 specimens; H5343, 1 specimen; D5712, 1 specimen; D5735, 3 specimens; Sausalito, 3½ feet, March 2, 1912, 4 specimens; Red Rock, 4 feet, March 22, 1912, 150+ specimens.

Distribution.—Known from California and the shores of British Columbia.

Remarks.—This species may be recognized by the following characters:

(1) The carapace (fig. 90, *a*) is hardly produced as a rostral plate, anterior margin broadly and evenly rounded, anterolateral angles acute.

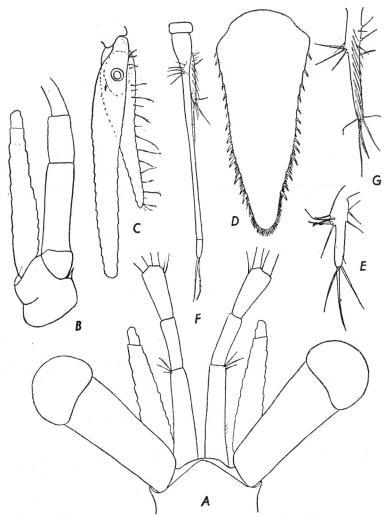

FIGURE 90.—*Acanthomysis macropsis* (Tattersall): *a*, Anterior end of female to show rostral plate, eye, and antennule; *b*, antennal scale and peduncle, × 78; *c*, uropod, × 60; *d*, telson, × 78; *e*, third pleopod of male, × 78; *f*, fourth pleopod of male, × 62; *g*, fifth pleopod of male, × 78.

(2) The eye (fig. 90, *a*) is greatly elongated, three and one-third times as long as broad, cornea occupying the distal quarter of the entire eye. The eye is longer than the antennal scale and the antennal peduncle and is remarkably like that of *Macropsis*.

(3) Antennal scale (fig. 90, a, b) much shorter than the antennular peduncle, six times as long as broad, with a well marked distal joint.

(4) The labrum is without the spinelike process characteristic of most members of the genus.

(5) The thoracic limbs are long and slender. The endopod of the third to the eighth pairs is divided into five to seven subjoints.

(6) The telson (fig. 90, d) is linguiform, twice as long as broad at the base, apex bluntly rounded. The lateral margins are armed with 13 to 15 larger spines somewhat widely spaced and extending about five-sixths of the way along the margins from the base; between the last four or five large spines are a varying number of small spines; the whole of the apex posterior to the last pair of large spines is armed by a very closely set row of small spines, which are more like the closely set teeth of a saw than a series of articulated spines.

(7) The inner uropod (fig. 90, c) has a single spine near the statocyst.

(8) The fourth pleopod of the male (fig. 90, f) is long and slender; the proximal joint of the exopod is 10 times as long as the distal; the terminal setae are twice as long as the distal joint.

This very distinct species is readily identified by its elongate eye, the short antennal scale, and the form and armature of the telson.

ACANTHOMYSIS PSEUDOMACROPSIS (Tattersall)

FIGURES 91, 92

Neomysis pseudomacropsis TATTERSALL, 1933, p. 14, figs. 7, 8.

Occurrence.—BERING SEA REGION: Bering Island, L. Stejneger collector, 6 adult females, breeding; Petropavlovsk, Kamchatka, collected by the *Albatross*, 1 adult male; *Albatross* station 3235, 1 female, 1 male.

Distribution.—Hitherto this species was known only from the coast of British Columbia. The present records indicate a considerable extension northward to the Bering Sea and down the east coast of Siberia to Petropavlovsk.

Remarks.—This species may be recognized by the following characters: (1) The carapace (fig. 91, a) is hardly produced into a rostral plate; the front margin is broadly and evenly rounded and the antero-lateral corners acute. (2) The eye (fig. 91, a; 92, a) is elongate but less so than in *A. macropsis;* it is two and a half times as long as broad and the cornea occupies the distal third. The eye is shorter than the antennal scales. (3) The antennal scale (figs. 91, a; 92, d) is about as long as the antennular peduncle, five times as long as broad, with a distinct distal joint. (4) The labrum has a small spinous process. (5) The endopod of the third to the eighth thoracic limbs (fig. 92, e) has the sixth joint subdivided into eight subjoints. (6) The telson (fig. 91, *b*) is linguiform in shape, three times as long as broad at the base, apex bluntly rounded; the lateral margins are armed with short blunt spines which are grouped into series in the center third of the margin; apex armed with a closely set row of short blunt spines, all equal in size and set like the teeth of a saw. (7) The inner uropod has no spines on the lower margin near the statocyst. (8) The fourth pleopod of the male (fig. 92, *f*) of curious form, rather short and stout, exopod three (?)-jointed, curved, with two very stout and heavily barbed setae, one at the tip and the other arising from the inner corner of the penultimate joint, outer margin of the exopod with about seven long simple setae.

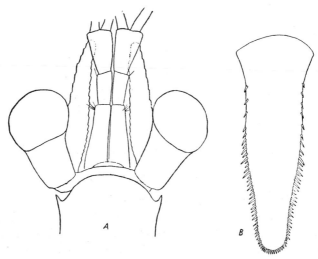

FIGURE 91.—*Acanthomysis pseudomacropsis* (Tattersall): *a*, Anterior end to show rostral plate, eye, antennal scale, and antennular peduncle, × 22½; *b*, telson, × 25.

This species is closely allied to *A. macropsis* but differs from it in the shorter eye, longer antennal scale, the presence of a spine on the labrum, the absence of spines on the inner uropod, and in the proportions of the telson. The fourth pleopod of the male is very distinctive and enables males to be readily recognized.

ACANTHOMYSIS LONGICORNIS (Milne-Edwards)

Mysis longicornis MILNE-EDWARDS, 1837, p. 459 ; 1840, pl. 26, figs. 7–9.

Occurrence.—Naples*, identified by A. M. Norman.

Distribution.—The Mediterranean Sea and Atlantic coasts of Europe.

ACANTHOMYSIS sp. ?

Reference to this species may be found on page 249.

Genus PRONEOMYSIS Tattersall

Proneomysis TATTERSALL, 1933, p. 21.

This genus was instituted for a species from British Columbia. Its chief characters are the 3-jointed exopod of the fourth pleopod of the male and the modified fifth pleopod of the male, which consists of a

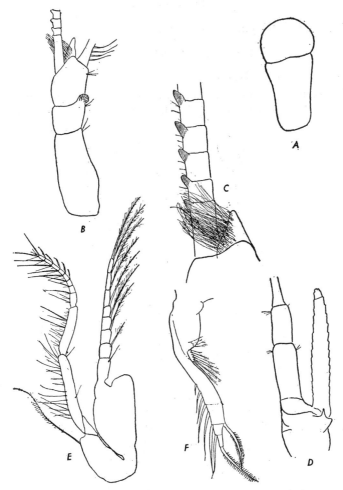

FIGURE 92.—*Acanthomysis pseudomacropsis* (Tattersall): *a*, Eye, × 25; *b*, antennular peduncle of male, × 25; *c*, proximal portion of inner flagellum of antennular peduncle of male to show curious spines on joints, × 25; *d*, antennal scale and peduncle, × 25; *e*, third thoracic limb, × 25; *f*, fourth pleopod of male, × 25.

long sympod terminated by a very long seta. Otherwise it is closely allied to *Acanthomysis*.

Ii (1936a) described four new species of the genus from Japanese waters in which none had the fifth pleopod of the male modified in any way but was exactly like the same appendage in the female. He has, accordingly, modified the original definition of the genus and relies solely on the 3-jointed exopod of the fourth pleopod of the male to separate the genus from *Acanthomysis*.

PRONEOMYSIS WAILESI Tattersall

FIGURES 93, 94

This species is diagnosed on page 249.

Genus PARACANTHOMYSIS Ii

Paracanthomysis Ii, 1936b, p. 7.

This genus is closely related to the genera *Acanthomysis* and *Proneomysis* and differs only in the structure of the exopod of the

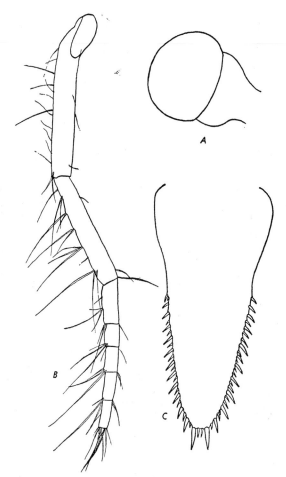

FIGURE 93.—*Proneomysis wailesi* Tattersall: *a*, Eye, × 45; *b*, endopod of third thoracic limb, × 75; *c*, telson, × 75.

fourth pleopod of the male, which is composed of a single joint only whereas in *Acanthomysis* it is 2-jointed and in *Proneomysis* 3-jointed.

PARACANTHOMYSIS KURILENSIS Ii

FIGURE 95

Paracanthomysis kurilensis Iı, 1936b, p. 11, figs. 29–41.

Occurrence.—BERING ISLAND: L. Stejneger collector, 35 females, 6 males up to 14 mm., breeding; No. 2541, L. Stejneger collector, 1882–83,

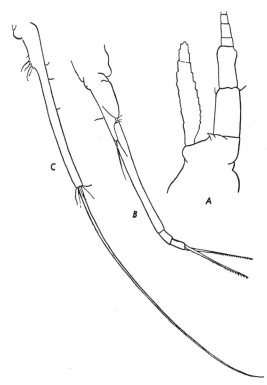

FIGURE 94.—*Proneomysis wailesi* Tattersall: *a*, Antennal scale and peduncle, × 39; *b*, fourth pleopod of male, × 39; *c*, fifth pleopod of male, × 39.

1 adult female; from mouth of cod, N. Grebnitzky collector, 9 males up to 18 mm.

Distribution.—Hitherto known only from the Kurile Islands, the present material from Bering Island indicates a considerable northern extension of the known geographical range of this species.

Remarks.—These specimens agree closely with the careful description and clear figures of Ii, and I have nothing to add to his account. I give here figures (fig. 95, *a–c*) of the antennal scale, telson, and fourth pleopod of the male for comparison with Ii's figures. I can see no suture in the exopod of the fourth pleopod of the male and agree that it appears to be single-jointed, though I have to confess that it is exceedingly difficult to be quite definite on this point.

Genus MYSIDIUM Dana

Mysidia DANA, 1850, p. 130.—ZIMMER, 1918, p. 24.
Macromysis DANA, 1852b, p. 638 (*nec* White, 1847, p. 81).
Mysidium DANA, 1852b, p. 638.
Diamysis ZIMMER, 1915a, p. 214.

The name *Mysidia* is preoccupied by a genus of Hemiptera founded by Westwood in 1840, and there is no doubt that the later form of the

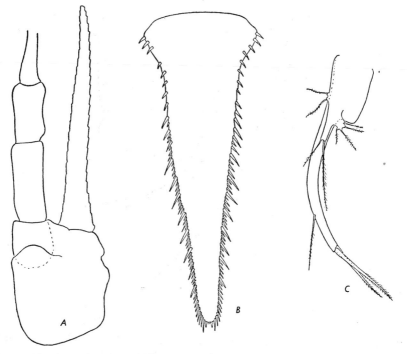

FIGURE 95.—*Paracanthomysis kurilensis* Ii: *a*, Antennal scale, × 55; *b*, telson, × 55; *c*, fourth pleopod of male, × 55.

name, *Mysidium*, given by Dana in 1852, is the correct one for this genus.

Two species of the genus have been described, *M. gracile* (Dana) and *M. columbiae* (Zimmer). A third species is herein described as new. All three species are known only from American waters at present and all are represented in the present material. They may be distinguished according to the key.

KEY TO THE SPECIES OF MYSIDIUM

a^1. Apex of telson evenly rounded, neither incised nor emarginate; spines on lateral margins, including the apex, about 35 on each half; antennal scale 5 times as long as broad_____integrum (p. 223)

a^2. Apex of telson incised or emarginate.

b^1. Telson incised at apex; spines on telson, including the incision, 23 on each half; antennal scale 7 times as long as broad_____columbiae (p. 223)

b^2. Apex of telson emarginate; spines on telson, including the emarginate, 25 on each half; antennal scale 4 times as long as broad____gracile (p. 223)

MYSIDIUM COLUMBIAE (Zimmer)

Diamysis columbiae ZIMMER, 1915b, p. 172, figs. 23–29.
Mysidia columbiae ZIMMER, 1918, p. 26.

Occurrence.—VENEZUELA: Puerto Cabello, January 1892, collected by K. Levinsen, 24 females, 13 males. VIRGIN ISLANDS: St. Croix, February 19, 1906, 4 fathoms, 1 male, 1 female.

Distribution.—Previously known only from Cartagena, Colombia, where the type specimens were collected, the range now includes Venezuela and the Virgin Islands.

MYSIDIUM GRACILE (Dana)

Macromysis gracilis DANA, 1852b, p. 653; 1855, pl. 43, figs. 5a–m.
Mysidium gracile CZERNIAVSKY, 1887, p. 85.
Mysidia gracilis ZIMMER, 1918, p. 24.

Occurrence.—VIRGIN ISLANDS: St. Croix, February 19, 1906, 4 fathoms, 1 female.

Distribution.—Known previously only from the harbor of Rio de Janeiro, the Virgin Islands are now included in the range.

MYSIDIUM INTEGRUM, new species

FIGURE 96

Description.—Carapace short, leaving the last two thoracic somites exposed in the middorsal line, front margin only slightly produced as a rostral plate, which is broadly triangular, with a blunt apex, not covering the eyestalks.

Eyes large and globose, pigment light brown.

Antennal scale (fig. 96, *a*) five times as long as broad, extending only slightly beyond the antennular peduncle, setose all around, with a distinct distal joint and a prominent spine on the outer corner of the joint from which it arises; antennal peduncle very short, less than half as long as the scale and composed of three short more or less equal joints.

The mouth appendages and thoracic limbs resemble closely those of *M. gracile* as described and figured by Zimmer (1918). The sixth joint of the endopods of the third to the seventh thoracic limbs (fig.

96, *d*) is divided into three subjoints and that of the eighth into two. The basal joint of the exopods of all the thoracic limbs has the outer distal corner rounded, without spine.

Sixth somite of the pleon 1½ to 1⅔ as long as the fifth.

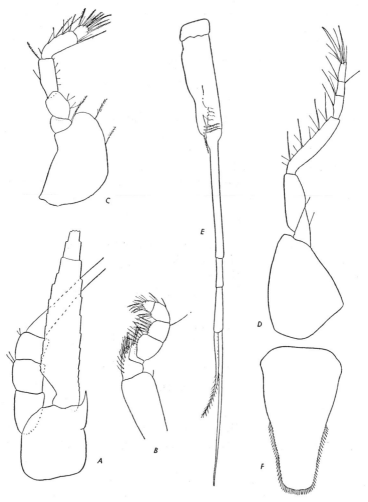

FIGURE 96.—*Mysidium integrum*, new species: *a*, Antennal scale, × 64; *b*, endopod of first thoracic limb, × 56; *c*, endopod of second thoracic limb, × 56; *d*, endopod of third thoracic limb, × 56; *e*, fourth pleopod of male, × 64; *f*, telson, × 64.

Telson (fig. 96, *f*) only three-quarters of the length of the sixth segment of the pleon, spatulate in shape, 1¾ times as long as broad at the base, gradually narrowing to a broadly rounded apex which is not incised or even emarginate, but straight with rounded lateral corners; the armature of very closely set and regularly arranged spines is confined to the distal half of the margins and the whole of the apex; the spines form a continuous series of about 70, 35 on each half of the telson, without distinction between lateral and apical spines.

Inner uropod more than 1½ times as long as the telson, without spines on its lower margin; outer uropod about twice as long as the telson.

Pleopods of the male almost exactly the same as described by Zimmer (1918) for *M. gracile*. Fourth pleopod (fig. 96, *e*) extending beyond the distal end of the pleon, its terminal setae reaching to the distal end of the telson; endopod represented by a short simple lobe with a single seta at the apex; exopod very long and slender, 4-jointed, the first joint much the longest, equal to the other three combined, penultimate and ultimate joints each with a single long plumose seta, that of the penultimate much the longer.

Length of adult male and female specimens, 7 mm.

Type lot.—From Cruz Bay, St. John, Virgin Islands.

Occurrence.—GULF OF MEXICO: Carlos Stansch collector, 8 males, 3 females. WEST INDIES (Virgin Islands): Cruz Bay, St. John, 1896, Chr. Lofting collector, 55 males, 76 females (type lot); Cruz Bay, St. John, 1896, Ch. Levinsen collector, several hundreds of both sexes; Water Island, St. Thomas, January 1896, Ch. Levinsen collector, 78 males, 91 females; St. Croix, February 21, 1906, Th. Mortensen collector, 2 males, 1 female, 1 immature.

Distribution.—*M. integrum* would appear to be an abundant species in the Caribbean Sea area among the islands of the West Indies; it likewise occurs in the Gulf of Mexico.

Remarks.—Except for the first lot, none of this material is in the collection of the U. S. National Museum. The second is the type lot. This new species is very closely allied to *M. gracile* (Dana) and differs from it only in the shape of the telson. In *M. gracile* the apex of the telson is emarginate so that it appears slightly bilobate, and the number of spines on each half of the telson is about 25. *M. integrum* has the apex of the telson entire without any trace of emargination, with the result that the telson appears to be longer and narrower than in *M. gracile*. There are 35 spines on each half of the telson. I have examined hundreds of specimens of this new form and the telson is similar in all of them. In its other characters it is almost exactly the same as *M. gracile*, and Zimmer's figures of the latter will serve almost as well for *M. integrum*. The other known species of the genus, *M. columbiae*, is rather more distinct. The telson is incised rather than emarginate at the apex so that the bilobate appearance of the apex is more marked than in *M. gracile*. The antennal scale is longer and narrower, 7 : 1 against 4 : 1 and 5 : 1. The fourth pleopod of the male differs from that of both the other species in being relatively shorter, in the larger endopod and in the fact that the exopod is only 3-jointed instead of 4-jointed. *M. columbiae* also has a more marked rostral plate with an acutely pointed apex.

Genus DIAMYSIS Czerniavsky

Diamysis CZERNIAVSKY, 1882a, pp. 57, 63 ; 1887, p. 84.
Pseudomysis CZERNIAVSKY, 1882a, p. 132 (nec Sars, 1879).
Euxinomysis CZERNIAVSKY, 1882a, pp. 58, 64, 132.
Potamomysis CZERNIAVSKY, 1882a, pp. 58, 64, 129.

In 1882 Czerniavsky founded the three genera *Diamysis*, *Euxinomysis*, and *Potamomysis*. In 1915 Zimmer united *Diamysis* and *Euxinomysis* (1915a, p. 214), and in 1924 Dershavin (p. 117) showed that *Potamomysis* should also be regarded as a synonym of *Diamysis*. In the same year Martynov (1924, p. 210) independently concluded that *Euxinomysis* and *Potamomysis* were synonymous. *Diamysis*, as the first of the three names to be used, is the name which must be applied to the genus. In 1878 Czerniavsky used the name *Pseudomysis*, without definition or description, for specimens of *Euxinomysis mecznikowi* in the collection of the University Museum of Zoology at Odessa. In 1879 (b) Sars instituted the genus *Pseudomysis* for a very striking mysid captured by the Norwegian North Polar Expedition, and in 1882 Czerniavsky substituted the name *Euxinomysis* for his former *Pseudomysis*, regarding the latter name as preoccupied by Sars. I have been unable to trace whether Czerniavsky actually published the name *Pseudomysis* in 1878 or whether it existed only in manuscript. In any case, as a nomen nudum, it can be disregarded.

DIAMYSIS AMERICANA, new species

FIGURE 97

Description.—Body somewhat slender; carapace hardly at all produced into a rostral plate, front margin evenly arcuate.

Eyes of moderate size, total length of cornea and stalk not quite twice the greatest breadth, cornea occupying about one-third of the total eye, hardly broader than the stalk, pigment black.

Antennular peduncle with the basal joint about equal to the second and third joints combined, setose lobe in the male well developed.

Antennal peduncle (fig. 97, *a*) shorter than the antennular, second joint about one-quarter longer than the third.

Antennal scale (fig. 97, *a*) nearly twice as long as its own peduncle and extending beyond the antennular peduncle for one-sixth of its length, narrow and lanceolate in shape, six times as long as broad, setose on both margins, with a distinct distal transverse suture.

Maxillule (fig. 97, *b*) without any protuberance on the front margin and the spines arming the apex of the outer lobe (third joint) very short and arranged in three rows.

Maxilla (fig. 97, *c*) with the exopod small and its setae feebly developed, terminal joint of the palp less expanded than in *D. bahirensis* and the spines arming the apex longer.

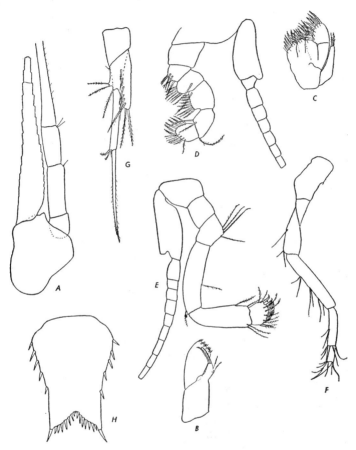

FIGURE 97.—*Diamysis americana*, new species: *a*, Antennal scale, × 64; *b*, maxillule, × 74⅔; *c*, maxilla, × 74⅔; *d*, first thoracic limb, × 74⅔; *e*, second thoracic limb, × 74⅔; *f*, endopod of third thoracic limb, × 64; *g*, fourth pleopod of male, × 74⅔; *h*, telson, × 74⅔.

Carpopropodal joint of the endopods of the third (fig. 97, *f*) to the eighth thoracic limbs divided into two subjoints, the proximal of which is twice as long as the distal, nail well developed, basal joint of the exopod with its outer corner rounded and not spiniform.

Sixth somite of the pleon about one-fifth longer than the fifth.

Telson (fig. 97, *h*) short, about two-thirds the length of the sixth somite of the pleon and only slightly more than half as long as the inner uropod, 1½ times as long as broad at the base, apex only two-thirds the width at the base with a shallow broad and angular cleft, lateral angles of the apex armed with a single spine, margins of the cleft armed with seven spines on each side of the central point, these spines shorter than those at the apical angles, lateral margins of the telson armed with five spines on the proximal two-thirds of their length, the distal third of the margins smooth and without spines.

Inner uropod 1¾ as long as the telson, without spines on its inner margin.

Outer uropod 2¼ times as long as the telson and one-third longer than the inner uropod.

Fourth pleopod of the male (fig. 97, *g*) with the endopod of normal structure except that the side lobe is much shorter than in *D. bahirensis*, exopod of one joint terminating in a very long stout plumose spine, which is longer than the joint, three short spinules at the angle at the base of the long spine.

Length of an adult male 5 mm.

Type lot.—Two males, 3 immature females, U.S.N.M. No. 81270, from Paramaribo, Dutch Guiana.

Occurrence.—South America: Paramaribo, Dutch Guiana, from a ditch in the botanical gardens, fresh water, A. Reyne collector, 2 males, 3 females (type lot).

Distribution.—The occurrence of the genus *Diamysis* on the American continent raises a point of geographical interest. The other three species of the genus are inhabitants of the Mediterranean basin. *D. bahirensis* is rather widely distributed along the shores of the Mediterranean and Black Seas, in water of low salinity. *D. mecznikowi* is characteristic of the fresh waters draining into the Black Sea, and *D. pusilla* is a Caspian Sea species. It is therefore of special interest to find a species on the American continent in fresh-water conditions similar to those of *D. mecznikowi*. It seems possible to explain this interesting distribution of *Diamysis* by regarding *D. americana* on the one hand and the Mediterranean species on the other hand as relicts of the fauna of the old Tethys sea of early Tertiary times, in which the genus was probably widely distributed. With the changes that led to the present constitution of the Atlantic Ocean and the Mediterranean basin the genus *Diamysis* gradually retreated on the one hand into the Mediterranean and on the other hand into the Caribbean Sea, penetrated into fresh water, and became the present-day Mediterranean and American species. The American species can therefore be seen to have a special interest for students of geographical distribution.

Remarks.—This species differs from the generic description of *Diamysis* in having only two subjoints in the sixth joint of the endopods of the thoracic limbs instead of three and in having only one joint in the exopod of the fourth pleopod of the male. It is, however, so essentially a *Diamysis* in all its main characters that I have regarded these differences as of only specific value. It differs from other species of the genus, in addition to the two characters already mentioned, in the many fewer spines on the margin of the telson, in the virtual absence of a rostral plate, and in the absence of spines on the inner uropod. From the data accompanying the specimens this species, like its congeners, lives in almost fresh water.

Genus ANTROMYSIS Creaser

Antromysis CREASER, 1936, p. 121.

The genus *Antromysis* was established in 1936 by Creaser for a small but very interesting cave-dwelling mysid found in caves in Yucatán. Unfortunately Creaser's account of the type species, *A. cenotensis*, contains several serious errors of mysidacean morphology. He describes the mandibular palp as composed of two joints and figures it as such (his fig. 22), yet in figure 15 he depicts correctly a 3-jointed mandibular palp that he labels as the "first thoracic appendage (gnathopod)." The endopod of the true first thoracic appendage (fig. 13) is labeled as the "second thoracic appendage (maxilliped)." The true second thoracic appendage (gnathopod) is described as the "third thoracic appendage (first true leg)," but in the text is referred to as "following thoracic appendages," and moreover the exopodite is called the endopodite and the endopodite the exopodite. Such grave mistakes make it difficult to decide how much reliance may be placed on apparent differences between my specimens and Creaser's description, whether such differences really exist or are the result of misinterpretations of the characters concerned. The most serious of these differences, and the most important because it is of generic significance, is the form of the fourth pleopod of the male. In his generic definition Creaser describes these appendages as biramous, the inner ramus composed of two joints without lateral processes. In my specimens the fourth pleopod of the male is biramous, but the inner ramus is composed of a single flattened platelike joint with a well-marked setose side lobe; it is in fact very similar to that described in so many Mysidae. The outer ramus is, as far as I can make out, composed of three joints terminated by a single strong barbed seta which is longer than the combined length of the three joints of the ramus. If Creaser's description of the fourth pleopod of the male is correct, the differences I have pointed out would preclude the reference of my species to his genus. A comparison of my figures with those of Creaser, however, shows a general broad agreement in essential points between the two species and forces the conclusion that we are dealing with species of the same genus. I have therefore referred my specimens to Creaser's genus and have modified his generic definition accordingly. The species described below appears to be distinct from *A. cenotensis*. The latter is described as having the eyes without pigment areas, whereas the new species has a definite narrow band of pigment along the outer edge of the ocular plate. There are also other differences in the telson.

Emended definition.—Eyes partially fused to form a thick ocular plate with a somewhat deep furrow in the median line separating the distal parts of the two eyes, visual elements imperfectly developed, pigment reduced or absent; antennal scale short, oval, setose, all around, a distal joint marked off by a distinct suture; maxilla with exopod; carpopropodal joint of the endopod of the third to the eighth thoracic limbs divided into two or three subjoints, nail well developed; telson short, quadrangular, apex entire without cleft or emargination, armed with a few strong spines, no plumose setae, lateral margins unarmed or armed with one or two spines; statocyst very small; first, second, third, and fifth pleopods of the male rudimentary as in the female, composed of small single-jointed plates; fourth pleopod of the male biramous, endopod composed of a single-jointed flat plate with a prominent side lobe, exopod three-jointed and terminated by a single very long, strong, barbed seta; female with two pairs of incubatory lamellae.

Remarks.—This interesting genus is a typical member of the tribe Mysini and in Zimmer's classification falls into his division III.A.a., thus showing closest affinity with the genera *Diamysis* and *Limnomysis*. It differs from both these genera in the form of the telson, which is entire and without cleft or emargination and has a truncate apex. The genera named have the apex of the telson with a shallow apical cleft. *Antromysis* has become specialized for life in deep holes or in underground cave waters and the eyes are profoundly modified accordingly.

ANTROMYSIS ANOPHELINAE, new species

FIGURES 98, 99

Description.—Carapace hardly at all produced into a rostral plate, anterior margin broadly arcuate (fig. 98, *a*).

Eyes (fig. 98, *a*) modified and reduced, fused proximally to form an ocular plate, each eye free distally with a deep furrow separating the anterior part of each eye, visual elements reduced and forming a narrow band along the edge of the ocular plate, where there is also a narrow band of black pigment.

Antennular peduncle (fig. 98, *a*) robust, with the third joint almost as long as the first; no setose lobe or process in the male.

Antennal scale (fig. 98, *b*) small and ovate in shape, considerably shorter than its own peduncle, setose all around, about 3½ times as long as broad, with a distinct distal joint marked off by a suture; antennal peduncle (fig. 98, *b*) longer than the scale, third joint two-thirds of the length of the second.

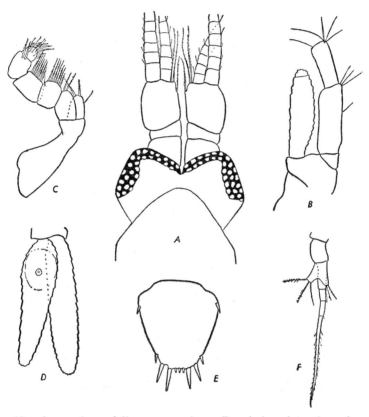

FIGURE 98.—*Antromysis anophelinae*, new species: *a*, Dorsal view of anterior end to show eyes and antennular peduncle; *b*, antennal scale and peduncle, × 68; *c*, endopod of first thoracic limb, × 68; *d*, uropod, × 68; *e*, telson, × 68; *f*, fourth pleopod of male, × 68.

Mouth parts not presenting any special features but agreeing closely with those of the Mysini in general; mandibular palp 3-jointed, terminal joint unusually short; maxilla with a well-developed exopod.

First thoracic limb (fig. 98, *c*) with a well-marked gnathobasic lobe on the second joint of the endopod; third and fourth joints somewhat expanded but hardly produced into lobes.

Third to the seventh thoracic limbs (fig. 99, *b*) with the carpo-propodal joint of the endopod divided into three subjoints, nail well developed.

Eighth thoracic limb (fig. 99, c) rather long and slightly modified as a fossorial limb, the proximal subjoint of the carpopropodal joint of the endopod being expanded and bearing a row of plumose setae along its anterior outer border.

Female with two pairs of incubatory lamellae attached to the seventh and eighth thoracic limbs.

First, second, third, and fifth pleopods of the male similar to those of the female, composed of single-jointed flat plates with well-marked setose side lobes. Fourth pleopod of the male (fig. 98, f) biramous, inner ramus of the same form as the remaining pleopods, a simple unjointed plate with a well-marked side lobe, outer ramus composed of three joints terminating in a single strong very stout barbed seta, longer than the combined length of the three joints of the ramus.

Telson (fig. 98, e) short, quadrangular in shape, only very slightly longer than broad at the base, apex entire and truncate or slightly arcuate, and armed by three small spinules in the center flanked by a pair of stout long spines on each side at the outer angles of the apex; lateral margins armed by two spines, one near the proximal end of the margin, the other at the distal end slightly proximal to the outer of the two large spines at the corners of the apex, so that they appear and may be regarded as part of the apical armature.

Uropods (fig. 98, d) short and subequal in length without spines on the inner lower margin of the inner pair; statocyst very small and obviously reduced in size.

Length of adult specimens of both sexes, 3–3.5 mm.

Type lot.—Eight males, 11 females, U.S.N.M. No. 81271, from Río Aranjuez, Puntarenas, Costa Rica.

Occurrence.—COSTA RICA: Río Aranjuez, Puntarenas, in the holes of a shore crab (*Cardisoma crassum* Smith) with the larvae of a mosquito (*Deinocerites pseudes* Dyar and Knab), September 12, 1905, collected by F. Knab, 8 males, 11 females, 3 to 3.5 mm., type lot.

Remarks.—The number of eggs in the brood pouch of a breeding female was only four.

This species differs from the type and only known other species of the genus, *A. cenotensis*, in the following points:

(1) The presence of pigment in the ocular plate. This difference is to be correlated with its different mode of life. *A. cenotensis* is an underground cave-dwelling species. *A. anophelinae* is a surface-living form but lives at the bottom of deep crab holes.

(2) The armature of the telson. *A. cenotensis* has two median spinules on the apex of the telson and a single large spine at each corner. It apparently has no spines on the lateral margins of the telson at all.

(3) In the form of the fourth pleopod of the male. The exopod of this appendage in *A. cenotensis* is not at all unlike that of the present species except in the number of joints, and as these are so very difficult to make out in so small an animal, this difference is not

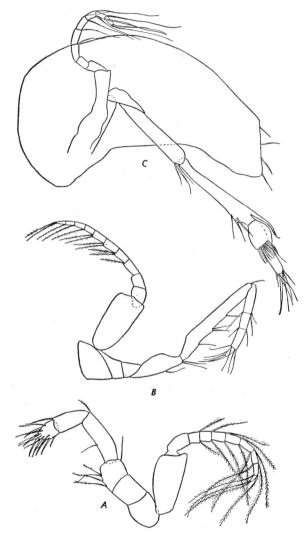

FIGURE 99.—*Antromysis anophelinae*, new species: *a*, Second thoracic limb, × 68; *b*, third thoracic limb, × 68; *c*, eighth thoracic limb, × 68.

serious. The endopod, is, however very different. It is figured as a two-jointed ramus terminating in two long setae. In the present species the endopod is a single unjointed plate with a prominent side lobe furnished with setae.

The habits of *A. anophelinae* are extremely interesting and specialized. It was discovered in the holes made by the large shore crab, *Cardisoma crassum* Smith, living with the larvae of a mosquito *Deinocerites pseudes* Dyar and Knab (1909, p. 260). According to Knab, the collector (1906, p. 95), these mosquitoes were found far up the mangrove inlets behind Puntarenas. The crab holes were near the head of tide water, above overflow, often a considerable distance from the water, and the water in them must have been very nearly if not quite fresh. The mysid *Antromysis anophelinae* must, therefore, be regarded as a brackish-water form at least, with a wide range of salinity tolerance up to water that is occasionally quite fresh. The reduced and specialized structure of the eyes is a point of great interest. Knab does not mention the depth of the crab holes at Puntarenas, but he says that similar holes at Port Limon on the east coast of Costa Rica, inhabited by *Deinocerites cancer*, went to a great depth to reach water, so that the mosquitoes living in them never see the light until they attain the winged state. There were no mysids in the holes at Port Limon, but if the holes at Puntarenas were similarly deep and dark, the reduction of the eye can be correlated with this specialized habit. The type species, *A. cenotensis*, is a cave-dwelling species, found in fresh water in caves in Yucatán, and in this species the eyes are further reduced and have lost all pigment. *A. cenotensis* has probably been derived from a species similar to *A. anophelinae* in which the first stages of specialized habit with the corresponding specialization of structure are exhibited.

ANTROMYSIS CENOTENSIS Creaser

Antromysis cenotensis CREASER, 1936, p. 121, figs. 13–24; 1938, p. 159.

Occurrence.—Paratypes * from Yucatán, identified by E. P. Creaser.

Distribution.—Known only from caves in Yucatán.

Tribe HETEROMYSINI

Endopods of the third to the eighth thoracic limbs with the carpus and propodus fused; the fused carpopropodus is undivided in the third pair of limbs but is divided by vertical articulations into a number of subjoints in the fourth to the eighth pair; all the pleopods of the male rudimentary as in the female; antennal scale ovate, setose all around; telson cleft.

Remarks.—Only one genus is included in this tribe *Heteromysis*. Numerous species of the genus have been described, of which three, possibly four, are known from American waters.

Genus HETEROMYSIS S. I. Smith

Heteromysis S. I. SMITH, 1873, p. 553.
Chiromysis G. O. SARS, 1877, p. 56.
Gnathomysis BONNIER AND PÉRÈZ, 1902, p. 117.

This genus is represented on both the east and west coasts of America, on the east coast by *H. formosa, H. bermudensis,* and *H. antillensis,* and on the west coast by *H. odontops,* with which I regard *H. spinosa* as synonymous. The west coast species can be distinguished from all the east coast forms by the extension of the spines arming the lateral margins of the telson along the whole length of the margins, whereas in the east coast species the spines occupy only the distal half of the margins. The key will help to identify the species:

KEY TO THE SPECIES OF HETEROMYSIS

a^1. Telson with spines along full extent of lateral margins; 20 to 24 spines on lateral margins of telson; cleft of telson one-fourth to one-third length of telson with spines along full extent of margins of cleft; eye with a tubercular process on inner corner of stalk_____ odontops (p. 239)

a^2. Telson with spines along distal half of lateral margins only.

b^1. Twelve to 16 spines on lateral margins of telson; cleft of telson one-third length of telson with spines along full extent of its margins.
formosa (p. 235)

b^2. Six spines on lateral margins of telson; cleft of telson one-third length of telson with spines along proximal part of its margins only; distal part of each margin being smooth and devoid of spines___bermudensis (p. 237)

I am unable to place *H. antillensis* in this key. Verrill's description is entirely inadequate and does not record any of the fundamental characters of the species. In all probability it is not specifically separable from *H. bermudensis.*

HETEROMYSIS FORMOSA S. I. Smith

FIGURES 100, 101

Heteromysis formosa S. I. SMITH, 1873, p. 553; 1879, p. 101.—BENEDICT, 1885, p. 175.—PAULMIER, 1905, p. 129.—M. RATHBUN, 1905, p. 28.—FOWLER, 1912, p. 541.—SUMNER, OSBORN, and COLE, 1913, p. 663.—PRATT, 1916, p. 383; 1935, p. 423.—ALLEE, 1923a, p. 180; 1923b, p. 227.—FISH, 1925, p. 152.

Occurrence.—EAST COAST OF UNITED STATES: Woods Hole, 1 immature female; Woods Hole region, 18 females, 9 males; Woods Hole, surface, 8 p. m., October 2, 1882, 2 immature specimens; Vineyard Sound, 1875, 84 breeding females, 60 adult males, 13 immature; Vineyard Sound, December 28, 1877, V. N. Edwards collector, 4 females, 3 males; Vineyard Sound, 1 breeding female; Vineyard Sound, identified by S. I. Smith*; Newport, R. I., 1880, shore to 30 fathoms, 2 imma-

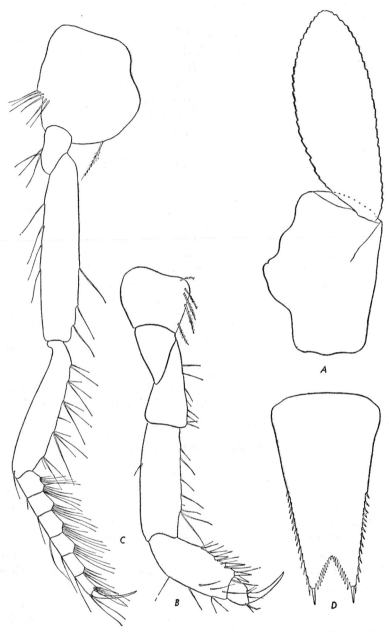

FIGURE 100.—*Heteromysis formosa* S. I. Smith: *a*, Antennal scale, × 40; *b*, endopod of third thoracic limb, × 40; *c*, endopod of fourth thoracic limb, × 40; *d*, telson, × 40.

ture specimens; in washings of oysters, mouth of New Haven Harbor, May 28, 1880, R. Rathbun collector, 1 adult female; New Haven, Conn., identified by S. I. Smith*; Long Island Sound, 1874, 3 breeding females, 1 adult male; *Fish Hawk* stations 917, latitude 40°22′ N., longitude 70°42′ W., 44 fathoms, July 16, 1881, 1 male, 1 female; 934, Nobska Light, 9 fathoms, July 20, 1881, 1 breeding female (another specimen from this station, identified by S. I. Smith, was not examined by me); 1242*, Vineyard Sound, 18 fathoms, 10 :50 a. m., September 5, 1887, identified by S. I. Smith; *Albatross* stations 2402, 1 immature female, 12 mm.; 2603, 1 breeding female, 13 mm., 2 males, 8 to 13 mm.; no locality, 4 breeding females.

Distribution.—Smith (1879) has given a full account of the distribution of this species on the American coasts as known at that time. Subsequent records, a full list of which is given above in the references to this species, and the long list of records given here, do not add considerably to the facts presented by Smith except for the records from *Albatross* stations 2402 and 2603, which extend the geographical range of the species considerably southward, and for those records which increase its bathymetric range to 124 fathoms. The species is common on the coasts in shallow water from New Jersey to the northern boundary of the United States. It has not yet been recorded from Canada or in shallow water to the south of New Jersey.

Remarks.—The specimens from Fish Hawk station 917 and *Albatross* stations 2402 and 2603 are of special interest. Not only do they come from much deeper water than any so far recorded, but they are of larger size. The largest male from station 2402 measured 15 mm., and an adult male and female from station 2603 measured 13 mm., the usual size of adult specimens being 8 to 10 mm. I thought at first that these deep-water specimens might represent a new species, but a careful examination shows that they cannot be separated from the shallow-water forms by any fundamental characters except their size and the fact that the endopods of the third thoracic limbs are relatively larger and more massive, though essentially of the same form. I figure the chief appendages of these deep-water specimens for comparison with those of the shallow-water form (figs. 100, *a–d*; 101).

HETEROMYSIS BERMUDENSIS G. O. Sars

Heteromysis bermudensis G. O. SARS, 1885, p. 216, pl. 38, figs. 1–7.—VERRILL, 1923, p. 184.

Occurrence.—Bermuda; No. 60, 1876–77, G. Brown Goode, collector, 2 females.

Distribution.—This species is so far not known from any locality outside Bermuda, from which it has been recorded only twice, by Sars in 1885 and by Verrill in 1923.

Remarks.—These specimens are rather badly damaged, but they agree substantially with Sars' description and figures.

HETEROMYSIS ANTILLENSIS Verrill

This species is recorded on page 250.

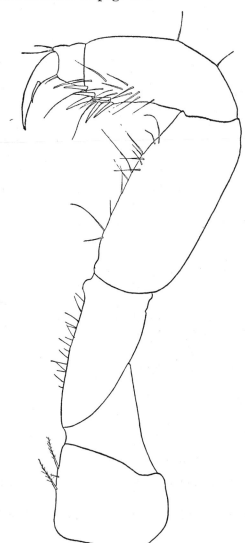

FIGURE 101.—*Heteromysis formosa* S. I. Smith: Endopod of third thoracic limb of a specimen 13 mm. long, from *Albatross* station 2402, × 40.

HETEROMYSIS ODONTOPS Walker

FIGURES 102, 103

Heteromysis odontops WALKER, 1898, p. 278, pl. 15, figs. 3–6.—HOLMES, 1900, p. 225.—TATTERSALL, 1933, p. 24.
Heteromysis spinosus HOLMES, 1900, p. 225, pl. 4, figs. 73–76.

Occurrence.—WEST COAST OF PANAMA : Taboguilla, 3 fathoms, sand, November 29, 1915, Dr. T. Mortensen collector, 1 male; Taboga, from *Pagurus* shells, 4 fathoms, January 14, 1916, Dr. T. Mortensen collec-

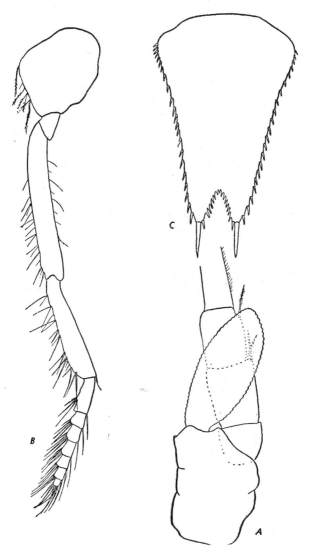

FIGURE 102.—*Heteromysis odontops* Walker: *a*, Antennal scale and peduncle, × 40; *b*, endopod of third thoracic limb, × 40; *c*, telson, × 62.

tor, 7 males, 16 females; Pontadora, Perlas Islands, 8 to 10 fathoms, January 28, 1916, 2 females.

Distribution. — Puget Sound (Walker); San Pedro, Calif. (Holmes); west coast of Panama.

Remarks.—Walker (1898) described *H. odontops* from Puget Sound and Holmes (1900) *H. spinosus* from California. These two supposedly distinct species are obviously very closely allied. The only character that Holmes points out as distinguishing his species from Walker's is that the latter has the inner margin of the antennal scale devoid of setae, whereas in the California species the scale is setose all around. I cannot believe that this is a real difference. Walker makes no mention of this special character in his description. On the other hand, Holmes gives no description of the eye, nor does he make any mention of spines on the inner uropods of his species, characters which could have been compared with those given by Walker as specific to *H. odontops.* The two forms agree in such fundamental characters as the telson, the endopods of the third thoracic limbs, and the number of articulations in the sixth joint of the endopods of the succeeding limbs. Both Walker's and Holmes' descriptions are inadequate, and it is difficult to decide whether the two species are really distinct.

The specimens here recorded are from the Pacific coast of the Panama region. They agree substantially with both Walker's and Holmes' species, yet they present certain differences which are best given in tabular form.

TABLE 8.—*Principal differences between the present Panama specimens of* Heteromysis odontops *and* spinosus *and those previously described*

Character	Previously described		Panama specimens
	odontops	*spinosus*	
Antennal scale_____	Inner margin without setae	Setose all around_____	Setose all around
Eye_____	With a toothlike process on the stalk	(?) _____	Looked at from above, the inner distal margin of the stalk is produced slightly as a blunt process overhanging the cornea.
Inner uropod_____	Four spines_____	(?)_____	One spine.
Cleft of telson_____	One-third of the telson in depth; 15 spines	One-third of the telson in depth; 12–13 spines	One-fourth of the telson in depth; 7–8 spines
Length_____	11 mm_____	½ inch_____	10 mm.

The Panama specimens agree with both *H. odontops* and *H. spinosus* in having the lateral margins of the telson armed with 20 to 24 spines, which extend along the entire margin, and also in that the apical lobes of the telson are furnished with two spines, the outer about twice as long as the inner. The form of the endopod of the third thoracic limbs and the number of articulations in the sixth joint of the endopods of the remaining thoracic limbs are substantially the same in all three forms.

FIGURE 103.—*Heteromysis odontops* Walker: *a*, Endopod of third thoracic limb of a small male, × 32; *b*, endopod of third thoracic limb of a large male, × 32.

The most serious differences presented by the Panama specimens is in the extent of the cleft of the telson. It is distinctly shallower and has fewer spines on its margins.

It is impossible to escape from the conclusion that we are dealing here with a single species with a geographical range extending from British Columbia to Panama on the west coast of America. Consequently I record these specimens as *H. odontops* Walker, with *H. spinosus* Holmes, as a synonym. I give here figures of the main appendages in the Panama specimens for comparison with those published for the other two species. (Figs. 102, *a–c;* 103, *a–b.*)

I have already expressed the opinion that Walker's figure of the antennal scale in his species is not correct, considering the characters in table 8. It is easy to understand the appearance depicted by Walker if the setae of the inner margin are folded under the lamina of the scale, and this is very likely to occur in manipulating the specimen for examination under a microscope. I do not think the inner margin of the scale in Walker's specimen was really without setae, and this supposed difference may be ignored.

With regard to the eye there is a distinct blunt process in all the Panama specimens. It is not so acutely pointed as shown by Walker.

I have examined the uropods of the Panama specimens very carefully and cannot detect more than one spine on the inner margin of the inner uropod near the statocyst. Since Holmes gives no particulars of the eye or uropods of his species, direct comparison is impossible.

In the Panama specimens the sixth joint of the endopod of the fourth thoracic limbs is 4-jointed and in the fifth to the eighth limbs it is 7- or 8-jointed. This agrees with Walker. Holmes gives the number of articulations in this joint as 8 to 10.

The endopod of the third thoracic limbs agrees substantially with both Walker and Holmes. The number of spines on the lower margins of the carpus varies, but it is generally about four pairs arranged in two rows. The limb is more robust in the male than in the female but otherwise it is the same in general form and armature. The propodal jont is much smaller and less evident than in *H. formosa.*

SPECIES NOT REPRESENTED IN THE COLLECTIONS OF THE UNITED STATES NATIONAL MUSEUM

LOPHOGASTER HAWAIENSIS Fage

Lophogaster hawaiensis FAGE, 1940, p. 323.

Occurrence.—Hawaii: *Albatross* stations 3847*, 3857*, 3858*, 3884*, 3965*, and 4101*, identified by Ortmann.

Distribution.—Hawaii.

Remarks.—The paper in which Fage described this species (mentioned also in Biological Abstracts, No. 5837) is unavailable both in England and America and the assignment of the name to the material listed must be regarded as tentative. For these reasons the species has not been included in the key.

These Hawaiian specimens need to be reexamined in the light of Fage's report and the discussion of the species of *Lophogaster* given above.

SCOLOPHTHALMUS LUCIFUGUS Faxon

Scolophthalmus lucifugus FAXON, 1893, p. 219; 1895, p. 226, pl. 55, figs. 1–1e.

Distribution.—Known only from the Pacific Ocean off the Galápagos Islands.

BOREOMYSIS NOBILIS G. O. Sars

FIGURE 6

Boreomysis nobilis G. O. SARS, 1879b, p. 428.—STEPHENSEN, 1933, p. 9.—TATTERSALL, 1939b, p. 282.

Distribution.—Recorded by Stephensen (1933) from Greenland and by Tattersall (1939) from the eastern waters of Canada off the coast of Newfoundland. The species is an Arctic one confined to waters where the bottom temperature is below zero, and in consequence it is not likely to be met with in the deep boreal waters of the eastern coasts of America.

Remarks.—Figure 6 illustrates the salient characters of this species and may serve as a guide to its identification.

PSEUDOMMA BERKELEYI Tattersall

FIGURE 48

Pseudomma berkeleyi TATTERSALL, 1933, p. 6, fig. 1.

Description.—I reproduce here the original description and figures of this species.

Ocular plate (fig. 48, *a*) with a well-marked and relatively deep incision in the median front margin; anterolateral margins armed with about nine very coarse teeth.

Antennal scale (fig. 48, *b*) extending about one-quarter of its length beyond the antennular peduncle; three and a half times as long as broad; outer margin terminating in a strong spine beyond which the apex of the scale barely extends.

Sixth segment of the abdomen 1⅔ as long as the fifth.

Telson (fig. 48, *c*) without the terminal spines as long as the sixth segment of the abdomen; 1⅔ as long as broad at its base and 3½ times as long as broad at the apex; apex arcuate and armed with three pairs of very strong spines, the median pair about one-quarter as long as the telson; a pair of delicate plumose setae between the median spines (broken in all the specimens); distal half of the lateral margins armed with four or five spines, the distal one about half as long as the outer pair of apical spines, the remaining spines short.

Outer uropod almost 1½ as long as the telson; inner uropod equal in length to the telson plus the terminal spines, thus only slightly shorter than the outer uropod.

Length of adult male 8 mm.

Distribution.—Known only from the type locality off British Columbia* in 65 fathoms.

Remarks.—This species is distinguished by the combination of characters afforded by the eyes, the antennal scale, and the telson. In having the terminal portion of the antennal scale barely extending beyond the terminal spine of the outer margin, *P. berkeleyi* differs from all the northern species of *Pseudomma*, *P. roseum*, *P. affine*, *P. truncatum*, and *P. frigidum*. In this character it agrees with *P. nanum* from the west coast of Ireland and *P. kruppi* from the Mediterranean. It differs from *P. nanum* in the much coarser teeth on the ocular plates and in having spines on the lateral margins of the telson. *P. kruppi* has smooth ocular plates and only a single pair of spines on the apex of the telson. *P. berkeleyi* is remarkable for the coarse character of the teeth on the ocular plates, and by the long and very stout spines arming the apex of the telson.

PSEUDOMMA sp. ?

Pseudomma sp. ESTERLY, 1914, p. 15.

Distribution.—Known only from San Diego, Calif.*.

Remarks.—Esterly (1914) recorded a female specimen of *Pseudomma* from California that is very closely allied to *P. berkeleyi*. The antennal scale is identical in both species, and the armature of the telson is closely similar. The ocular plate, to judge by Esterly's meager description and not too clear figure of the California specimen, appears to be more microscopically and more finely serrate than in the British Columbia species.

CAESAROMYSIDES LIGURIAE Colosi

Caesaromysides liguriae COLOSI, 1916, p. 138, fig. 1; 1919, p. 9; 1920, p. 242, pl. 18, figs. 5a-c.

Distribution.—The references in the synonymy, which all refer to the same material, record this species from the western coasts of South America, off Valparaiso*. This is the only known locality.

MYSIDOPSIS ACUTA Hansen

Mysidopsis acuta HANSEN, 1913a, p. 16, pl. 2, figs. 1a–1m; 1921, p. 3.

Distribution.—Falkland Islands*, 16 meters (Hansen, 1913); Tierra del Fuego*, 6 to 10 fathoms (Hansen, 1921).

Remarks.—This species is readily recognized by the very acutely pointed apex to the antennal scale. The telson is linguiform in shape, twice as long as broad at the base, without apical cleft, terminated by a single pair of long spines, lateral margins with 30 to 31 short spines extending along the entire margin from the base to the apex.

MYSIDOPSIS INERMIS Coifmann

Mysidopsis inermis COIFMANN, 1937, p. 8, fig. 4.

Distribution.—Known only from the original record from Guayas*.

Remarks.—This species is closely related to *M. californica* Tattersall, but it differs in the following characters: (1) The elongate form of the eye; (2) the absence of a distal joint to the antennal scale; (3) the absence of spines on the inner uropod.

METAMYSIDOPSIS PACIFICA (Zimmer)

Mysidopsis pacifica ZIMMER, 1918, p. 19, figs. 16–24.—COIFMANN, 1937, p. 11, fig. 6.

Distribution.—Known only from Callao, Chile*.

Remarks.—This species is very similar to *M. elongata* Holmes, from which it may be distinguished by the following characters: (1) The form of the telson, which has the apex much less convex and the spines terminating the lateral margins more sharply marked than in *M. elongata*. (2) The antennal peduncle, which is longer than the first joint of the scale, whereas in *M. elongata* it is shorter. (3) Absence of the three separate distal spines on the inner margin of the inner uropods.

Coifmann examined numerous specimens of this species from Callao, the type locality of the species, and finds that these differences are constant. She considers the differences sufficient to justify the separation of *M. pacifica* from *elongata*.

PROMYSIS ATLANTICA Tattersall

FIGURE 56

Promysis atlantica TATTERSALL, 1923, p. 286, pl. 1, figs. 5–6.

Distribution.—The type and only known specimen was taken off Rio de Janeiro. It has not again been recorded.

Remarks.—This Atlantic representative of the genus is closely allied to the type species, but it may be distinguished by the following characters:

(1) The eyes (fig. 56, *a*) are longer in proportion to their breadth (2¾ : 1), and the cornea is only half as long as the stalk. In *P. orientalis* the eye is 1½ times as long as broad, and the cornea is only slightly shorter than the stalk.

(2) The rostral plate (fig. 56, *a*) is shorter and more broadly rounded.

(3) The antennal scale (fig. 56, *a*) extends only to the middle of the third joint of the antennular peduncle. In *P. orientalis* it is slightly longer than the antennular peduncle.

(4) The cleft of the telson (fig. 56, *b*) is equal to one-seventh of the total length of the telson. In *P. orientalis* it is one-quarter.

(5) There are 18 spines on the lateral margin of the telson, confined to the distal three-fifths of the margin. In *P. orientalis* there are 12 spines occupying the distal five-sixths of the margin. In *P. atlantica*, therefore, there is a proportionately longer part of the margins of the telson unarmed, and the spines are more numerous and more crowded.

(6) The endopod of the uropods (fig. 56, *b*) is at least as long as, even slightly longer than, the exopod. It bears 16 spines on its inner margin, the two distal ones longer than the rest, slightly curved and situated at the apex. In *P. orientalis* the endopod of the uropods is slightly shorter than the exopod, though the arrangement of the spines is closely similar to that in *P. atlantica*.

DOXOMYSIS MICROPS Colosi

Doxomysis microps COLOSI, 1920, p. 249, pl. 20, figs. 9a–f.

Distribution.—The only known specimens were recorded by Colosi from the Galápagos Islands*.

MYSIDETES CRASSA Hansen

Mysidetes crassa HANSEN, 1913a, p. 18, pl. 2, figs. 3a–g; pl. 3, figs. 1a–c; 1921, p. 5.

Distribution.—Known only from a single immature specimen collected at Port Albemarle, Falkland Islands, in 40 meters*.

ARTHROMYSIS MAGELLANICA (Cunningham)

Macromysis magellanica CUNNINGHAM, 1871, p. 497.
Antarctomysis sp. ZIMMER, 1915b, p. 170.
Arthromysis chierchiae COLOSI, 1924, p. 4, figs. 1–3.

Distribution.—Known only from the Straits of Magellan, from which all the specimens referred to in the synonymy were collected.

Remarks.—This species was named by Cunningham in 1871 from specimens collected by H. M. S. *Nassau* in 1867 at the eastern entrance of the Strait of Magellan. Cunningham's description, which was not accompanied by any figures, is very inadequate, and beyond the one positive character, "terminal segment of pleon deeply bilobate," there is no way the species could be recognized. Learning that the *Nassau* collections were presented to the British Museum, I applied to Dr.

I. Gordon, who very kindly instituted a search for Cunningham's types and fortunately found them. They comprise four fully adult breeding females bearing eggs or embryos in the brood pouch, 24 to 27 mm. in length, in fairly good condition. An examination of this material at once showed that it belonged without any question of doubt, as indeed I had long suspected, to the species described in 1924 by Colosi as *Arthromysis chierchiae*, which must therefore now be known as *Arthromysis magellanica* (Cunningham). It is very gratifying to have this hitherto obscure species cleared up.

I think there is very little doubt that the specimen recorded by Zimmer (1915b) from the Strait of Magellan as *Antarctomysis* sp. belongs to the same species. Zimmer's remarks about the eye of his specimen are particularly significant, as the greatly elongate eye is one of the most striking features of this species.

Unfortunately there were no males in Cunningham's material, so the position of the genus in the classification must still remain obscure. Colosi comments on its superficial resemblance to certain species of the genus *Tenagomysis* and refers it to the tribe Leptomysini, but I believe its true position is that indicated by Zimmer's identification of his single specimen, i. e., in the tribe Mysini near *Antarctomysis*.

PRAUNUS FLEXUOSUS (O. F. Müller) [14]

Cancer flexuosus O. F. MÜLLER, 1776, p. 196, No. 2352.

Occurrence.—Channel Islands, France, 1884, E. Lovett collector, 8 males; Kiel Bay* (identified by Mobius); Guernsey* (identified by A. M. Norman); Baltic Sea*; Channel Island*; Helgoland*; Stockholm*; Plymouth*.

Distribution.—Atlantic coasts of Europe and the North Sea.

NEOMYSIS INTEGER (Leach) [14]

Praunus integer LEACH, 1814, p. 401.

Distribution.—Kiel Bay*, identified by Mobius; Helgoland*; Guernsey*, identified by A. M. Norman.

NEOMYSIS PATAGONA Zimmer

Neomysis patagona ZIMMER, 1907, p. 3, figs. 1–17.—HANSEN, 1913a, p. 21, pl. 3, figs. 3a–h; 1921, p. 5.—COIFMANN, 1937, p. 13, fig. 7.

Distribution.—Apparently not uncommon on the coast of Patagonia and the Falkland Islands*.

NEOMYSIS MERIDIONALIS Colosi

Neomysis meridionalis COLOSI, 1924, p. 5, figs. 4–6.

Distribution.—Known only from the original record of Colosi from the coast of Chile*.

---

[14] These records are based on specimens which are now included in the U. S. National Museum collection, but which were not seen by Dr. Tattersall.—ED.

NEOMYSIS MONTICELLI Colosi

Neomysis monticelli Colosi, 1924, p. 6, figs. 7–9.

Distribution.—Known only from the original record of Colosi from the Strait of Magellan*.

ACANTHOMYSIS SCULPTA (Tattersall)

FIGURES 83–85

Neomysis sculpta TATTERSALL, 1933, p. 17, figs. 9–11.

Distribution.—This species has so far been collected only on the coast of British Columbia.

Remarks.—This species may be recognized by the following characters:

(1) The somites of the pleon (fig. 83, *a, b*) are furnished with transverse ridges, which represent folds of the integument and give the impression that the somite is subdivided into subsidiary segments. There are three ridges on the first somite and two on each of the succeeding somites. The fourth abdominal somite has a posterior dorsal median spine. The fifth somite has a similar spine but in addition a prominent lateral spine on each side. The sixth abdominal somite has a median dorsal spine and, in addition, is furnished with an anterior median blunt plate and a posterior pair of blunt spines, with grooves and carinae.

(2) The carapace is produced in front into a short triangular rostral plate with a pointed apex; the anterolateral corners are rounded.

(3) The eyes (fig. 84, *a*) are large and prominent, pigment black, one and a third times as long as broad, cornea occupying about half of the eye.

(4) Antennal scale (fig. 84, *b*) is six times as long as broad with a distinct distal segment. The scale extends beyond the antennular peduncle for about one-third of its length.

(5) The endopods (fig. 85, *a*) of the third to the eighth thoracic limbs have the sixth joint divided into 7 or 8 subjoints.

(6) The telson (fig. 84, *d*) is linguiform, about three times as long as broad at the base. The apex is narrowly truncate and armed with two pairs of spines, the inner pair of which is longer than the outer. The lateral margins are armed throughout their length with about 50 spines, which, on the distal two-thirds of the margin, are arranged in groups of from 2 to 10 small spines between the larger spines.

(7) The inner uropod (fig. 85, *b*) has a group of seven spines on the inner margin near the statocyst.

(8) The fourth pleopod of the male (fig. 84, *c*) has the proximal joint of the exopod twice as long as the distal. The terminal setae

are short and stout and only about one-sixth of the length of the distal joint.

This species is most closely related to *A. costata* and to *A. stelleri*. All three are characterized by the folds of the integument on the pleon. *A. sculpta* is distinguished from the other two by the details of the ornamentation of the pleon, by the form of the telson, and by the structure of the fourth pleopod of the male.

ACANTHOMYSIS sp. ?

Neomysis sp. TATTERSALL, 1941, p. 6.

Distribution.—Known only from Magdalena Bay, Baja California, in 10 to 15 fathoms.

Remarks.—In 1941 I recorded the occurrence of two female specimens of a species of *Acanthomysis* from Baja California, which, in the absence of males, I could not satisfactorily determine, though suspecting that they probably represent a new species. The specimens come nearest to *Acanthomysis macropsis* (Tattersall), *A. pseudomacropsis* (Tattersall), and *A. columbiae* (Tattersall). They differ from the first two of these species in having more or less normal eyes without specially elongate eyestalks, and from the last of the above species in the absence of a supraocular spine on the anterior margin of the carapace. The carapace is broadly rounded anteriorly and somewhat vaulted, very similar to the condition seen in *A. pseudomacropsis* except that the rostral plate is perhaps more produced in relation to the anterolateral spines of the carapace. The telson resembles most closely that of *A. pseudomacropsis* in that the lateral margins are closely set with spines and the shape is lingular.

PRONEOMYSIS WAILESI Tattersall

FIGURES 93, 94

Proneomysis wailesi TATTERSALL, 1933, p. 21, figs. 12, 13.

Distribution.—This species is known only from the waters of British Columbia in 3 to 25 fathoms.

Remarks.—This species may be recognized by the following characters: (1) The carapace is hardly produced into a rostral plate, the anterior margin is broadly and evenly rounded, and the anterolateral corners are acute. (2) The eyes (fig. 93, *a*) are not elongate, are large and globose, cornea occupying much more than half the eye and wider than the stalk, pigment black. (3) The antennal scale (fig. 94, *a*) is very short, not longer than the antennular peduncle, five times as long as broad. (4) The labrum has a spinous process. (5) The endopods of the third to the eighth thoracic limbs (fig. 93, *b*) with the sixth joint divided into five subjoints. (6) The telson (fig. 93, c) is triangular, twice as long as broad at the base, apex narrowly truncate, almost rounded, and armed with two pairs of spines, the outer of which are twice as long as the inner; the lateral margins are armed along the distal part of their length only, by 25 spines grouped in series of one or two shorter spines between the longer spines. (7) The inner uropods have two spines on the inner lower margin near the statocyst. (8) The fourth pleopod of the male (fig. 94, b), with the exopod three-jointed, the proximal joint very long, four times as long as the combined length of the second and third joints, which are small and subequal; the third joint is terminated by two long barbed setae, which are nearly three times as long as the combined length of the last two joints of the exopod. (9) The fifth pleopod of the male (fig. 94, c) consists of a greatly elongated sympod terminated by an exceedingly long seta, which is nearly twice as long as the sympod and extends backward beyond the outer uropods.

HETEROMYSIS ANTILLENSIS Verrill

Heteromysis antillensis VERRILL, 1923, p. 184, pl. 49, fis. 2, *a–2, f*.

Distribution.—Dominica Island.

Remarks.—As mentioned above this species* is not recognizable from the description given by Verrill. It is probably synonymous with *H. bermudensis*, but this point must await solution until more material is available.

NEW GENERA, SPECIES, AND VARIETIES DESCRIBED HEREIN

Lophogaster americanus (p. 17)
Lophogaster japonicus (p. 19)
Siriella vulgaris var. *rostrata* (p. 63)
Siriella panamensis (p. 76)
Gastrosaccus philippinensis (p. 90)
Gastrosaccus mexicanus (p. 98)
Anchialina zimmeri (p. 103)
Meterythrops microphthalma (p. 113)
Gibberythrops philippinensis (p. 122)
Synerythrops cruciata (p. 124)
Amblyops ohlinii (p. 130)
Pseudomma oculospinum (p. 135)
Mysidopsis mortenseni (p. 145)
Metamysidopsis (p. 146)
Bathymysis renoculata (p. 153)
Pseudomysis dactylops (p. 157)
Inusitatomysis serrata (p. 160)
Stilomysis major (p. 177)
Mysidium integrum (p. 223)
Diamysis americana (p. 226)
Antromysis anophelinae (p. 230)

TABLE 9.—Albatross *dredging stations from which collections are reported*

Sta-tion No.	Locality	Date	Latitude			Longitude		
		1883	*North*			*West*		
			°	′	″	°	′	″
[1] 2034	Between Cape May and Nantucket_____	July 17	39	27	10	69	56	20
2036	_____do_____	July 18	38	52	40	69	24	40
2038	_____do_____	July 26	38	30	30	69	08	25
2039	_____do_____	July 28	38	19	26	68	20	20
2044	_____do_____	July 31	40	00	30	68	37	20
2045	_____do_____	___do_____	40	04	20	68	43	50
2046	_____do_____	___do_____	40	02	49	68	49	00
2047	_____do_____	___do_____	40	02	30	68	49	40
2072	Between Nantucket and Cape Sable, Nova Scotia_____	Sept. 2	41	53	00	65	35	00
2078	_____do_____	Sept. 4	41	11	30	66	12	20
2083	_____do_____	Sept. 5	40	26	40	67	05	15
2091	Between Cape Hatteras and Nantucket_____	Sept. 21	40	01	50	70	59	00
2094	_____do_____	___do_____	39	44	30	71	04	00
2095	_____do_____	Sept. 30	39	29	00	70	58	40
[2] 2096s	_____do_____	___do_____	39	22	20	70	52	20
2098	_____do_____	Oct. 1	37	40	30	70	37	30
2099	_____do_____	Oct. 2	37	12	20	69	39	00
2101	_____do_____	Oct. 3	39	18	30	68	24	00
2103	_____do_____	Nov. 5	38	47	20	72	37	00
2104	_____do_____	___do_____	38	48	00	72	40	30
2105	_____do_____	Nov. 6	37	50	00	73	03	50
		1884						
2117	Caribbean Sea_____	Jan. 27	15	24	40	63	31	30
2140	_____do_____	Mar. 11	17	36	10	76	46	05
2149	_____do_____	Apr. 4	13	01	30	81	25	00
2171	Between Cape Hatteras and Nantucket_____	July 20	37	59	30	73	48	40
2172	_____do_____	___do_____	38	01	15	73	44	00
2174s	_____do_____	July 21	38	15	00	72	03	00
2179	_____do_____	July 23	39	30	10	71	50	00
2180	_____do_____	___do_____	39	29	50	71	49	30
2182	_____do_____	___do_____	39	25	30	71	44	00
2186	_____do_____	Aug. 2	39	52	15	70	55	30
2187	_____do_____	Aug. 3	39	49	30	71	10	00
2190	_____do_____	Aug. 4	39	40	00	70	20	15
2192	_____do_____	Aug. 5	39	46	30	70	14	45
2193	_____do_____	___do_____	39	44	30	70	10	30
2195	_____do_____	___do_____	39	44	00	70	03	00
2201	_____do_____	Aug. 19	39	39	45	71	35	15
2202	_____do_____	___do_____	39	38	00	71	39	45
2203	_____do_____	___do_____	39	34	15	71	41	15
2210s	_____do_____	Aug. 21	39	37	45	71	18	45
2211	_____do_____	___do_____	39	35	00	71	18	00
2213	_____do_____	Aug. 22	39	58	30	70	30	00
2215	_____do_____	___do_____	39	49	15	70	31	45
2221	_____do_____	Sept. 6	39	05	30	70	44	30
2226	_____do_____	Sept. 10	37	00	00	71	54	00
2229	_____do_____	Sept. 11	37	38	40	73	16	30
2230	_____do_____	Sept. 12	38	27	00	73	02	00
2233	_____do_____	___do_____	38	36	30	73	06	00
2235	_____do_____	Sept. 13	39	12	00	72	03	30
2237	_____do_____	___do_____	39	12	17	72	09	30
2272	_____do_____	Oct. 19	35	20	10	75	14	00

[1] Townsend, C. H., Dredging and other records of the U. S. Fish Commission steamer *Albatross*, with bibliography relative to the work of the vessel. U. S. Fish Commission Report for 1900 [1901], pp. 393–419.

[2] Surface collections are denoted by an "s" following the station number.

TABLE 9.—Albatross *dredging stations from which collections are reported*—Con.

Station No.	Locality	Date	Latitude			Longitude		
		1885	° North ′ ″			° West ′ ″		
2314	Between Charleston and Savannah	Jan. 5	32	43	00	77	51	00
2351	Between Habana, Cuba, and Yucatán	Jan. 21	22	11	00	84	16	30
2383	Gulf of Mexico	Mar. 3	28	32	00	88	06	00
2384	_____do	___do____	28	45	00	88	15	30
2399	_____do	Mar. 14	28	44	00	86	18	00
2401	_____do	___do____	28	38	30	85	52	30
2402	_____do	___do____	28	36	00	85	33	30
2403	_____do	Mar. 15	28	42	30	85	29	00
2418	Between Savannah and Cape Charles	Apr. 2	33	20	00	77	05	00
2427	Off Newfoundland	June 23	42	46	00	51	00	00
2428	_____do	___do____	42	48	00	50	55	30
2429	_____do	___do____	42	55	30	50	51	00
2437	_____do	June 24	43	36	00	50	05	00
2453	_____do	June 26	47	10	00	51	02	00
2528	Between Cape Sable and Cape May	July 13	41	47	00	65	37	30
2535	_____do	July 15	40	03	30	67	27	15
2546	_____do	Aug. 8	39	53	30	70	17	30
2550	_____do	Aug. 9	39	44	30	70	30	45
2569s	_____do	Aug. 31	39	26	00	68	03	30
2585s	_____do	Sept. 19	39	08	30	72	17	00
2601	Between Cape Hatteras and Charleston, S. C	Oct. 18	34	39	15	75	33	30
2602	_____do	___do____	34	38	30	75	33	30
2603	_____do	___do____	34	38	30	75	33	30
		1886						
2642	Bahamas, Florida, and Cuba	Apr. 9	25	20	30	79	58	00
2654	_____do	May 2	27	57	30	77	27	30
2666	Between Bahamas and Cape Fear, N. C	May 5	30	47	30	79	49	00
2674	_____do	May 6	32	32	00	77	17	00
2689	Between Long Island and Nantucket	July 18	39	42	00	71	15	30
2709	Between Cape Breton and Nantucket	Aug. 28	40	07	00	67	54	00
2715	Between Nantucket and Cape Charles	Sept. 18	38	29	30	70	54	30
2716	_____do	___do____	38	29	30	70	57	00
2723	_____do	Oct. 23	36	47	00	73	09	30
2728s	_____do	Oct. 25	36	30	00	74	33	00
2729	_____do	___do____	36	36	00	74	32	00
2734	_____do	Oct. 26	37	23	00	73	53	00
		1887						
2741	Between Cape Charles and Long Island	Sept. 17	37	44	00	73	57	00
2742s	_____do	___do____	37	46	30	73	56	30
2748	_____do	Sept. 19	39	31	00	71	14	30
2751	_____do	Nov. 28	16	54	00	63	12	00
		1888						
2839	Santa Barbara Islands, Calif	May 8	33	08	00	118	40	00
2842	Between Unalaska and Cook Inlet	July 23	54	15	00	166	03	00
2859	Between Sitka and Columbia River	Aug. 29	55	20	00	136	20	00
2860	_____do	Aug. 31	51	23	00	130	34	00
2861	_____do	___do____	51	14	00	129	50	00
2863	_____do	Sept. 5	48	58	00	123	10	00
2883	Off Oregon	Oct. 18	45	56	00	124	01	30
2884	_____do	___do____	45	55	00	124	02	00
2890	_____do	Oct. 19	43	46	00	124	57	00

TABLE 9.—Albatross *dredging stations from which collections are reported*—Con.

Station No.	Locality	Date	Latitude North ° ′ ″	Longitude West ° ′ ″
		1889		
2892	Off southern California	Jan. 5	34 15 00	120 36 00
2896	----do	Jan. 6	33 55 30	120 28 00
2919	----do	Jan. 17	32 17 00	119 17 00
2923	----do	Jan. 19	32 40 30	117 31 30
2925	----do	---do----	32 32 30	117 24 00
2927	----do	Jan. 23	32 43 00	117 51 00
2928	----do	---do----	32 47 30	118 10 00
2929	----do	Jan. 26	32 27 30	117 26 30
2936	----do	Feb. 4	32 49 00	117 27 30
2937	----do	---do----	33 04 30	117 42 00
2980	----do	Feb. 12	33 49 45	119 24 30
2986	Off Baja California	Feb. 28	28 57 00	118 14 30
2992	Revillagigedo Islands	Mar. 6	18 17 30	114 43 15
3071	Off Oregon and Washington	June 28	47 29 00	125 33 30
3073	----do	---do----	47 28 00	125 15 00
3074	----do	June 29	47 22 00	125 48 30
3075	----do	---do----	47 22 00	125 41 00
		1890		
3112	Off central California	Mar. 12	37 08 00	122 47 00
3126	----do	Mar. 13	36 49 20	122 12 30
3127	----do	---do----	36 45 00	122 10 20
3128	----do	---do----	36 41 50	122 07 30
3162	----do	Mar. 22	37 54 10	123 30 00
3211	South of Alaska	May 21	54 02 00	162 52 00
3227	Bering Sea	May 23	54 36 30	166 54 00
3235	----do	June 7	58 16 30	158 13 00
3236	----do	---do----	58 11 00	158 05 30
3239	----do	June 8	58 22 20	159 23 15
3240	----do	---do----	58 30 00	159 35 50
3241	----do	---do----	58 38 30	159 33 30
3243	----do	---do----	58 45 10	160 28 00
3307	----do	Aug. 3	53 55 00	170 50 00
3308	----do	Aug. 4	56 12 00	172 07 00
3315	----do	Aug. 15	54 02 40	166 42 00
3316	----do	Aug. 16	54 01 00	166 48 45
3324	----do	Aug. 20	53 33 50	167 46 50
3325	----do	---do----	53 37 10	167 50 10
3326	----do	---do----	53 40 25	167 41 40
3327	----do	---do----	53 43 40	167 29 30
3329	----do	Aug. 21	53 56 50	167 08 15
3330	----do	---do----	54 00 45	166 53 50
3331	----do	---do----	54 01 40	166 48 50
3332	----do	---do----	54 02 50	166 45 00
3337	Unalaska to Kodiak	Aug. 27	53 55 30	163 26 00
3340	----do	Aug. 29	55 26 00	155 26 00
3342	Off British Columbia	Sept. 3	52 39 30	132 38 00
3343	Off Washington	Sept. 21	47 40 40	125 20 00
3346	----do	Sept. 22	45 30 00	124 52 00
3348	Off northern California	Sept. 25	39 02 40	124 06 15
		1891		
3361	Off Panama	Feb. 25	6 10 00	83 06 00
			South	
3400	Off Galápagos Islands	Mar. 27	0 36 00	86 46 00
3406	----do	Apr. 3	0 16 00	90 21 30

TABLE 9.—Albatross *dredging stations from which collections are reported*—Con.

Sta-tion No.	Locality	Date	Latitude			Longitude		
		1891	*North*			*West*		
			°	′	″	°	′	″
3411	Off Galápagos Islands	Apr. 4	0	54	00	91	09	00
3413	____do	Apr. 5	2	34	00	92	06	00
3420	Off Mexico	Apr. 12	16	46	00	100	08	20
3425	____do	Apr. 18	21	19	00	106	24	00
3444	Off Washington	Aug. 27	48	16	30	123	29	40
3459	____do	Sept. 2	48	24	20	124	24	40
3467	Hawaiian Islands	Dec. 3	21	13	00	157	43	37
3473	____do	Dec. 6	21	15	00	157	30	00
3475	____do	___do	21	08	00	157	43	00
		1893						
3486	Bering Sea	July 13	57	19	00	173	53	00
3488	____do	___do	57	05	00	173	47	00
3514	____do	Aug. 2	59	22	00	168	21	00
3548	____do	Sept. 1	54	44	00	165	42	00
		1894						
3600	____do	June 26	55	06	00	163	28	00
		1895						
3603	____do	Aug. 11	55	23	00	170	31	00
3604	____do	Aug. 12	54	54	00	168	59	00
3607	____do	Aug. 18	54	11	30	167	25	00
3608	____do	Aug. 20	55	19	00	168	11	00
		1896						
3627	West of Cortez and Tanner Banks	Apr. 13	32	44	00	119	32	00
		1897						
3669	Monterey Bay and vicinity	Apr. 16	36	47	00	122	11	00
3670	____do	Apr. 17	36	43	00	122	12	00
		1899						
3681	Off San Francisco	Aug. 27	28	23	00	126	57	00
		1900						
3696	Manazuru Zaki, off Honshu Island, Japan	May 5						
3697	____do	___do						
3707	Ose Zaki, off Honshu Island, Japan	May 8						
3710	Entrance to Port Heda, off Honshu Island, Japan	May 10						
3714	Ose Zaki, off Honshu Island, Japan	May 11						
3715	____do	___do						
3717	____do	___do						
3718	____do	___do						
3740	____do	May 17						
3783	Copper Island, off Kamchatka	June 25						
						East		
3784	North of Aleutian Islands	June 27	54	32	00	178	31	00
		1902				*West*		
[3] 3797	Hawaiian Islands	Mar. 17	31	55	00	136	00	00
3799	____do	Mar. 18	29	22	00	139	31	00
3801	____do	Mar. 19	28	31	00	141	47	00
3802	____do	Mar. 20	27	04	15	144	18	30
3812	South coast of Oahu Island, Hawaiian Islands	Mar. 27						

[3] Townsend, C. H., Records of the dredging and other collecting stations of the U. S. Fish Commission steamer *Albatross* in 1901 and 1902. U. S. Fish Commission Report for 1902 [1903], pp. 401–431.

TABLE 9.—Albatross *dredging stations from which collections are reported*—Con.

Sta-tion No.	Locality	Date	Latitude North ° ′ ″	Longitude West ° ′ ″
		1902		
3824	South coast of Molokai Island, Hawaiian Islands_____	Apr. 1		
3826	____do_____	___do____		
3829	_____do_____	{Apr. 1} {Apr. 2}		
3847	_____do_____	Apr. 8		
3857	Pailolo Channel, Hawaiian Islands_____	Apr. 9		
3858	_____do_____	___do____		
3867	_____do_____	Apr. 10		
3884	_____do_____	Apr. 16		
3887	North coast of Molokai Island, Hawaiian Islands_____	Apr. 17		
3889	_____do_____	___do____		
3907	South coast of Oahu Island, Hawaiian Islands_____	May 5		
3908	_____do_____	___do____		
3909	_____do_____	___do____		
3911	_____do_____	___do____		
3912	_____do_____	___do____		
3921	_____do_____	May 6		
3925	_____do_____	May 7		
3926	Between Honolulu and Laysan Islands, Hawaiian Islands__	May 10	21 13 00	158 43 00
3927	_____do_____	May 11	21 31 00	161 55 00
3929	_____do_____	May 13	23 19 00	166 54 00
3930	_____do_____	May 15	25 07 00	170 50 00
3965	Vicinity of Laysan Island, Hawaiian Islands_____	May 23		
3980	Between Honolulu and Kauai Island, Hawaiian Islands_____	June 9	21 23 00	158 19 00
4005	_____do_____	June 17		
4009	Between Kauai and Oahu Islands, Hawaiian Islands_____	___do____	21 50 30	159 15 00
4011	_____do_____	June 18	21 20 00	158 21 00
4014	Vicinity of Kaui Island, Hawaiian Islands_____	June 20		
4018	_____do_____	June 21		
4038	West coast of Hawaii Island, Hawaiian Islands_____	July 10		
4086	Puniawa Point, north coast of Maui Island, Hawaiian Islands_____	July 21		
4101	Pailolo Channel, between Maui and Molokai Islands, Hawaiian Islands_____	July 23		
4105	Kaiwi Channel, between Molokai and Oahu Islands, Hawaiian Islands_____	July 24		
4106	_____do_____	___do____		
4107	_____do_____	___do____		
4109	_____do_____	___do____		
4142	Vicinity of Kauai Island, Hawaiian Islands_____	Aug. 2		
4144	_____do_____	___do____		
4145s	Between Kaui and Bird Islands, Hawaiian Islands_____	Aug. 4		
4166	Bird Island, Hawaiian Islands_____	Aug. 8		
		1903		
⁴ 4192	Gulf of Georgia, Vancouver Island, B. C._____	June 19		
4251	Stephens Passage, Alaska_____	July 14		
4257	Clear Point, Lynn Canal, Alaska_____	July 23		
4264	Off Freshwater Bay, Chatham Strait, Alaska_____	July 25		
4267	Cape Edgecumbe, off Sitka Sound, Alaska_____	July 31		
4272	Point Lipsett, Afognak Island, Alaska_____	Aug. 3		
		1904		
⁵ 4307	Point Loma Lighthouse, vicinity of San Diego, Calif._____	Mar. 2		
4317	_____do_____	Mar. 5		

⁴ Fassett, Harry C., Records of the dredging and other collecting and hydrographic stations of the U. S. Fisheries steamer *Albatross* in 1903. U. S. Fish Commission Report for 1903 [1904], pp. 124–134.

⁵ Fassett, Harry C., Dredging and hydrographic records of the U. S. Fisheries steamer *Albatross* for 1904 and 1905. Bur. Fish. Doc. No. 604, 1906, pp. 10–79.

TABLE 9.—Albatross *dredging stations from which collections are reported*—Con.

Station No.	Locality	Date	Latitude			Longitude		
		1904	° *North* ′ ″			° *West* ′ ″		
4334	Point Loma Lighthouse, vicinity of San Diego, Calif_____	Mar. 9						
4335	____do_____	___do____						
4337	____do_____	Mar. 10						
4351	____do_____	Mar. 14						
4352	____do_____	___do____						
4353	____do_____	___do____						
4354	____do_____	___do____						
4379	North Coronado Island, vicinity of San Diego, Calif_____	Mar. 18						
4380	____do_____	___do____						
4383	____do_____	___do____						
4389	Point Loma Lighthouse, vicinity of San Diego, Calif_____	Mar. 24						
4390	Off Santa Catalina Island, Calif_____	Mar. 28	33	02	15	120	42	00
4393	____do_____	Mar. 30	32	54	20	121	11	15
4397	____do_____	Apr. 1	33	10	15	121	42	15
4399	Vicinity of San Diego, Calif_____	Apr. 7	32	44	50	117	48	45
4400	____do_____	Apr. 8	32	50	20	118	03	30
4401	____do_____	___do____	32	52	40	118	13	40
4403	San Clemente Island, Calif_____	___do____						
4405	____do_____	Apr. 9						
4406	Santa Catalina Island, Calif_____	___do____						
4407	____do_____	___do____						
4415	Santa Barbara Island, Calif_____	Apr. 11						
4423	San Nicolas Island, Calif_____	Apr. 13						
4427	Point San Pedro, Santa Cruz Island, Calif_____	Apr. 14						
4428	____do_____	___do____						
4429	Gull Islet, off Santa Cruz Island, Calif_____	___do____						
4435	San Miguel Island, Calif_____	Apr. 15						
4440	Point Pinos Lighthouse, Monterey Bay, Calif_____	May 10						
4441	____do_____	___do____						
4461	____do_____	May 12						
4493	Santa Cruz Lighthouse, Monterey Bay, Calif_____	May 18						
4513	Point Pinos Lighthouse, Monterey Bay, Calif_____	May 23						
4515	____do_____	___do____						
4516	____do_____	May 24						
4522	____do_____	May 26						
4528	____do_____	May 27						
4529	____do_____	___do____						
4533	____do_____	May 28						
4536	____do_____	May 31						
4537	____do_____	___do____						
4540	____do_____	June 1						
4541	____do_____	___do____						
4544	____do_____	June 2						
4571	Santa Rosa Island, Calif_____	Oct. 7	33	40	00	119	35	00
4576	West coast of Baja California_____	Oct. 8	29	52	00	116	56	00
4592	Southwest coast of Mexico_____	Oct. 13	18	17	30	103	35	00
4607	Southwest coast of Central America_____	Oct. 171	2	00	00	91	30	00
4615	_____do_____	Oct. 19	9	06	00	85	08	00
4617	South coast of Panama_____	Oct. 20	7	21	00	82	21	00
4619	_____do_____	___do____	7	17	00	82	11	00
4627	Between Panama and Galápagos Islands_____	Nov. 2	7	21	00	79	56	00
4635	_____do_____	Nov. 4	3	52	30	84	15	00
				South				
4640	Mt. Pitt, Chatham Island_____	Nov. 6	0	40	00	88	11	00
4641	Hood Island, Galápagos Islands_____	Nov. 7	1	35	00	89	30	00
4645	Between Galápagos Islands and Peru_____	Nov. 8	3	37	30	89	43	00
4646	_____do_____	___do____	4	02	00	89	16	00

TABLE 9.—Albatross *dredging stations from which collections are reported*—Con.

Station No.	Locality	Date	Latitude			Longitude		
		1904	*South*			*West*		
			°	′	″	°	′	″
4648	Between Galápagos Islands and Peru	Nov. 9	4	43	00	87	07	30
4650	____do	Nov. 10	5	21	00	84	39	00
4651	Aguja Point, Peru	Nov. 11	5	42	00	83	00	00
4652	____do	___do	5	45	00	82	40	00
4653	____do	Nov. 12	5	47	00	81	24	00
4655	____do	___do	5	57	30	81	50	00
4656	Off Peru	Nov. 13	6	55	00	83	34	00
4657	____do	___do	7	12	30	84	09	00
4664	____do	Nov. 17	11	30	00	87	19	00
4667	____do	Nov. 18	12	00	00	83	40	00
4668	____do	Nov. 19	12	09	00	81	45	00
4671	Palominos Lighthouse, Peru	Nov. 20	12	07	00	78	28	00
4672	____do	Nov. 21	13	11	30	78	18	00
4675	____do	Nov. 22	12	54	00	78	33	00
4676	Between Callao, Peru, and Easter Island	Dec. 5	14	29	00	81	24	00
4677	____do	___do	14	37	30	81	41	00
4678	____do	Dec. 6	16	31	00	85	04	00
4679	____do	Dec. 7	17	26	00	86	46	00
4682	____do	Dec. 8	19	07	30	90	10	00
4683	____do	Dec. 9	20	02	30	91	52	30
4685	____do	Dec. 10	21	36	00	94	56	00
4688	____do	Dec. 11	23	17	00	98	37	30
4692	Sala y Gomez Island, between Peru and Easter Island	Dec. 13	25	40	30	104	01	00
4694	North Cape, Easter Island	Dec. 22	26	34	00	108	57	30
4695	____do	Dec. 23	25	22	30	107	45	00
4696	Between Easter and Galápagos Islands	___do	24	40	00	107	05	00
4698	____do	Dec. 24	22	50	00	105	32	00
4700	____do	Dec. 25	20	29	00	103	26	00
4702	____do	Dec. 26	18	40	00	102	00	00
4704	____do	Dec. 27	16	55	00	100	25	00
4706	____do	Dec. 28	14	19	00	98	46	00
4709	____do	Dec. 30	10	15	00	95	41	00
4710	____do	___do	9	30	00	95	08	00
		1905						
4715	Hood Island, Galápagos Islands	Jan. 2	2	40	30	90	19	00
4716	____do	___do	2	18	30	90	02	30
4717	Between Galápagos and Paumotu Islands	Jan. 13	5	11	00	98	56	00
4718	____do	___do	5	32	30	99	32	00
4719	____do	Jan. 14	6	30	00	101	17	00
4720	____do	___do	7	13	00	102	31	30
4721	____do	Jan. 15	8	07	30	104	10	00
4723	____do	Jan. 16	10	14	00	107	45	00
4724	____do	Jan. 17	11	13	30	109	29	00
4725	____do	___do	11	38	00	110	05	00
4727	____do	Jan. 18	13	00	00	112	45	00
4729	____do	Jan. 19	14	15	00	115	13	00
4733	____do	Jan. 21	16	57	30	120	48	00
4734	____do	Jan. 22	17	36	00	122	15	00
4741	Between Paumotu Islands and Acapulco, Mexico	Feb. 11	8	29	00	122	56	00
			North					
4753	Bushy Point, between Yes Bay and Seattle	Oct. 1	55	41	30	131	46	12
4756	West Point Light, between Yes Bay and Seattle	Nov. 16	47	37	48	122	26	20

TABLE 9.—Albatross *dredging stations from which collections are reported*—Con.

Station No.	Locality	Date	Latitude			Longitude		
		1906	°North'	'	''	°West'	'	''
[6] 4759	Cape St. James, Queen Charlotte Islands_____	May 20	53	05	00	138	31	00
4760	Between Union Bay, British Columbia, and Dutch Harbor, Alaska_____	May 21	53	53	00	144	53	00
4763	Bogoslof Islands, Aleutian Islands_____	May 28	53	57	00	168	06	00
4765	Yunaska Island, between Dutch Harbor, Alaska, and Aleutian Islands_____	May 29	53	12	00	171	37	00
4766	Koniuji Island, vicinity of Aleutian Islands_____	May 31	52	38	00	174	49	00
						East		
4767	Bering Sea_____	June 3	54	12	00	179	07	30
4775	____do__	June 4	54	33	30	178	44	00
4780	Between "Petrel Bank," Bering Sea, and Agattu, Aleutian Islands_____	June 7	52	10	00	174	39	00
4781	____do__	___do____	52	14	30	174	13	00
4785	Vicinity of Attu Island_____	June 12	53	20	00	170	33	00
4788	Copper Island_____	June 14	54	50	24	167	13	00
4793	Bering Island_____	June 16	54	48	00	164	54	00
4800	Chirinkotan Island, Sea of Okhotsk_____	June 22	49	06	00	153	06	00
4815	Sea of Japan__	July 18	38	16	00	138	52	00
4816	____do__	___do____	38	14	00	138	54	00
4817	____do__	___do____	38	12	00	138	52	00
4861	____do__	July 31	36	19	00	129	47	00
4862	____do__	___do____	36	20	00	129	50	00
4867	____do__	Aug. 1	36	31	00	129	46	00
4891	Ose Saki Light, Eastern Sea_____	Aug. 9	32	27	00	128	34	00
4903	____do__	Aug. 10	32	31	10	128	33	20
4905	Tsurikake Saki Light, Eastern Sea_____	Aug. 11	31	39	00	129	19	00
4906	____do__	___do____	31	39	00	129	20	30
4907	____do__	___do____	31	39	30	129	24	00
4908	____do__	___do____	31	40	00	129	29	40
4909	____do__	___do____	31	38	30	129	27	30
4911	____do__	Aug. 12	31	38	30	129	19	00
4912	____do__	___do____	31	39	40	129	20	00
4913	____do__	___do____	31	39	10	129	22	30
4914	____do__	___do____	31	33	00	129	26	30
4915	____do__	___do____	31	31	00	129	25	30
4919	____do__	Aug. 13	30	34	00	129	19	30
4944	Kagoshima Gulf, Japan_____	Aug. 17	31	38	15	130	46	50
4953	____do__	Aug. 22	31	39	00	132	54	40
4954	____do__	___do____	32	05	00	133	02	00
4956	____do__	Aug. 23	32	32	00	132	25	00
4960	____do__	___do____	32	34	00	132	21	45
4988	Sea of Japan_____	Sept. 20	42	23	10	140	21	10
5003	Saghalin Island, Okhotsk Sea_____	Sept. 23	47	32	30	141	45	00
5015	____do__	Sept. 26	46	44	00	144	02	00
5030	Okhotsk Sea_____	Sept. 29	46	29	30	145	46	00
5050	Between Hakodate and Yokohama, Japan_____	Oct. 10	38	11	00	142	08	00
5060	Ose Saki, Suruga Gulf, Japan_____	Oct. 13	35	06	00	138	40	10
5063	____do____	___do____	35	01	10	138	38	50
5082	Omai Saki Light, Japan_____	Oct. 20	34	05	00	137	59	00
5091	Uraga Strait, Japan_____	Oct. 26	35	04	10	139	38	12
		1908						
[7] 5115	Sombrero Island, Philippine Islands_____	Jan. 20	13	37	11	120	43	40
5121	Malabrigo Light, east coast of Mindoro, Philippine Islands___	Feb. 2	13	27	20	121	17	45

[6] Fassett, Harry C., Dredging and hydrographic records of the U. S. Fisheries steamer *Albatross* for 1906. Bur. Fish. Doc. No. 621, 1907, pp. 8–49.

[7] Fassett, Harry C., Dredging and hydrographic records of the U. S. Fisheries steamer *Albatross*, during the Philippine Expedition, 1907–10. Bur. Fish. Doc. No. 741, 1910, pp. 14–97.

TABLE 9.—Albatross *dredging stations from which collections are reported*—Con.

Sta-tion No.	Locality	Date	Latitude	Longitude
		1908	*North* ° ′ ″	*East* ° ′ ″
5195s	Capitancillo Island Light, off northern Cebu, Philippine Islands	Apr. 3	10 47 00	124 06 30
5219	Mompog Island, between Marinduque and Luzon, Philippine Islands	{Apr. 23 {Apr. 24	13 21 00	122 18 45
5233	Between Bohol and Leyte, Philippine Islands	May 7	10 00 22	124 45 06
5238	Point Lambajon, east coast of Mindanao, Philippine Islands	{May 12 {May 13	7 34 45	126 38 15
5287	Sombrero Island, China Sea	July 20	13 37 40	120 39 00
5288	Matocot Point, Luzon, Philippine Islands	July 22	13 43 30	121 00 00
5299	China Sea, vicinity of southern Luzon	Aug. 8	20 05 00	116 05 00
5320	China sea, vicinity of Formosa	Nov. 6	20 58 00	120 03 00
5321	Ibugos Island, China Sea, vicinity of Formosa	Nov. 9	20 19 30	121 51 15
		1909		
5359	Jolo Sea, Philippine Islands	Jan. 9	8 12 45	120 37 15
5364	Cape Santiago Light, Balayan Bay, Luzon, Philippine Islands	Feb. 20	13 48 30	120 43 45
5422s	Between Panay and Guimaras, Philippine Islands	Mar. 30	10 31 00	122 18 45
5435s	Biscuay Island, Cuyos Islands, Philippine Islands	Apr. 9	10 50 00	120 58 10
5438	Hermana Mayor Light, west coast of Luzon, Philippine Islands	May 8	15 54 42	119 44 42
5449	East Point, Batan Island, east coast of Luzon, Philippine Islands	June 4	13 21 36	124 00 30
5456s	Legaspi Light, east coast of Luzon, Philippine Islands	June 7	13 11 10	123 51 52
5463	Sialat Point Light, east coast of Luzon, Philippine Islands	June 16	13 40 57	123 57 45
5466	Atulayan Island, east coast of Luzon, Philippine Islands	June 17	13 38 36	123 41 45
5468	____do____	June 18	13 35 39	123 40 28
5471	Sialat Point Light, east coast of Luzon, Philippine Islands	June 19	13 34 57	123 47 06
5498	Bantigue Island, between Leyte and Mindanao, Philippine Islands	Aug. 3	9 07 15	124 59 30
5500	Macabalan Point Light, Mindanao, Philippine Islands	Aug. 4	8 37 45	124 35 45
5540s	Apo Island, between Negros and Siquijor, Philippine Islands	Aug. 19	9 03 00	123 24 30
5544	Coronado Point, Mindanao, Philippine Islands	Sept. 6	8 16 30	122 26 30
5550	Jolo Light, Jolo Island, Philippine Islands	Sept. 17	6 02 00	120 44 40
5568s	Singaan Island, north of Tawi Tawi, Philippine Islands	Sept. 21	5 45 50	120 26 00
5595s	Off Zamboanga, Mindanao, Philippine Islands	Oct. 6	6 54 00	122 04 30
5596s	____do____	Oct. 10	6 54 00	122 04 30
5597s	____do____	Oct. 12	6 54 00	122 04 30
5601	Gulf of Tomini, Celebes	Nov. 13	1 13 10	125 17 05
			South	
5611s	____do____	Nov. 19	0 40 30	121 50 00
			North	
5618	Mareh Island, Molucca Passage	Nov. 27	0 37 00	127 15 00
5619	____do____	---do----	0 35 00	127 14 40
			South	
5628	St. Lamo Island, Patiente Strait	{Nov. 30 {Dec. 1	0 28 30	127 45 00
5630	Doworra Island, south of Patiente Strait	Dec. 2	0 56 30	128 05 00
5631	____do____	---do----	0 57 00	127 56 00
5637	Amblau Island, vicinity of Bouro Island	Dec. 10	3 53 20	126 48 00
5638	Tifu Bay, vicinity of Bouro Island	{Dec. 10 {Dec. 11	3 47 15	126 23 40
5650	Lamulu Point, Gulf of Boni	Dec. 17	4 53 45	121 29 00

TABLE 9.—Albatross *dredging stations from which collections are reported*—Con.

Station No.	Locality	Date	Latitude	Longitude
		1909	° ′ ″ *South*	° ′ ″ *East*
5655	Cape Tabako, Gulf of Boni	Dec. 18	3 34 10	120 50 30
5667	Onkona Point, Macassar Strait	Dec. 29	2 56 00	118 47 30
5669s	Mamuju Island, Macassar Strait	---do----	2 19 30	118 50 00
5670	Chenoki Point, Macassar Strait	Dec. 30	1 19 00	118 43 00
		1912		
[8] 5712	Lime Point, San Francisco Bay	Feb. 16		
5735	Bonita Point Light, San Francisco Bay	Mar. 11		
5761	Point Edith Beacon, San Francisco Bay, Calif	Apr. 2		
5764	Pt. Campbell, San Francisco Bay, Calif	Apr. 3		
5777	Fort Point Light, San Francisco Bay, Calif	Apr. 17		
5778	----do	---do----		
5797	Angel Island, San Francisco Bay, Calif	Oct. 29		
5798	----do	---do----		
5799	----do	---do----		
5803	Mission Rock, San Francisco Bay, Calif	Oct. 30		
5805	Vicinity of Shag Rock, San Francisco Bay, Calif	---do----		
5822	Vicinity of Brothers Light, San Francisco Bay, Calif	Dec. 17		
		1913		
5828	Vicinity of Southampton Light, San Francisco Bay, Calif	Jan. 20		
5830	Vicinity of Alcatraz Light, San Francisco Bay, Calif	Jan. 21		

[8] Dredging and hydrographic records of the U. S. Fisheries steamer *Albatross*, 1911-20. Bur. Fish. Doc. No. 897, 1921, pp. 22-65.

TABLE 10.—Albatross *hydrographic stations from which collections are reported*

Station No.	Locality	Date	Latitude	Longitude
		1891	° ′ ″ *North*	° ′ ″ *West*
[1] H2619	Off west coast South America and Mexico	Mar. 11	7 31 00	78 42 30
H2627	----do	Mar. 25	0 36 00	82 45 00
H2670	Between California and Hawaiian Islands	Oct. 11	36 47 34	121 50 20
H2682	----do	---do----	36 43 00	122 17 00
H2728	----do	Oct. 16	33 04 30	133 56 30
H2788	----do	Nov. 8	32 35 00	135 03 00
H2820	----do	Nov. 11	30 23 00	140 26 30
		1896		*East*
H3710	Sea of Okhotsk	Sept. 6	45 18 00	147 31 00
		1899		*West*
H3784	California to Marquesas Islands	Sept. 2	16 52 00	136 12 00
		1912		
[2] H4988	Upper section of San Francisco Bay	Feb. 20		
H4989	----do	---do----		
H4990	----do	---do----		

[1] Townsend, C. H., Dredging and other records of the U. S. Fish Commission steamer *Albatross*, with bibliography relative to the work of the vessel. U. S. Fish Commission Report for 1900 [1901], pp. 454-471.

[2] Dredging and hydrographic records of the U. S. Fisheries steamer *Albatross*, 1911-20. Bur. Fish. Doc. No. 897, 1921, pp. 22-65.

TABLE 10.—Albatross *hydrographic stations from which collections are reported—*
Continued

Station No.	Locality	Date	Latitude	Longitude
		1912	*North* ° ′ ″	*West* ° ′ ″
H4991	Upper section of San Francisco Bay	Feb. 20		
H4992	_____do_____	Feb. 21		
H4995	Middle section of San Francisco Bay	___do____		
H4996	_____do_____	___do____		
H4997	_____do_____	___do____		
H4998	_____do_____	___do____		
H5000	_____do_____	___do____		
H5003	Lower section of San Francisco Bay	Feb. 23		
H5005	_____do_____	___do____		
H5007	_____do_____	___do____		
H5008	_____do_____	___do____		
H5011	_____do_____	Feb. 27		
H5012	_____do_____	___do____		
H5013	_____do_____	___do____		
H5082	Upper section of San Francisco Bay	Apr. 23		
H5084	_____do_____	___do____		
H5085	_____do_____	___do____		
H5090	Lower section of San Francisco Bay	Apr. 26		
H5091	_____do_____	___do____		
H5097	Middle section of San Francisco Bay	Apr. 29		
H5098	_____do_____	___do____		
H5099	_____do_____	___do____		
H5100	_____do_____	___do____		
H5101	_____do_____	___do____		
H5106	Upper section of San Francisco Bay	Apr. 30		
H5107	_____do_____	___do____		
H5110	_____do_____	___do____		
H5113	Lower section of San Francisco Bay	May 1		
H5114	_____do_____	Apr. 30		
H5115	_____do_____	May 1		
H5120	Middle section of San Francisco Bay	May 6		
H5122	_____do_____	___do____		
H5123	_____do_____	___do____		
H5125	_____do_____	___do____		
H5126	_____do_____	___do____		
H5127	_____do_____	___do____		
H5128	_____do_____	May 14		
H5130	_____do_____	July 22		
H5133	_____do_____	___do____		
H5136	_____do_____	___do____		
H5137	_____do_____	___do____		
H5138	Lower section of San Francisco Bay	July 23		
H5140	_____do_____	___do____		
H5141	_____do_____	___do____		
H5146	Upper section of San Francisco Bay	July 24		
H5147	_____do_____	___do____		
H5149	_____do_____	___do____		
H5151	Middle section of San Francisco Bay	July 29		
H5152	_____do_____	___do____		
H5154	_____do_____	___do____		
H5155	_____do_____	___do____		
H5159	Lower section of San Francisco Bay	July 30		
H5166	Upper section of San Francisco Bay	July 31		
H5168	_____do_____	___do____		
H5172	_____do_____	___do____		
H5177	_____do_____	Oct. 7		
H5184	Lower section of San Francisco Bay	Oct. 8		
H5186	_____do_____	___do____		

TABLE 10.—Albatross *hydrographic stations from which collections are reported*—
Continued

Station No.	Locality	Date	Latitude	Longitude
		1912	*North* ° ′ ″	*West* ° ′ ″
H5188	Middle section of San Francisco Bay	Oct. 9		
H5190	____do	___do		
H5193	____do	___do		
H5195	____do	___do		
H5196	Upper section of San Francisco Bay	Oct. 10		
H5198	____do	___do		
H5199	____do	___do		
H5211	Middle section of San Francisco Bay	Oct. 12		
H5216	____do	___do		
H5219	Outside Golden Gate, San Francisco Bay	Oct. 15		
H5228	Middle section of San Francisco Bay	Nov. 4		
H5232	Lower section of San Francisco Bay	Nov. 11		
H5242	Upper section of San Francisco Bay	Nov. 26		
H5244	____do	___do		
H5245	____do	___do		
H5246	____do	___do		
H5247	____do	___do		
H5248	Lower section of San Francisco Bay	Nov. 27		
H5249	____do	___do		
H5255	____do	___do		
H5257	____do	___do		
H5261	____do	___do		
H5264	Upper section of San Francisco Bay	Dec. 3		
H5266	____do	___do		
H5267	____do	___do		
H5273	Lower section of San Francisco Bay	Dec. 4		
H5274	____do	___do		
H5275	____do	___do		
H5277	Middle section of San Francisco Bay	Dec. 5		
H5282	____do	___do		
		1913		
H5286	Upper section of San Francisco Bay	Jan. 13		
H5287	____do	___do		
H5288	____do	___do		
H5291	____do	___do		
H5292	____do	___do		
H5298	Middle section of San Francisco Bay	Jan. 20		
H5299	____do	___do		
H5300	____do	___do		
H5301	____do	___do		
H5302	____do	___do		
H5303	____do	___do		
H5304	____do	___do		
H5305	Lower section of San Francisco Bay	Jan. 21		
H5306	____do	___do		
H5307	____do	___do		
H5310	____do	___do		
H5312	____do	___do		
H5313	____do	Jan. 27		
H5314	____do	___do		
H5316	____do	___do		
H5319	____do	___do		
H5320	____do	___do		
H5321	Middle section of San Francisco Bay	Jan. 28		
H5322	____do	___do		
H5323	____do	___do		
H5324	____do	___do		
H5325	____do	___do		

TABLE 10.—Albatross *hydrographic stations from which collections are reported*—Continued

Station No.	Location	Date	Latitude	Longitude
		1913	*North* ° ′ ″	*West* ° ′ ″
H5326	Middle section of San Francisco Bay	---do----		
H5328	-----do----	---do----		
H5337	-----do----	July 22		
H5338	-----do----	---do----		
H5339	-----do----	---do----		
H5341	-----do----	---do----		
H5343	Lower section of San Francisco Bay	July 23		
H5346	-----do----	---do----		
H5347	-----do----	---do----		

LITERATURE CITED [15]

ADAMS, ARTHUR.
1852. Crustacea Decapoda, *in* Peter C. Sutherland, Journal of a voyage in Baffin's Bay and Barrow Straits, in the years 1850–1851 . . ., vol. 2, Appendix, pp. ccv–ccvii. London.

Records *Mysis flexuosus* from Union Bay, Beechey Island. The record refers without doubt to *Mysis oculata.*

ALLEE, W. C.
1923a. Studies in marine ecology, I : The distribution of common littoral invertebrates of the Woods Hole region. Biol. Bull., vol. 44, pp. 167–191.

Record of *Heteromysis formosa, Mysis stenolepis,* and *Michtheimysis mixta.*

1923b. Studies in marine ecology, III : Some physical factors related to the distribution of littoral invertebrates. Biol. Bull., vol. 44, pp. 205–253.

Record of *Heteromysis formosa.*

AURIVILLIUS, CARL W. S.
1896. Das Plankton der Baffins Bay und Davis' Strait, eine thiergeographische Studie. Festskrift för Lilljeborg, Upsala, pp. 181–212, pl. 10.

Record of *Mysis oculata* and *Mysis mixta.*

BAJKOV, ALEXANDER.
1930. Biological conditions of Manitoban lakes. Contr. Can. Biol. and Fish., new ser., vol. 5, pp. 165–204 (383–422), 8 figs.

Records *Mysis relicta* from Lake Winnipeg.

BELL, THOMAS.
1855. Account of the Crustacea, *in* Edward Belcher, The last of the Arctic voyages . . ., vol. 2, pp. 400–411, 2 pls.

Records *Mysis fabricii* and *Mysis oculata.*

BENEDEN, PIERRE-J. VAN.
1861. Recherches sur la faune littorale de Belgique. Crustacés, 180 pp., 31 pls. Brussels.

American species are included.

---

[15] References that deal with American forms are annotated.

BENEDICT, JAMES E.
    1885. *In* Z. L. Tanner, Report on the work of the United States Fish Com-
        mission steamer *Albatross* for the year ending December 31st, 1883.
        Rep. Comm. Fish and Fisheries for 1883, pp. 175–177.
            Mysis stenolepis and *Heteromysis formosa* caught by the use of
        electric light.

BIRSTEIN, J. A.
    1939. On some peculiarities in the geographical distribution of freshwater
        Malacostraca of the Far-East. Zool. Journ. Moscow, vol. 18, pp.
        54–69, 6 figs.

BONNIER, JULES, and PÉRÈZ, CHARLES.
    1902. Sur un crustacé commensal des pagures, *Gnathomysis gerlachi*, nov.
        sp., type d'une famille nouvelle de schizopodes. Comptes Rend.
        Acad. Sci. Paris, vol. 134, pp. 117–119.

BOONE, LEE.
    1930. Scientific results of the cruises of the yachts *Eagle* and *Ara*, 1921–1928,
        William K. Vanderbilt, commanding. Crustacea: Anomura, Ma-
        cura, Schizopoda, Isopoda, Amphipoda, Mysidacea, Cirripedia, and
        Copepoda. Bull. Vanderbilt Marine Mus., vol. 3, 221 pp., 83 pls.
            Records *Gnathophausia willemoesii* from off Panama.

BRANDT, JOHANN F.
    1851. Krebse *in* A. Th. v. Middendorf, Reise in den aussersten norden und
        osten Siberiens, vol. 2, pt. 1, Zool., pp· 79–148.

CALMAN, W. T.
    1901. A catalogue of Crustacea and of Pycnogonida contained in the museum
        of the University College, Dundee. Edited by D'Arcy Wentworth
        Thompson.
            Several records of species from America.

    1904. On the classification of the Crustacea Malacostraca. Ann. Mag. Nat.
        Hist., ser. 7, vol. 13, pp. 144–158.

CAULLERY, MAURICE.
    1896. Résultats scientifiques de la Campagne du *Caudan* dans le Golfe de
        Gascogne. Crustacés Schizopodes et Décapodes. Ann. Univ. Lyon,
        vol. 26, pp. 362–419, pls. 13–17.

CHUN, CARL.
    1900. Aus den Tiefen des Weltmeeres, ed. 1, pp. vi, 549, 46 pls., 2 charts,
        390 figs. Jena.
    1903. Aus den Tiefen des Weltmeeres, ed. 2, 592 pp., 46 pls., 482 figs. Jena.

CLEMENS, WILBERT A., and BIGELOW, N. K.
    1922. The food of ciscoes (*Leucichthys*) in Lake Erie. Contr. Can. Biol.
        (1921), No. 5, pp. 89–101.
            Record of *Mysis relicta.*

CLEMENS, WILBERT A.; DYMOND, JOHN R.; BIGELOW, N. K.; ADAMSTONE, F. B.;
        and HARKNESS, W. J. K.
    1923. The food of Lake Nipigon fishes. Univ. Toronto Stud., biol. ser., No.
        22. Publ. Ontario Fish. Res. Lab., No. 16, pp. 173–188.
            Record of *Mysis relicta.* American bibliography.

COIFMANN, ISABELLA.
  1936. I misidacei del Mar Rosso: Studio del materiale raccolto dal Prof.
         L. Sanzo durante la campagna idrografica della R. Nave Ammiraglio
         Magnaghi (1923–24). R. Comitato Talassografico Italiano, Mem.
         233, 52 pp., 25 pls.
  1937. Misidacei raccolti dalla R. corvetta *Vettor Pisani* negli anni 1882–85.
         Ann. Mus. Zool. Univ. Napoli, new ser., vol. 7, No. 3, pp. 1–14, 7 figs.

         Records of *Siriella chierchiae, Gastrosaccus dissimilis, Mysidopsis
         inermis, M. pacifica,* and *Neomysis patagona* from the coasts of South
         America.

COLOSI, GIUSEPPE.
  1916. *Caesaromysides liguriae,* n. gen., n. sp.; Nota preliminare. Monitore
         Zool. ital., vol. 27, pp. 136–139, 1 fig.

         Contains American species.

  1919. Nota preliminare sui misidacei raccolti dalla R. N. *Liguria* nel 1903–
         05. Bull. Soc. Ent. Ital., vol. 49 (1917), pp. 3–11.

         American species are included.

  1920. Crostacei, Part IV. Misidacei. Raccolte Planctoniche fatte dalla R.
         Nave *Liguria,* vol. 2, fasc. 9, pp. 229–260, 3 pls.

         Includes American species.

  1924. Euphausiacea e Mysidacea raccolti dalla R. Nave *Vettor Pisani* nel
         1882–1885. Ann. Mus. Zool. Univ. Napoli, new ser., vol. 5, No. 7,
         pp. 1–7, 9 figs.

         Describes *Arthromysis chierchiae, Neomysis meridionalis,* and *N. mon-
         ticelli* from Magellan and Chile.

COUCH, R. Q.
  1856. On Crustacea new to the British fauna. Zoologist, ser. 1, vol. 14,
         pp. 5281–5288, 13 figs.

         Contains American species.

COUTIÈRE, H.
  1906. Crustacés Schizopodes et Décapodes. Exp. Antarc. Franç. (1903–
         1905). Crustacés, pp. 1–10, 2 pls.

CREASER, EDWIN P.
  1936. Crustaceans from Yucatán. Carnegie Inst. Washington Publ. 457,
         pp. 117–132, 43 figs.

         Description of *Antromysis cenotensis* from caves.

  1938. Larger cave Crustacea of the Yucatán Peninsula. Carnegie Inst.
         Washington, Publ. No. 491, pp. 159–164, 8 figs.

         Further records of *Antromysis cenotensis.*

CUNNINGHAM, ROBERT O.
  1871. Notes on the reptiles, Amphibia, fishes, Mollusca, and Crustacea ob-
         tained during the voyage of H. M. S. *Nassau* in the years 1866–69.
         Trans. Linn. Soc. London, ser. 1, vol. 27, pp. 491–502, 2 pls.

         Description of *Macromysis magellanica* Cunningham.

CZERNIAVSKY, VOLDEMARO.
  1882a. Monographia Mysidarum imprimis Imperii Rossici (marin., lacustr.
         et fluviatilium). Trudy St. Petersburg Nat., pt. 1, vol. 12, 170 pp.

CZERNIAVSKY, VOLDEMARO—Continued

1882b. Monographia mysidarum imprimis Imperii Rossici (marin., lacustr. et fluviatilium). Trudy St. Petersburg Nat., pt. 2, vol. 13, 85 pp., 4 pls.

1887. Monographia mysidarum imprimis Imperii Rossici (marin., lacustr. et fluviatilium). Trudy St. Petersburg Nat., pt. 3, vol. 18 (1883), 102 pp., 28 pls.

DANA, JAMES DWIGHT.

1850. Synopsis generum crustaceorum ordinis "Schizopoda" J. D. Dana elaboratus, et descriptiones specierum hujus ordinis quae in orbis terrarum circumnavigatione, Carolo Wilkes e Classe Reipublicae Faederatae Duce, auctore lectae (pars I). Amer. Journ. Sci. and Arts, ser. 2, vol. 9, pp. 129–133.

1852a. Conspectus Crustaceorum . . . . Conspectus of the Crustacea of the exploring expedition under Capt. Wilkes, U. S. N. Proc. Acad. Nat. Sci. Philadelphia, vol. 6, pp. 6–28.

1852b. United States Exploring Expedition during the years 1838, 1839, 1840, 1841, 1842, under the command of Charles Wilkes, U. S. N., vol. 13. Crustacea, pt. 1, 685 pp. Philadelphia.

Records *Macromysis gracilis.*

1855. United States Exploring Expedition during the years 1838, 1839, 1840, 1841, 1842, under the command of Charles Wilkes, U. S. N., vol. 13. Crustacea, pt. 1. Folio atlas, 96 pls. Philadelphia.

Records *Macromysis gracilis.*

DAWSON, J. WILLIAM.

1886. Handbook of zoology with examples from Canadian species, recent and fossil, ed. 3, 304 pp., 317 figs., 9 pls. Montreal.

Records *Mysis spinulosus* and *M. oculatus.*

DE KAY, J. E.

1844. Zoology of New York, or the New York fauna, pt. 6, Crustacea, 70 pp., 13 pls.

Mysis spinulosus is recorded and figured on plate 7.

DELSMAN, H. C.

1939. Preliminary plankton investigations in the Java Sea. Treubia, vol. 17, pp. 139–181, 41 figs.

DERSHAVIN, A. N.

1913. Neue Mysiden von der Küste der Halbinsel Kamtschatka. Zool. Anz., vol. 43, pp. 197–204, 15 figs.

1923. Malacostraca der Süsswasser-Gewässer von Kamtschatka. Russ. Hydrobiol. Zeit., vol. 2, pp. 180–194, 7 pls.

1924. Freshwater Peracarida from the coast of the Black Sea of the Caucasus. Russ. Hydrobiol. Zeit., vol. 3, pp. 113–129, 1 pl.

1930. The freshwater Malacostraca of the Russian Far East. Russ. Hydrobiol. Zeit., vol. 9, pp. 1–8.

DOHRN, ANTON.

1870. Untersuchungen uber Bau und Entwicklung der Arthropoden. 10. Beitrage zur Kenntniss der Malacostraken und ihrere Larven. Zeit. Wiss. Zool., vol. 20, pp. 607–626, 3 pls.

Includes American species.

DYAR, HARRISON GRAY, and KNAB, FREDERICK.
    1909. Descriptions of some new species and a new genus of American
        mosquitoes. Smithsonian Misc. Coll., vol. 52, pp. 253–266, 1 fig.

ESTERLY, CALVIN OLIN.
    1914. The Schizopoda of the San Diego region. Univ. California Publ.
        Zool., vol. 13, pp. 1–20, 2 pls.

        Records *Holmesiella anomala, Pseudomma* sp., and *Mysis costata*.

FABRICIUS, OTTO.
    1780. Fauna Groenlandica, xvi+452 pp., 12 figs.

        American species are included.

FAGE, LOUIS.
    1936. Sur un Ellobiopside nouveau, *Amallocystis fasciatus*, g. et sp. nov.,
        parasite des Mysidacés bathypélagiques. Arch. Zool. Exper. Gen.,
        vol. 78, notes et revue, pp. 145–154.

    1939. Á propos d'un mysidacé bathypélagique peu connu: *Chalaraspis
        alata* G. O. Sars (Willemoes-Suhm *in lit.*). Arch. Zool. Exper.
        Gen., vol. 80, notes et revue, pp. 68–76, figs. 1–7.

    1940. Diagnoses préliminaires de quelques espèces nouvelles du genre
        Lophogaster (Crust. Mysidacés). Bull. Mus. Nat. Hist. Nat.
        [Paris], ser. 2, vol. 12, pp. 323–328.

FAXON, WALTER.
    1893. Reports on the dredging operations off the west coast of Central
        America to the Galápagos . . . by the *Albatross*, VI: Preliminary
        descriptions of new species of Crustacea. Bull. Mus. Comp. Zool.,
        vol. 24, pp. 149–220.

        Descriptions of *Gnathophausia dentata, Eucopia sculpticauda, Peta-
        lophthalmus pacificus, Scolophthalmus lucifugus,* and *Ceratomysis
        spinosa.*

    1895. Reports on an exploration off the west coasts of Mexico, Central and
        South America, and off the Galápagos Islands . . . by the . . .
        Albatross, XV: The stalk-eyed Crustacea. Mem. Mus. Comp. Zool.,
        vol. 18, 922 pp. pls. A–K, 1–56. Other American records.

        Full descriptions of the new species named in 1893 and records of
        Gnathophausia zoea, G. willemoesii, and *Eucopia australis.*

    1896. Reports on the results of dredging, under the supervision of Alex-
        ander Agassiz, in the Gulf of Mexico and the Caribbean Sea, and
        on the east coast of the United States, 1877 to 1880, by the U. S.
        Coast Survey Steamer *Blake*, Lieut.-Commander C. D. Sigsbee,
        U. S. N., and Commander J. R. Bartlett, U. S. N., commanding, 37:
        Supplementary notes on the Crustacea. Bull. Mus. Comp. Zool.,
        vol. 30, pp. 153–166, 2 pls.

        Description of *Lophogaster longirostris* and records of *Gnathophausia
        zoea, Eucopia sculpticauda,* and *Petalophthalmus armiger.*

FEWKES, JESSE WALTER.
    1888. Echinodermata, Vermes, Crustacea, and pteropod Mollusca in Inter-
        national Polar Expedition. Report on the proceedings of the
        United States expedition to Lady Franklin Bay, Grinnell Land,
        vol 2, App. 133, pp. 47–52, 3 pls.

        Records *Mysis oculata* ?.

FILHOL, H.
1885. La vie au fond des mers, viii+301 pp., 96 figs., 8 pls. Paris.

FISH, CHARLES J.
1925. Seasonal distribution of the plankton of the Woods Hole region.
Bull. Bur. Fisheries, vol. 41, Doc. No. 975, pp. 91–179, figs. 1–81.

Records *Neomysis americana, Heteromysis formosa,* and *Erythrops.*

FISH, CHARLES J., and JOHNSON, MARTIN W.
1937. The biology of the zooplankton population in the Bay of Fundy and
Gulf of Maine with special reference to production and distribution.
Journ. Biol. Board Canada, vol. 3, pp. 189–322, 45 figs.

Records *Neomysis americana* from the Bay of Fundy.

FORBES, STEPHEN A.
1876. List of Illinois Crustacea. Key to the species mentioned in the preceding paper. Illinois Mus. Nat. Hist. Bull. 1, pp. 3–24, 1 pl.

Records *Mysis relicta* in Lake Michigan.

FOWLER, HENRY W.
1912. The Crustacea of New Jersey. Ann. Rep. New Jersey State Mus.,
1911, pt. 2, pp. 29–650, 150 pls.

Repeats earlier records of *Gnathophausia gigas, G. zoea, Boreomysis
arctica, Pseudomma roseum, Mysis americana,* and *Heteromysis formosa.*

GARDINER, A. C.
1934. Variations in the amount of macroplankton by day and night. Journ.
Marine Biol. Assoc., new ser., vol. 19, pp. 559–567, 3 figs.

Erythrops erythrophthalma off Nova Scotia.

GOËS, AXEL.
1863. Crustacea Decapoda podophthalma marina Sueciae, interpositis
speciebus norvegicis aliisque vicinis, enumerat. Ofv. Vet.-Akad.
Forh., Stockholm, vol. 20, pp. 161–180.

GOULD, AUGUSTUS A.
1841. Report on the Invertebrata of Massachusetts, comprising the Mollusca,
Crustacea, Annelida, and Radiata, xiii+373 pp., 213 figs. Cam-
bridge.

Records *Mysis spinulosus* as abundant around the margins of the bays.
Probably refers to *Mysis stenolepis* Smith.

HANSEN, HANS JACOB.
1887. Malacostraca marina Groenlandiae occidentalis. Vid. Medd. Naturh.
Foren. Kjobenhaven, vol. 9, pp. 5–226, 6 pls.
1905a. Preliminary report on the Schizopoda collected by H. S. H. Prince
Albert of Monaco during the cruise of the *Princesse-Alice* in the
year 1904. Bull. Mus. Ocean. Monaco, No. 30, pp. 1–32, 24 figs.
1905b. Further notes on the Schizopoda. Bull. Mus. Ocean. Monaco, No. 42,
pp. 1–32.
1908a. Danish Ingolf-Expedition, Crustacea Malacostraca, I, vol. 3, pt. 2,
pp. 1–120, 2 figs., 5 pls.
1908b. Schizopoda and Cumacea. Res. Voyage S. Y. *Belgica,* Rapports Sci.,
Zool., 20 pp., 3 pls.
1910. The Schizopoda of the *Siboga* expedition. *Siboga*-Expeditie, vol. 37,
123 pp., 3 figs., 17 pls.

HANSEN, HANS JACOB—Continued

1912. Reports on the scientific results of the expedition to the tropical Pacific . . . by the U. S. Fish Commission Steamer *Albatross:* The Schizopoda. Mem. Mus. Comp. Zool., vol. 35, pp. 175–296, 12 pls.

Records other American species.

1913a. Report on the Crustacea Schizopoda collected by the Swedish Antarctic Expedition 1901–3, under the charge of Baron Otto Nordenskjöld, pp. 1–46, pls. 1–6.

Describes *Mysidopsis acuta, Mysidetes crassa,* and records *Neomysis patagona* from the Falkland Islands.

1913b. On some California Schizopoda. Univ. California Publ. Zool., vol. 11, pp. 173–180, pl. 9.

Redescribes *Siriella pacifica, Mysis costata,* and *Neomysis franciscorum.*

1921. On some malacostracous Crustacea (Mysidacea, Euphausiacea, and Stomatopoda) collected by Swedish Antarctic expeditions. Ark. för Zool., vol. 13, No. 20, pp. 1–7.

Records *Mysidopsis acuta* from Terra del Fuego and *Neomysis patagona* from Port Famine, Magellan.

1925. On the comparative morphology of the appendages in the Arthropoda. A, Crustacea. Studies on Arthropoda II, 7+176 pp., 8 pls. Copenhagen.

1927. Sergestides et schizopodes. Expéd. Sci. du *Travailleur* et du *Talisman,* 1880–1883, 26 pp., 1 pl.

HANSTRÖM, BERTIL.

1933. Neue untersuchungen über Sinnesorgane und Nervensystem der Crustaceen, II. Zool. Jahrb., vol. 56, pp. 387–520, 68 figs.

Records *Callomysis maculata* from Pacific Grove, Calif.

HOLMES, SAMUEL J.

1894. Notes on West American Crustacea. Proc. California Acad. Sci., ser. 2, vol. 4, pp. 563–588, 2 pls.

Description of *Callomysis maculata.*

1897. Description of a new schizopod from Lake Merced. Proc. California Acad. Sci., ser. 2, vol. 6, pp. 199–200, 1 pl.

Description of *Neomysis mercedis.*

1900. Synopsis of California stalk-eyed Crustacea. Occ. Pap. California Acad. Sci., vol. 7, pp. 1–262, 4 pls.

Descriptions of new species: *Mysis costata, Neomysis franciscorum, Heteromysis spinosus, Mysidopsis elongata, Siriella pacifica,* and records of *Neomysis mercedis, Callomysis maculata,* and *Heteromysis odontops.*

HOLT, ERNEST W. L., and BEAUMONT, W. I.

1900. Survey of fishing grounds, west coast of Ireland, 1890–1891, X: Report on the Crustacea Schizopoda of Ireland. Trans. Roy. Soc. Dublin, ser. 2, vol. 7, pp. 221–252, pl. 16, figs. 1–7; text fig. 1, figs. 1–9.

HOLT, ERNEST W. L., and TATTERSALL, WALTER M.

1905. Schizopodous Crustacea from the north-east Atlantic slope. Rep. Sea Inland Fisheries Ireland, 1902–1903, pt. 2, App. 4, pp. 99–152, 11 pls.

1906a. Preliminary notice of the Schizopoda collected by H. M. S. *Discovery* in the Antarctic region. Ann. Mag. Nat. Hist., ser. 7, vol. 17, pp. 1–11.

HOLT, ERNEST W. L., and TATTERSALL, WALTER M.—Continued

1906b. Schizopodous Crustacea from the north-east slope: Supplement. Fisheries Ireland, Sci. Invest. 1904, No. 5, 50 pp., 5 pls.

HOY, P. R.

1872. Deep-water fauna of Lake Michigan. Trans. Wisconsin Acad. Sci. Arts and Letters, 1870–1872, pp. 98–101.

> *Mysis diluvianus* from 50 to 70 fathoms. This refers to *Mysis relicta*.

HUMBERT, ALOIS.

1874. L'expédition scientifique du navire de S. M. Britannique le *Challenger*. Arch. Sci. Phys. Nat., vol. 49, new ser., pp. 189–212.

HUNTSMAN, A. G.

1913. Invertebrates other than insects and mollusks, *in* The natural history of the Toronto region, Ontario, Canada, pp. 272–287. Edited by Joseph H. Faull.

> Records *Mysis relicta*.

1915. The fresh-water Malacostraca of Ontario. Contr. Can. Biol., 1911–14, sessional paper 39b, pp. 145–163, 13 figs.

> Records *Mysis relicta*.

II, NAOYOSI.

1936a. Studies on Japanese Mysidacea, I: Descriptions of new and some already known species belonging to the general *Neomysis*, *Acanthomysis*, and *Proneomysis*. Jap. Journ. Zool., vol. 6, pp. 577–619, 116 figs.

1936b. Studies on Japanese Mysidacea, II: Descriptions of three new species belonging to two new genera, *Parastilomysis* and *Paracanthomysis*. Jap. Journ. Zool., vol. 7, pp. 1–15, 41 figs.

1937. Studies on Japanese Mysidacea, III: Descriptions of four new species belonging to tribes Leptomysini and Erythropini. Jap. Journ. Zool., vol. 7, pp. 191–209, 60 figs.

1940. Studies on Japanese Mysidacea, IV: Descriptions of three new species belonging to tribe Mysini. Jap. Journ. Zool., vol. 9, pp. 153–173, 47 figs.

ILLIG, G.

1906a. Bericht über die neuen Schizopodengattungen und -arten der Deutschen Tiefsee Expedition 1898–1899. Zool. Anz., vol. 30, pp. 194–211, 17 figs.

1906b. Ein weiterer bericht über die Schizopoden der Deutschen Tiefsee Expedition 1898–1899. Supplement. I, II: Gnathophausien. Zool. Anz., vol. 30, pp. 227–230, 2 figs.; pp. 319–322, 1 fig.

1930. Die Schizopoden der Deutschen Tiefsee Expedition. Wiss. Ergeb. Deutsch. Tiefsee Exped., vol. 22, pp. 400–625, 215 figs.

JOHANSEN, FRITS.

1922. The crustacean life of some Arctic lagoons, lakes, and ponds. Rep. Can. Arctic Exped., 1913–1918, vol. 7, Crustacea, pt. N, pp. 1–31.

> Records *Mysis relicta*.

JUDAY, CHANCEY, and BIRGE, EDWARD A.

1927. *Pontoporeia* and *Mysis* in Wisconsin lakes. Ecology, vol. 8, pp. 445–452.

> *Mysis relicta* in Green and Trout Lakes.

KELLICOTT, D. S.

1878. Notes on microscopic life in the Buffalo water supply. Amer. Journ. Micr. Pop. Sci., vol. 3, pp. 250–252.

In American bibliography, as recording *Mysis* species from Lake Erie. Text of paper gives no name. The only crustacean mentioned is "occasionally a small crustacean comes through the faucet bearing on its surface numerous individuals of a beautiful *Acineta*."

KINDLE, E. M., and WHITTAKER, E. J.

1918. Bathymetric check list of the marine invertebrates of eastern Canada with an index to Whiteaves' catalogue. Contr. Can. Biol. for 1917–1918: Sessional paper No. 38A, pp. 228–294.

Lists *Meterythrops robusta, Mysis mixta, M. oculata, M. stenolepis, Pseudomma roseum,* and *P. truncatum.*

KNAB, FREDERICK.

1906. Notes on *Deinocerites cancer* Theobald. Psyche, vol. 13, pp. 95–97, pls. 5, 6.

KOSSMANN, ROBBY.

1880. Zoologische Ergebnisse . . . Reise in die Küsten gebiete des Rothen Meeres, vol. 2, III: Malacostraca (2 Theil, *Anomura*), pp. 67–140, 12 pls.

KROPP, BENJAMIN, and PERKINS, EARLE B.

1933. The occurrence of the humoral chromatophore activator among marine crustaceans. Biol. Bull., vol. 64, pp. 28–32.

Records *Mysis stenolepis.*

KRØYER, HENRIK.

1861. Et bidrag til Kundskab om Krebsdyrfamilien Mysidae. Naturh. Tidsskr., ser. 3, vol. 1, pp. 1–75, 2 pls.

Records *Promysis galatheae* from the West Indies. The species is a *Siriella*, probably *S. thompsonii.*

LATREILLE, P. A.

1803. Histoire naturelle, génerale et particulière, des crustacés et des insectes, vol. 6, 391 pp., 12 pls. Paris.

LEACH, WILLIAM ELFORD.

1814. Crustaceology, *in* Brewster's Edinburgh Encyclopaedia, vol. 7, pp. 383–437.

Contains American species.

1830. On the genus *Megalophthalmus*, a new and very interesting genus, completely proving the theory of Jules-Caesar Savigny to be correct. Trans. Plymouth Inst., 1830, pp. 176–178.

LEAVITT, BENJAMIN B.

1938. The quantitative vertical distribution of macrozooplankton in the Atlantic Ocean basin. Biol. Bull., vol. 74, pp. 376–394, 5 figs.

Records *Eucopia biunguiculata, Gnathophausia,* and other unnamed mysids.

LILLJEBORG, WILHELM.

1852. Hafs-Crustaceer vid Kullaberg. Öfv. Vet.-Akad. Forh., Stockholm vol. 9, pp. 1–13.

Contains American species.

Lovén, S.
    1861.   Om några i Vettern och Venern funna Crustaceer. Öfv. Vet.-Akad.
        Forh., Stockholm, vol. 18, pp. 285–314.

Marsh, C. Dwight.
    1891.   Preliminary list of deep-water Crustacea in Green Lake, Wisc., U. S. A.
        Zool. Anz., Jahrg. 14, pp. 275–276.

            Records *Mysis relicta.*

    1900.   The plankton of fresh-water lakes. Science, new ser., vol. 11, pp.
        374–389.

            Records *Mysis relicta.*

Martynov, A. B.
    1924.   On some interesting Malacostraca from freshwaters of European
        Russia. Russ. Hydrobiol. Zeit., vol. 3, pp. 210–216.

Marukawa, Hisatosi.
    1928.   Ueber neue 5 Arten der Schizopoden. Annot. Oceanogr. Rech., vol. 2,
        pp. 4–8, 3 pls.

Milne-Edwards, Henri.
    1837.   Histoire naturelle des crustacés, vol. 2, 531 pp. Paris.

            Contains American species.

    1840.   Histoire naturelle des crustacés, vol. 3, 638 pp., 42 pls. Paris.

            American species are included.

Miyadi, Denzaburo.
    1932a.   Studies on the bottom fauna of Japanese lakes, III: Lakes of the
        Kwanto plain. Jap. Journ. Zool., vol. 4, pp. 1–39, 6 figs., 31 pls.
    1932b.   Studies on the bottom fauna of Japanese lakes, VII: Lakes of Hok-
        kaido. Jap. Journ. Zool., vol. 4, pp. 223–252, 20 pls.
    1933a.   Marine relict Mysidacea of Japanese lakes. Proc. Imp. Acad. Japan,
        vol. 9, pp. 27–30.
    1933b.   Studies on the bottom fauna of Japanese lakes, XI: Lakes of Etorohu-
        Sima surveyed at the expense of the Keimei-Kwai fund. Jap. Journ.
        Zool., vol. 5, pp. 171–208.
    1938a.   Bottom fauna of the lakes in Kunasirisima of the South Kurile Is-
        lands. Int. Rev. Hydrobiol. Hydrogr., vol. 37, pp. 125–163, 23 figs.,
        21 pls.
    1938b.   Ecological studies on marine relicts and landlocked animals in inland
        waters of Nippon. Philippine Journ. Sci., vol. 65, pp. 239–249, 2 figs.

Müller, Otto Frederick.
    1776.   Zoologiae Danicae Prodromus, seu Animalium Daniae et Norvegiae
        indigenarum: Characters, nomina, et synonyma imprimis popu-
        larium, xii+274 pp., Havniae.

Murdoch, John.
    1885a.   Description of seven new species of Crustacea and one worm from
        Arctic Alaska. Proc. U. S. Nat. Mus., vol. 7, pp. 518–522.

            First description of *Mysis rayii.*

    1885b.   Report on the International Polar Expedition to Point Barrow, Alaska,
        pt. 4, natural history. V, Marine invertebrates (exclusive of mol-
        lusks), pp. 136–176, 2 pls.

            Description and figures of *Mysis rayii.*

NAKAZAWA, K.
  1910. Notes on Japanese Schizopoda. Annot. Zool. Japonensis, vol. 7, pt. 4, pp. 247–261, 1 pl.

NORMAN, ALFRED MERLE.
  1860. On an undescribed crustacean of the genus *Mysis*. Ann. Mag. Nat. Hist., ser. 3, vol. 6, pp. 429–431, 1 pl.
  1862. On the Crustacea, Echinodermata, and zoophytes obtained in deep-sea dredging off the Shetland Isles in 1861. Rep. British Assoc. Adv. Sci., vol. 31 (1861), pp. 151, 152.
  1868. Preliminary report on the Crustacea, Molluscoida, Echinodermata, and Coelenterata, procured by the Shetland Dredging Committee in 1867. Rep. British Assoc. Adv. Sci., vol. 37 (1867), pp. 437–441.
  1892. On British Mysidae, a family of Crustacea Schizopoda. Ann. Mag. Nat. Hist., ser. 6, vol. 10, pp. 143–166, 242–263, 2 pls.
  1902. Notes on the natural history of East Finmark. Ann. Mag. Nat. Hist., ser. 7, vol. 10, pp. 472–486.
  1905. Museum Normanianum, III: Crustacea, ed. 2, 47 pp.

NORMAN, ALFRED MERLE, and SCOTT, THOMAS.
  1906. The Crustacea of Devon and Cornwall, xv+232 pp., 24 pls. London.

OHLIN, AXEL.
  1895a. Zoological observations during Peary Auxiliary Expedition 1894. Preliminary report. Biol. Centralb., vol. 15, pp. 161–174, 2 figs.

    Records *Mysis* sp. from Murchison Sound.

  1895b. Bidrag till kannedomen om malakostrakfaunan i Baffin Bay och Smith Sound. Lund Univ. Års-Skrift., vol. 31, pp. xxii, 70, 1 pl., 1 map.

    Several records of *Mysis oculata.*

  1901a. On a new "bipolar" schizopod. Ann. Mag. Nat. Hist., ser. 7, vol. 7, pp. 371–374.
  1901b. Arctic Crustacea collected during the Swedish Arctic Expeditions, 1898, 1899, and 1900, under the direction of Professor A. G. Nathorst and Mr. G. Kolthoff, II: Decapoda, Schizopoda. Bih. Svenska Vet.-Akad. Handl., vol. 27, afd. 4, No. 8, pp. 1–92, 3 pls.

ORTMANN, ARNOLD E.
  1893. Decapoden und Schizopoden. Ergebnisse der Plankton-Expedition der Humboldt-Stiftung, vol. 2, 120 pp., 1 fig., 7 pls.

    Description of *Chlamydopleon aculeatum* from Brazil. Records other American species.

  1894. Report on the dredging operations off the west coast of Central America to the Galápagos . . . by the U. S. Fish Commission steamer *Albatross* . . ., XIV: The pelagic Schizopoda. Bull. Mus. Comp. Zool., vol. 25, No. 8, pp. 99–111, 1 pl.

    Description of *Boreomysis californica,* new species, and records of *Siriella thompsoni, S. gracilis,* and *Euchaetomera typica.*

  1901. Crustacea and Pycnogonida collected during the Princeton expedition to North Greenland. Proc. Acad. Nat. Sci. Philadelphia, 1901, pp. 144–168.

    Records *Mysis oculata.*

  1905. Schizopods of the Hawaiian Islands collected by the *Albatross* in 1902. Bull. U. S. Fish Comm., 1903, pt. 3, pp. 961–973.

ORTMANN, ARNOLD E.—Continued

1906. Schizopod crustaceans in the U. S. National Museum. The families Lophogastridae and Eucopiidae. Proc. U. S. Nat. Mus., vol. 31, pp. 23–54, 2 pls.

> Descriptions of *Lophogaster spinosus* and *Gnathophausia scapularis* and a revision of the genus *Gnathophausia*. Records other American species.

1908. Schizopod crustaceans in the United States National Museum: Schizopods from Alaska. Proc. U. S. Nat. Mus., vol. 34, pp. 1–10, 1 pl.

> Descriptions of *Holmesiella anomala* and *Neomysis kadiakensis* and record of *Gnathophausia gigas*.

1918. Higher crustaceans (Malacostraca), *in* H. B. Ward, and G. C. Whipple, Fresh-water biology, pp. 828–850.

> Records *Mysis relicta*.

PACKARD, ALPHEUS S.

1863. A list of animals dredged near Caribou Island, southern Labrador, during July and August, 1860. Can. Nat. Geol., vol. 8, pp. 401–429, 2 pls.

> Records *Mysis spinulosus* in swarms in tide pools. The species is certainly *Mysis oculata*.

1867. Observations on the glacial phenomena of Labrador and Maine, with a view of the recent invertebrate fauna of Labrador. Mem. Boston Soc. Nat. Hist., vol. 1, pp. 210–303, 2 pls.

> Records *Mysis oculata* as abundant along the whole coast.

PARKER, GEORGE HOWARD.

1891. The compound eyes in crustaceans. Bull. Mus. Comp. Zool., vol. 21, pp. 45–140, 10 pls.

> *Mysis stenolepis* from Woods Hole.

PAULMIER, FREDERICK CLARK.

1905. Higher Crustacea of New York City. New York State Mus. Bull. 91, Zoology 12, pp. 117–189, 59 figs.

> Records *Mysis stenolepis*.

PEARSE, ARTHUR SPERRY.

1910. A preliminary list of the Crustacea of Michigan. Twelfth Rep. Michigan Acad. Sci., pp. 68–76.

> Records *Mysis relicta*.

PRATT, HENRY SHERRING.

1916. A manual of the common invertebrate animals exclusive of insects, 737 pp., 1,017 figs. Chicago.

> Three species of American mysids briefly described: *Mysis stenolepis, M. relicta,* and *Heteromysis formosa*.

1935. A manual of the common invertebrate animals exclusive of insects, rev. ed., 854 pp., 974 figs. Philadelphia.

> Contains American species.

PROCTOR, WILLIAM.

1933. Biological survey of the Mount Desert region, pt. 5. Marine fauna, pp. 1–402, 42 figs., 15 pls.

> Mentions *Erythrops erythrophthalma, Michtheimysis mixta,* and *Neomysis americana*.

RATHBUN, MARY JANE.
1905. Fauna of New England. 5. List of the Crustacea., Occ. Pap. Boston Soc. Nat. Hist., vol. 7, pp. 1–117.

Includes a list of seven recorded species.

1909. *In* W. T. Grenfell, Labrador: The country and the people. App. 2: The marine Crustacea, pp. 447–452. App. 6: List of Crustacea on the Labrador coast, pp. 480–487.

Mysis relicta in pools of fresh water near the sea.

RATHBUN, RICHARD.
1880. List of marine Invertebrata from the New England coast, distributed by the U. S. Commission of Fish and Fisheries, ser. 1. Proc. U. S. Nat. Mus., vol. 2, pp. 227–232.

Mysis mixta from Massachusetts Bay.

1881. The littoral fauna of Provincetown, Cape Cod, Massachusetts. Proc. U. S. Nat. Mus., vol. 3, pp. 116–133.

Record of *Mysis stenolepis*.

1883. List of duplicate marine invertebrates distributed by the United States National Museum. Proc. U. S. Nat. Mus., vol. 6, pp. 212–216.

Records *Mysis mixta*.

RATHKE, HEINRICH.
1843. Beitrage zur Fauna Norvegens. Nov. Act. Acad. Caes. Leop.-Carolinae, vol. 20, pp. 1–264c, 12 pls.

RICHTERS, FERD.
1884. Beitrag zur Kenntnis der Crustaceenfauna des Behringsmeeres. Abh. Senckenb. Naturf. Ges., vol. 13, pp. 401–406, 1 pl.

Records of *Mysis oculata, Mysideis grandis,* and *Pseudomma truncatum*.

RODGER, ALEXANDER.
1895. Preliminary account of natural history collections made on a voyage to the Gulf of St. Lawrence and Davis Straits. Proc. Roy. Soc. Edinburgh, vol. 20, pp. 154–163.

Record of *Mysideis grandis* from the Gulf of St. Lawrence.

SARS, GEORG OSSIAN.
1864. Beretning om en i Sommeren 1863 foretagen zoologisk Reise i Christiania Stift. Nyt. Mag. Naturv., vol. 13, pp. 225–260.

1866. Beretning om i Sommeren 1865 foretagen zoologisk Reise ved Kysterne af Christianias og Christiansands Stifter. Nyt. Mag. Naturv., vol. 15, pp. 84–128.

1869. Undersogelser over Christiania-fjordens Dybvandsfauna, anstillede paa en i Sommeren 1868 foretagen Zoologisk Reise. Nyt. Mag. Naturv., vol. 16, pp. 305–362.

1870a. Nye Dybvandscrustaceer fra Lofoten. Vidensk.-Selsk. Forh., 1869, pp. 147–174.

1870b. Carcinologiske Bidrag til Norges Fauna. I. Monographi over de ved Norges Kyster forekommende Mysider. Heft 1, pp. 1–64, 5 pls.

1872a. Undersogelser over Hardanger-fjorden Fauna I. Forh. Vidensk.-Selsk. Christiania (1871), pp. 263, 284.

1872b. Carcinologiske Bidrag til Norges Fauna. I. Monographi over de ved Norges Kyster forekommende Mysider. Heft 2, pp. 1–34, 3 pls.

SARS, GEORG OSSIAN—Continued

1877. Nye bidrag til Kundskaben om Middelhavets Invertebratfauna. I. Middelhavets Mysider. Arch. Math. Naturv., vol. 2, pp. 10–119, 36 pls.

1879a. Carcinologiske Bidrag til Norges Fauna, I: Monographi over de ved Norges Kyster forekommende Mysider, Heft 3, pp. 1–131, 34 pls.

1879b. Crustacea et Pycnogonida nova in itinere 2do et 3tio expeditionis norvegicae anno 1877 . . . 1878 collecta. (Prodromus descriptionis.) Arch. Math. Naturv., vol. 4, pp. 427–476.

1884. Preliminary notices on the Schizopoda of H. M. S. *Challenger*-Expedition. Forh. Vidensk.-Selsk. Christiania, 1883, No. 7, pp. 1–43.

1885. Report on the Schizopoda collected by H. M. S. *Challenger* during the years 1873–76. *Challenger* Reports, Zoology, vol. 13, pt. 37, 225 pp., 3 figs., 38 pls.

> Includes American species.

SARS, MICHAEL.

1857. Om 3 nye norske Krebsdyr. Forh. Skand. Naturf., vol. 7 (1856), pp. 160–175.

1869. Fortstatte Bemaerkninger over det dyriske Livs Udbredning i Havets Dybder. Vidensk.-Selsk. Forh., 1868, pp. 246–275.

SCHMITT, JOSEPH.

1904. Monographie de l'Île d'Anticosti (Golfe Saint-Laurent), 367 pp., 42 figs.

> Records *Mysis stenolepis* as common.

SCHMITT, WALDO L.

1919. Schizopod crustaceans. Report of the Canadian Arctic Expedition 1913–18, vol. 7, Crustacea, pt. B, pp. 1–8.

> Records *Mysis oculata* and *Mysis relicta* from the Northwest Territories and describes *Neomysis andersoni* from the same locality.

SHIINO, SUEO M.

1937. Two species of the gigantic mysidacean *Gnathophausia* found in Japan. Annot. Zool. Jap., vol. 16, pp. 181–187, 2 figs.

SIM, GEORGE.

1872. Stalk-eyed Crustacea of the N. E. coast of Scotland. Scottish Nat., vol. 1, pp. 182–190, 2 pls.

SMITH, SIDNEY I.

1871. Preliminary report on the dredging in Lake Superior. Rep. Sec. War, vol. 2: Rep. Chief Engineer, pp. 1–7.

> Records *Mysis relicta* from Lake Superior.

1873. *In* A. E. Verrill, Report upon the invertebrate animals of Vineyard Sound and the adjacent waters, with an account of the physical characters of the region. Rep. Comm. Fish and Fisheries, 1871 and 1872, pp. 295–747, 37 pls.

> First descriptions of *Mysis stenolepis, M. americana,* and *Heteromysis formosa.*

1874a. The Crustacea of the fresh waters of the United States. Rep. Comm. Fish and Fisheries, 1872 and 1873, pp. 637–665.

> *Mysis relicta* from Lakes Michigan and Superior.

SMITH, SIDNEY I.—Continued

1874b. Sketch of the invertebrate fauna of Lake Superior. Rep. Comm. Fish and Fisheries, 1872 and 1873, pp. 690–707.

Records *Mysis relicta.*

1879. The stalk-eyed crustaceans of the Atlantic coast of North America north of Cape Cod. Trans. Connecticut Acad., vol. 5, pp. 27–136, 5 pls.

The most important work on American Mysidae. Descriptions of *Pseudomma truncatum,* new species, and *Meterythrops robusta,* new genus and species, and a summary of all known American species.

1881. Preliminary notice of the Crustacea dredged in 64–325 fathoms, off the south coast of New England, by the United States Fish Commission in 1880. Proc. U. S. Nat. Mus., vol. 3, pp. 413–452. (Reprinted in summary in Ann. Mag. Nat. Hist., ser. 5, vol. 7, pp. 143–146.)

Records of *Lophogaster* sp., *Boremysis arctica,* and *Pseudomma roseum.*

1883. List of the Crustacea dredged on the coast of Labrador by the expedition under the direction of W. A. Stearns, in 1882. Proc. U. S. Nat Mus., vol. 6, pp. 218–222.

Mysis oculata abundant along all the coasts.

1884. Crustacea of the *Albatross* dredgings in 1883. Amer. Journ. Sci., ser. 3, vol. 28, pp. 53–56.

Mention of *Gnathophausia* and *Lophogaster.*

1885. List of Crustacea from Port Burwell collected by Dr. R. Bell in 1884, *in* Robert Bell, Observations on the geology, mineralogy, zoology, and botany of the Labrador coast, Hudson's Strait and Bay. Rep. Prog. Geol. Nat. Hist. Surv. Mus. Canada, 1882–83–84, (sect.) DD, Appendix 4, pp. 57–58.

Records *Mysis oculata.*

SMITH, SIDNEY I., and VERRILL, ADDISON E.

1871. [Notice of the Invertebrata dredged in Lake Superior in 1871, by the U. S. Lake Survey, under the direction of Gen. C. B. Comstock, S. I. Smith, Naturalist.] Amer. Journ. Sci. and Arts, ser. 3, vol. 2, pp. 448–454.

Mysis relicta from Lake Superior.

STAFFORD, J.

1912. On the fauna of the Atlantic coast of Canada: Third Report—Gaspé, 1905–6. Contr. Can. Biol., 1906–10, V, pp. 45–67.

Mentions *Mysis oculata.*

STEBBING, THOMAS R. R.

1893. A history of Crustacea. Recent Malacostraca, 466 pp.

1900. Arctic Crustacea: Bruce collection. Ann. Mag. Nat. Hist., ser. 7, vol. 5, pp. 1–16.

Mysideis grandis from west Greenland.

STEPHENSEN, K.
   1913. Grønlands Krebsdyr og Pycnogonider. (Conspectus Crustaceorum et
         Pycnogonidorum Groenlandiae.) Medd. Grønland, vol. 22, 479 pp.
   1933. The Godthaab Expedition 1928. Schizopoda. Medd. Grønland, vol.
         79, pp. 1–20, 6 figs.

         Records of Mysidacea mainly from East Greenland but some of them
         from localities near the Canadian coast.

STIMPSON, WILLIAM.
   1853. Synopsis of the marine Invertebrata of Grand Manan. Smithsonian
         Contr. Knowl., vol. 6, art. 4, pp. 1–66, pls. 1–3.

         Records *Mysis oculata* ? as abundant in the Bay of Fundy. Smith has
         suggested that these were euphausians.

   1863. Synopsis of the marine Invertebrata collected by the late Arctic ex-
         pedition, under Dr. I. I. Hayes. Proc. Acad. Nat. Sci. Philadelphia,
         1863, pp. 1–5.

         Records *Mysis oculata* from Port Foulke.

   1871. On the deep-water fauna of Lake Michigan. Amer. Nat., vol. 4, pp.
         403–405.

         Mysis [sp.] from stomach of whitefish (p. 404).

SUMNER, FRANCIS B.; OSBURN, RAYMOND C.; and COLE, LEON J.
   1913. A biological survey of the waters of the Woods Hole and vicinity.
         Bull. Bur. Fish., vol. 31 (1911), pt. 2, Section 3—A catalogue of
         the marine fauna, pp. 547–860.

         Records of *Michtheimysis mixta, Neomysis americana,* and *Heteromysis
         formosa.*

TATTERSALL, WALTER M.
   1907. Preliminary diagnoses of six new Mysidae from the west coast of
         Ireland. Ann. Mag. Nat. Hist., ser. 7, vol. 19, pp. 106–118.
   1908. Crustacea. VII. Schizopoda. Nat. Antarctic Exped., Nat. Hist., vol.
         4, Zool., pp. 1–42, pls. 1–8.
   1911a. The Percy Sladen Trust expedition to the Indian Ocean in 1905 . . .,
         No. 9. On the Mysidacea and Euphausiacea collected in the Indian
         Ocean during 1905. Trans. Linn. Soc. London, ser. 2, Zool., vol. 15,
         pp. 119–136, 2 pls.
   1911b. Schizopodous Crustacea from the North-east Atlantic slope, 2d suppl.
         Fisheries Ireland Sci. Invest. 1910, No. 2, pp. 1–77, 8 pls.
   1913. The Schizopoda, Stomatopoda, and non-Antarctic Isopoda of the
         Scottish National Antarctic Expedition. Trans. Roy. Soc. Edin-
         burgh, vol. 49, pt. 4, pp. 865–894, 1 pl.
   1921. Zoological results of a tour in the Far East. Pt. 7. Mysidacea,
         Tanaidacea, and Isopods. Mem. Asiatic Soc. Bengal, vol. 6, pp. 403–
         433, 3 pls.
   1922. Indian Mysidacea. Rec. Indian Mus., vol. 24, pp. 445–504, 28 figs.
   1923. British Antarctic (Terra Nova) Expedition, 1910; Crustacea. Part
         7: Mysidacea. Nat. Hist. Rep., Zool., vol. 3, No. 10, pp. 273–304,
         4 pls.

         Contains American species.

   1925. Mysidacea and Euphausiacea of marine survey, South Africa. Fish.
         Mar. Biol. Surv., Rep. No. 4 (1924). Special Reports: No. 5, pp.
         1–12, 2 pls.

TATTERSALL, WALTER M.—Continued

1926. Crustaceans of the orders Euphausiacea and Mysidacea from the western Atlantic. Proc. U. S. Nat. Mus., vol. 69, art. 8, 31 pp., 2 pls.

Records of *Lophogaster typicus, L. spinosus, Paralophogaster glaber, Eucopia unguiculata, Siriella thompsonii, Anchialina typica, Katerythrops oceanae, Euchaetomera typica, E. tenuis, Neomysis americana,* and a description of *Mysidopsis bigelowi.*

1928. Further records of Australian opossum shrimps (Mysidacea). Rec. South Australian Mus., vol. 4, pp. 105–110, 3 figs.

1932a. Contributions to a knowledge of the Mysidacea of California, I: On a collection of Mysidae from La Jolla, California. Univ. of California Publ. Zool., vol. 37, pp. 301–314, 38 figs.

Records for California *Siriella pacifica, Archaeomysis maculata, Mysidopsis elongata,* and *M. californica,* new species.

1932b. Contributions to a knowledge of the Mysidacea of California, II: The Mysidacea collected during the survey of San Francisco Bay by the U. S. S. *Albatross* in 1914. Univ. California Publ. Zool., vol. 37, pp. 315–347, 27 figs.

Records *Neomysis mercedis, N. franciscorum, N. costata, N. kadiakensis,* and *N. macropsis,* new species.

1933. Euphausiacea and Mysidacea from western Canada. Contr. Can. Biol. and Fish., vol. 8, No. 15, ser. a, Gen. No. 38, pp. 1–25, 13 figs.

A summary of all the species known from western Canada. Descriptions of new species : *Pseudomma berkeleyi, Neomysis columbiae, N. pseudomacropsis,* and *Proneomysis wailesi.*

1936a. Plankton of the Bermuda oceanographic expeditions. V. Notes on the Schizopoda. Zoologica, vol. 21, pp. 95, 96.

Records of *Anchialina typica, Euchaetomera tenuis,* and *Longithorax* sp.

1936b. Great Barrier Reef expedition 1928–29. Mysidacea and Euphausiacea. Sci. Rep., vol. 5, pp. 143–176, 14 figs.

1937. New species of mysidacid crustaceans. Smithsonian Misc. Coll., vol. 91, No. 26, pp. 1–18, 10 figs.

Descriptions of *Siriella occidentalis, Gastrosaccus johnsoni, Hypererythrops caribbaea, Metamblyops macrops,* and *Paralophogaster atlanticus* and records of *Lophogaster longirostris, L. spinosus,* and *Petalophthalmus oculatus,* all from the Caribbean.

1939a. The Euphausiacea and Mysidacea of the John Murray Expedition to the Indian Ocean. Sci. Rep. John Murray Exped., vol. 5, pp. 203–246, 21 figs.

1939b. The Mysidacea of eastern Canadian waters. Journ. Fish. Res. Board Canada, vol. 4, pp. 281–286.

A full list of all the species known from the area. New records for nine species ; *Boreomysis tridens* new to the area.

1940. Report on a small collection of Mysidacea from the coastal waters of New South Wales. Rep. Australian Mus., vol. 20, pp. 327–340, 6 figs.

1941. Euphausiacea and Mysidacea collected on the Presidential Cruise of 1938. Smithsonian Misc. Coll., vol. 99, No. 13, pp. 1–7, 2 figs.

Describes *Siriella roosevelti,* new species.

THOMSON, WYVILLE.
  1873. Notes from the *Challenger*. VII. Nature, vol. 8, pp. 400–403, 6 figs.

UENO, MASUZO.
  1933a. Freshwater Crustacea of Iturup. Annot. Zool. Jap., vol. 14, pp. 109–
        113, 1 fig.
  1933b. Inland water fauna of the North Kurile Islands. Bull. Biogeogr.
        Soc. Jap., vol. 4, pp. 171–212, pls. 15–18, 18 figs.
  1936a. Crustacea Malacostraca of the northern Kurile Islands. (Inland
        water fauna of the Kurile Islands. II.) Bull. Biogeogr. Soc. Jap.,
        vol. 6, pp. 241–246, 1 fig.
  1936b. Crustacea Malacostraca collected in the lake of the Island of
        Kunasiri. (Inland water fauna of the Kurile Islands. III.) Bull.
        Biogeogr. Soc. Jap., vol. 6, pp. 247–252, 1 fig.

UNDERWOOD, LUCIEN M.
  1886. List of the described species of fresh-water Crustacea from America,
        north of Mexico. Bull. Illinois State Lab. Nat. Hist., vol. 2, pp.
        323–386.
        Record of *Mysis relicta.*

VANHÖFFEN, ERNST.
  1897. Die Fauna und Flora Grönlands, *in* E. von Drygalski, Grönland-
        Expedition. Ges. Erdkunde Berlin, 1891–1893, vol. 2, pp. 1–383,
        map 10, 30 figs., 8 pls.
  1907. Crustaceen aus dem kleinen Karajakfjord in West-Grönland. Zool.
        Jahrb., vol. 25, abt. f. Syst., pp. 507–524, 3 pls.

VERRILL, ADDISON E.
  1873a. Brief contributions to zoology from the museum of Yale College, No.
        23. Results of recent dredging expeditions on the coast of New
        England. Amer. Journ. Sci. and Arts, ser. 3, vol. 5, pp. 1–16.
        Record of *Mysis* sp.

  1873b. Brief contributions to zoology from the museum of Yale College. No.
        25. Results of recent dredging expeditions on the coast of New
        England. Amer. Journ. Sci. and Arts, ser. 3, vol. 6, pp. 435–441.
        Record of *Mysis* sp.

  1874a. Brief contributions to zoology from the museum of Yale College. No.
        26. Amer. Journ. Sci. and Arts, ser. 3, vol. 7, pp. 38–46.
        Records of *Mysis americanus, M. stenolepis,* and *Mysis* sp. from the
        coasts of New England.

  1874b. Brief contributions to zoology from the museum of Yale College. No.
        27. Amer. Journ. Sci. and Arts, ser. 3, vol. 7, pp. 131–138.
        Records *Mysis stenolepis.*

  1874c. Brief contributions to zoology from the museum of Yale College, No.
        28. Amer. Journ. Sci. and Arts, ser. 3, vol. 7, pp. 405–414, 2 pls.
        Records *Pseudomma* sp. and *Mysis* sp.

  1874d. Brief contributions to zoology from the museum of Yale College, No.
        29. Amer. Journ. Sci. and Arts, ser. 3, vol. 7, pp. 478–505, 3 pls.
        Records *Mysis* sp.

VERRILL, ADDISON E.—Continued

1882. Notice of the remarkable marine fauna occupying the outer banks off the southern coast of New England, No. 7, and of some additions to the fauna of Vineyard Sound. Amer. Journ. Sci., ser. 3, vol. 24, pp. 360–371.

    Record of *Boreomysis tridens*.

1884. Notice of the remarkable marine fauna occupying the outer banks off the southern coast of New England, and of some additions to the fauna of Vineyard Sound. Rep. U. S. Fish Comm., 1882, pp. 641–669.

    Records *Boreomysis tridens*.

1885. Results of the explorations made by the steamer *Albatross* off the northern coast of the United States, in 1883. Rep. Comm. Fish and Fisheries for 1883, pp. 503–699, 44 pls.

    Records *Gnathophausia, Lophogaster, Boreomysis tridens,* and *Pseudomma roseum*.

1923. Crustacea of Bermuda: Schizopoda, Cumacea, Stomatopoda, and Phyllocarida. Trans. Connecticut Acad. Arts and Sci., vol. 26, pp. 181–211, 2 figs., 18 pls.

    Records *Heteromysis bermudensis* and describes *H. antillensis*.

WALKER, ALFRED O.

1898. Crustacea collected by W. A. Herdman, F. R. S., in Puget Sound, Pacific coast of North America, September 1897. Trans. Liverpool Biol. Soc., vol. 12, pp. 268–287, 2 pls.

    Description of *Heteromysis odontops*.

WALKER, DAVID.

1862. Notes on the zoology of the last Arctic expedition under Captain Sir F. L. M'Clintock, R. N. Journ. Roy. Dublin Soc., vol. 3 (1860–61), pp. 61–77.

    Records *Mysis flexuosus* from Port Kennedy. The record refers to *Mysis oculata*.

WARD, HENRY B.

1896. A biological examination of Lake Michigan in the Traverse Bay region. Bull. Michigan Fish Comm., No. 6, pp. 3–71.

    Records *Mysis relicta*.

WATERMAN, TALBOT H.; NUNNEMACHER, RUDOLF F.; CHACE, FENNER A.; and CLARKE, GEORGE L.

1939. Diurnal vertical migrations of deep-water plankton. Biol. Bull., vol. 76, pp. 256–279, 6 figs.

    Records *Boreomysis microps* and *Eucopia unguiculata*.

WHITE, ADAM.

1847. List of the specimens of Crustacea in the collection of the British Museum, 143 pp. London.

WHITEAVES, J. F.

1874a. On recent deep-sea dredging operations in the Gulf of St. Lawrence. Amer. Journ. Sci. and Arts, ser. 3, vol. 7, pp. 1–9.

    Records of *Pseudomma, Erythrops,* and *Parerythrops*.

WHITEAVES, J. F.—Continued
    1874b. Report on further deep-sea dredging operations in the Gulf of St. Lawrence, with notes on the present condition of the marine fisheries and oyster beds of part of that region. 6th Ann. Rep. Dept. Marine and Fisheries (1873), Appendix U, pp. 178–204.

        Records of *Pseudomma roseum, Pseudomma,* new species, and Mysidae near *Erythrops* and *Parerythrops.*

    1901. Catalogue of the marine Invertebrata of eastern Canada. Geol. Surv. Canada, pp. 1–271.

        List of five species of Mysidacea.

WILLEMOES-SUHM, RUDOLF VON.
    1873. Von der *Challenger* expedition: Briefe an C. Th. E. v. Siebold, I. Zeitschr. Wiss. Zool., vol. 23, pp. i–vii.

    1874a. Von der *Challenger* expedition: Briefe an C. Th. E. v. Siebold, II. Zeitschr. Wiss. Zool., vol. 24, pp. ix–xxiii.

    1874b. Von de *Challenger* expedition: Briefe an C. Th. E. v. Siebold, III. Zeitschr. Wiss. Zool., vol. 25, pp. xxv–xlvi.

    1875. On some Atlantic Crustacea from the *Challenger* expedition. Trans. Linn. Soc. London, ser. 2, Zool., vol. 1, pp. 23–59, 8 pls.

    1876a. Preliminary report to Prof. Wyville Thomson, F. R. S., director of the civilian scientific staff, on observations made during the earlier part of the voyage of H. M. S. *Challenger.* Proc. Roy. Soc. London, vol. 24, pp. 569–585.

    1876b. Preliminary report to Professor Wyville Thomson, F. R. S., director of the civilian scientific staff, on Crustacea observed during the cruise of H. M. S. *Challenger* in the Southern Sea. Proc. Roy. Soc. London, vol. 24, pp. 585–592.

    1876c. Von der *Challenger* expedition: Briefe an C. Th. E. v Siebold, IV, V, VI. Zeitschr. Wiss. Zool., vol. 26, pp. xlvii–lviii, lix–lxxv, lxxvii–xcvi.

    1876d. Von der *Challenger* expedition: Briefe an C. Th. E. v. Siebold, VII. Zeitschr. Wiss. Zool., vol. 27, pp. xcvii–cviii.

    1877. Von der *Challenger* expedition: Briefe an C. Th. E. v. Siebold, VIII. Zeitschr. Wiss. Zool., vol. 29, pp. cix–cxxxvi.

    1895. *In* Report of the voyage of H. M. S. *Challenger:* Summary of the scientific results, pt. 1, pp. vii–796.

WOOD-MASON, J., and ALCOCK, A.
    1891a. Natural history notes from H. M. Indian marine survey steamer *Investigator,* Commander R. F. Hoskyn, R. N., commanding, No. 21: Note on the results of the last season's deep-sea dredging. Ann. Mag. Nat. Hist., ser. 6, vol. 7, pp. 186–202.

    1891b. Natural history notes from H. M. Indian marine survey steamer *Investigator,* Commander R. F. Hoskyn, R. N., commanding, ser. 2, No. 1: On the results of deep-sea dredging during the season 1890–91. Ann. Mag. Nat. Hist., ser. 6, vol. 8, pp. 268–286.

ZIMMER, CARL.
    1904. Die Arktischen Schizopoden. Fauna Arctica, vol. 3, pp. 415–492, 172 figs.

        Includes American species.

    1907. Hamburger Magalhaensische Sammelreise, Schizopoden, pp. 3–5, 17 figs.

        Description of *Neomysis patagona.*

ZIMMER, CARL—Continued

1909. Nordisches Plankton, Lief 12, VI : Schizopoden, pp. 1–178, 384 figs.

1912. Südwestafrikanische Schizopoden. Jena Denkschr. med. Ges., vol. 17, pp. 1–11, 2 pls.

1914. Die Schizopoden der deutschen Südpolar-Expedition 1901–1903. Deutsche Südpolar-Expedition 1901–1903, vol. 15, Zool. 7, pp. 377–445, 4 pls.

1915a. Die systematik der Tribus Mysini H. J. Hansen. Zool. Anz., vol. 46, pp. 202–216, 19 figs.

1915b. Schizopoden des Hamburger Naturhistorischen (Zoologischen) Museums. Mitt. Nat. Mus. Hamburg, vol. 32, pp. 159–182, 41 figs.

> *Antarctomysis* sp. from the Magellan Straits and *Diamysis columbiae* from Cartagena, Colombia.

1918. ["Eingesandt in Mai 1917"]. Neue und wenig bekannte Mysidaceen des Berliner Zoologischen Museums. Mitt. Zool. Mus. Berlin, vol. 9, pp. 15–26, 44 figs.

> Describes *Mysidopsis munda* from Armacao, *M. pacifica* from Callao, and *Mysidia gracilis* from Rio de Janeiro.

1927. Mysidacea, *in* W. Kükenthal, Handbuch der Zoologie, vol. 3, pp. 607–650, 54 figs.

INDEX

abbreviata, Amblyops, 6, 128, 129 (fig.).
  Amblyopsis, 128.
  Hemisiriella, 80.
abbreviatum, Pseudomma, 128.
abyssi, Pseudomysis, 157–159.
abyssorum, Erythrops, 6, 111.
Acanthocaris, 89.
Acanthomysis, 1, 5, 164, 175, 179, 180, 202, 203, 219, 220, 249.
  columbiae, 8, 203, 204 (fig.), 205 (fig.), 206 (fig.), 249.
  costata, 202, 203, 208, 210 (fig.), 211 (fig.), 213, 249.
  dybowskii, 203, 213, 214 (fig.).
  longicornis, 218.
  macropsis, 8, 203, 207, 215, 216 (fig.), 218, 249.
  pseudomacropsis, 203, 207, 217, 218 (fig.), 219 (fig.), 249.
  sculpta, 202, 203, 208 (fig.), 209 (fig.), 213, 248.
  sp., 218, 249.
  stelleri, 202, 203, 210, 212 (fig.), 213, 249.
acanthura, Erythrops, 122.
  Gibberythrops, 122, 124.
  Parerythrops, 122.
aculeatum, Chlamydopleon, 10, 97, 98, 273.
acuta, Mysidopsis, 10, 138, 139, 147, 244, 269.
aequiremis, Siriella, 78.
affine, Pseudomma, 6, 132, 134, 244.
affinis, Holmesiella, 109.
  Lophogaster, 17.
  Siriella, 64, 79.
agilis, Anchialina, 105.
  Anchialus, 105.
alata, Chalaraspis, 13, 14, 267.
alatum, Chalaraspidum, 8, 14.
Amblyops, 128.
  abbreviata, 6, 128, 129 (fig.).
  crozeti, 130.
  crozetii, 130, 131.
  hispida, 7.
  ohlinii, 7, 130, 131 (fig.), 250.
  sp., 130.
Amblyopsis abbreviata, 128.
americana, Diamysis, 4, 226, 227 (fig.). 250.
  Mysis, 195, 268, 276.
  Neomysis, 180, 181, 195, 196 (fig.), 268, 274, 278, 279.
americanus, Lophogaster, 7, 16, 17, 18 (fig.), 250.
  Mysis, 195, 280.
Anchialina, 5, 81, 100.
  agilis, 105.
  frontalis, 102.
  grossa, 102.

Anchialina obtusifrons, 102.
  penicillata, 103, 104.
  typica, 10, 100, 279.
  zimmeri, 103, 104 (fig.), 250.
Anchialus, 100.
  agilis, 105.
  typicus, 100.
andersoni, Neomysis, 198, 200, 202, 276.
angusta, Mysidopsis, 139, 147.
anomala, Holmesiella, 7, 106, 107 (fig.), 108 (fig.), 267, 274.
  Siriella, 70, 79.
anophelinae, Antromysis, 4, 230, 231 (fig.), 233 (fig.), 250.
Antarctomysis, 163, 247.
  maxima, 163.
  sp., 246, 247, 283.
antillensis, Heteromysis, 235, 238, 250, 281.
Antromysis, 4, 229.
  anophelinae, 4, 230, 231 (fig.), 233 (fig.), 250.
  cenotensis, 4, 229, 230, 232, 233, 234, 265.
Archaeomysis, 5, 81.
  grebnitzkii, 8, 81, 82 (fig.), 84 (fig.), 89.
  maculata, 86, 87 (fig.), 88 (fig.), 279.
arctica, Arctomysis, 49.
  Boreomysis, 6, 49, 50 (fig.), 51, 268, 277.
  Mysis, 49.
Arctomysis, 43, 45.
  arctica, 49.
  fyllae, 43.
armata, Uromysis, 151.
armiger, Petalophthalmus, 7, 35, 36 (fig.), 38 (fig.), 42, 43, 46, 47, 267.
Arthromysis, 5, 163.
  chierchiae, 246, 247, 265.
  magellanica, 163, 246.
atlantica, Promysis, 10, 152 (fig.), 245.
atlanticus, Paralophogaster, 8, 22, 23, 24 (fig.), 279.
australis, Eucopia, 13, 32–34, 267.
awachensis, Neomysis, 188.
awatschensis, Mysis, 190.
  Neomysis, 180, 187, 188, 190, 191 (fig.).

bahirensis, Diamysis, 227, 228.
Bathymysis, 153.
  helgae, 153, 157.
  renoculata, 7, 153, 154 (fig.), 155 (fig.). 250.
berkeleyi, Pseudomma, 7, 135 (fig.), 137, 243, 279.
bermudensis, Heteromysis, 10, 235, 237, 250, 281.

bidentata, Gnathophausia, 28.
bidigitata, Dactylerythrops, 6, 126, 127 (fig.).
bigelowi, Mysidopsis, 138, 139, 140 (fig.), 147, 279.
biunguiculata, Eucopia, 34, 271.
Bereomysinae, 3, 45.
Boreomysis, 45.
　arctica, 6, 49, 50 (fig.), 51, 268, 277.
　californica, 8, 52 (fig.), 53 (fig.), 273.
　distinguenda, 46, 47.
　fragilis, 55.
　inermis, 8, 46, 56, 58–60.
　media, 52, 54, 55.
　microps, 8, 10, 55, 281.
　nobilis, 7, 47 (fig.), 243.
　obtusata, 55.
　rostrata, 8, 51, 54, 56, 57 (fig.), 58 (fig.), 59 (fig.).
　scyphops, 46, 47.
　sibogae, 51.
　subpellucida, 55.
　suhmi, 46, 47.
　tricornis, 48, 49.
　tridens, 6, 45, 48 (fig.), 279, 281.
　verrucosa, 58.
brevispinis, Gnathophausia, 28.

Caesaromysides, 137.
　liguriae, 8, 10, 137, 244, 265.
calcarata, Gnathophausia, 25.
californica, Boreomysis, 8, 52 (fig.), 53 (fig.), 273.
　Mysidopsis, 138, 142, 143 (fig.), 144 (fig.), 147, 245, 279.
Callomysis, 81.
　maculata, 81, 86, 269.
callopleura, Pseudomma, 137.
camtschatica, Stilomysis, 175.
Cancer flexuosus, 247.
　oculatus, 165.
　pedatus, 164.
capensis, Longithorax, 8, 120 (fig.).
caribbaea, Hypererythrops, 7, 118, 119 (fig.), 279.
cenotensis, Antromysis, 4, 229, 230, 232–234, 265.
Ceratolepis, 12.
Ceratomysis, 35, 37, 43.
　egregia, 44.
　spinosa, 8, 43, 267.
Chalaraspidum, 12–14.
　alatum, 8, 14.
Chalaraspis, 13, 32.
　alata, 13, 14, 267.
　unguiculata, 13, 34.
chierchiae, Arthromysis, 246, 247, 265.
　Siriella, 66, 67 (fig.), 68 (fig.), 72, 76, 265.
Chiromysis, 235.
Chlamydopleon, 89.
　aculeatum, 10, 97, 98, 273.
columbiae, Acanthomysis, 8, 203, 204 (fig.), 205 (fig.), 206 (fig.), 249.
　Diamysis, 223, 283.

columbiae, Mysidia, 223.
　Mysidium, 222, 223, 225, 226.
　Neomysis, 204, 279.
costata, Acanthomysis, 202, 203, 208, 210 (fig.), 211 (fig.), 213, 249.
　Mysis, 208, 267, 269.
　Neomysis, 208, 279.
crassa, Mysidetes, 10, 159, 246, 269.
cristata, Gnathophausia, 29.
crozeti, Amblyops, 130.
crozetti, Amblyops, 130, 131.
cruciata, Synerythrops, 7, 124, 125 (fig.), 250.
Crustacea, 11.
Ctenomysis, 15.
Cynthia thompsonii, 60.
czerniawskii, Neomysis, 179–181, 200, 201 (fig.).

Dactylamblyops, 126.
　sp., 7, 126.
Dactylerythrops, 126.
　bidigitata, 6, 126, 127 (fig.).
dactylops, Pseudomysis, 157, 158 (fig.), 250.
Dajus siriellae, 66, 78.
　siriellus, 62.
Dasymysis, 203.
dentata, Gnathophausia, 28, 267.
Diamysis, 4, 222, 226, 228, 229, 230.
　americana, 4, 226, 227 (fig.), 250.
　bahirensis, 227, 228.
　columbiae, 223, 283.
　mecznikowi, 228.
didelphys, Mysidopsis, 147.
diluvianus, Mysis, 167, 270.
dissimilis, Gastrosaccus, 89, 97 (fig.), 100, 265.
distinguenda, Boreomysis, 46, 47.
　Siriella, 79.
Doxomysis, 152.
　microps, 8, 10, 153, 246.
　pelagica, 152, 153.
　quadrispinosa, 152.
　tattersallii, 10, 152, 153.
　zimmeri, 152, 153.
drepanephora, Gnathophausia, 26.
dubia, Siriella, 79.
dybowskii, Acanthomysis, 203, 213, 214 (fig.).
　Neomysis, 180.
　Orientomysis, 213, 215.

Eclytaspis, 13.
egregia, Ceratomysis, 44.
elegans, Gnathophausia, 31.
elongata, Metamysidopsis, 149, 150 (fig.), 245.
　Mysidopsis, 146, 149, 269, 279.
erythraeus, Lophogaster, 17.
erythrophthalma, Erythrops, 6, 110 (fig.), 268, 274.
　Mysis, 110.
Erythrepini, 3, 105.

Erythrops, 5, 110, 111, 113, 120, 268, 281, 282.
  abyssorum, 6, 111.
  acanthura, 122.
  erythrophthalma, 6, 110 (fig.), 268, 274.
  goësii, 110.
  microphthalma, 111.
  microphthalmus, 110.
  microps, 6, 111.
  yongei, 111.
Eucarida, 11.
Euchaetomera, 112.
  plebeja, 112.
  tenuis, 7–10, 112, 279.
  typica, 7, 8, 112, 273, 279.
Eucopia, 13, 32.
  australis, 13, 32–34, 267.
  biunguiculata, 34, 271.
  intermedia, 32.
  major, 33.
  sculpticauda, 7, 32, 267.
  unguiculata, 7, 10, 34, 279, 281.
Eucopiidae, 3, 32.
Euxinomysis, 226.
  mecznikowi, 226.

fabricianus, Megalophthalmus, 164.
fabricii, Mysis, 165, 263.
flexuosa, Mysis, 37.
flexuosus, Cancer, 247.
  Mysis, 165, 263, 281.
  Praunus, 37, 175, 247.
formosa, Heteromysis, 5, 6, 235, 236 (fig.), 238 (fig.), 242, 263, 264, 268, 274, 276, 278.
fragilis, Boreomysis, 55.
franciscana, Neomysis, 181.
franciscorum, Neomysis, 179, 181, 183–186, 269, 279.
frigidum, Pseudomma, 244.
frontalis, Anchialina, 102.
fuscus, Longithorax, 121.
fyllae, Arctomysis, 43.
  Hansenomysis, 6, 39, 43.

galatheae, Promysis, 271.
Gastrosaccinae, 3, 80.
Gastrosaccus, 5, 81, 83, 89.
  dissimilis, 89, 97 (fig.), 100, 265.
  indicus, 90, 93.
  johnsoni, 89, 93, 94 (fig.), 95 (fig.), 96 (fig.), 97, 100, 279.
  mexicanus, 4, 89, 98, 99 (fig.), 250.
  normani, 83.
  pacificus, 90, 93.
  parva, 90.
  parvus, 93.
  philippinensis, 90, 91 (fig.), 250.
  sanctus, 90, 93.
  sp., 90.
  spinifer, 90.
Gibberythrops, 122, 124.
  acanthura, 122, 124.
  philippinensis, 122, 123 (fig.), 250.
gibbosa, Mysidopsis, 139, 147.

gigas, Gnathopausia, 26.
  Gnathophausia, 7, 26, 30, 31, 268, 274.
glaber, Paralophogaster, 22, 24, 25, 279.
Gnathomysis, 235.
Gnathopausia gigas, 26.
Gnathophansia, 25.
Gnathophausa, 25.
Gnathophausia, 12, 25, 46, 271, 274, 277, 281.
  bidentata, 28.
  brevispinis, 28.
  calcarata, 25.
  cristata, 29.
  dentata, 28, 267.
  drepanephora, 26.
  elegans, 31.
  gigas, 7, 26, 30, 31, 268, 274.
  gracilis, 8, 28.
  ingens, 7, 25, 26.
  longispina, 28, 31.
  sarsi, 29, 30.
  scapularis, 31, 274.
  sp., 26, 28, 30.
  willemoesi, 30.
  willemoesia, 29.
  willemoesii, 29, 264, 267.
  zoea, 7, 27, 29, 31, 178, 267, 268.
  zoea sarsi, 29.
  zoae scapularis, 8, 31.
goësii, Erythrops, 110.
goesii, Nematopus, 110.
gracile, Mysidium, 222, 223, 225.
gracilis, Gnathophausia, 8, 28.
  Leptomysis, 138.
  Macromysis, 223, 266.
  Mysidia, 223, 283.
  Siriella, 62, 63, 273.
grandis, Mysideis, 175, 275, 277.
  Mysis, 175.
  Stilomysis, 6, 175, 176 (fig.).
grebnitzkii, Archaeomysis, 8, 81, 82, (fig.), 84 (fig.), 89.
grossa, Anchialina, 102.

Hansenomysis, 35, 37, 39, 43, 44.
  fyllae, 6, 39, 43.
Haplostylus, 89.
hawaiensis, Lophogaster, 17, 242.
helgae, Bathymysis, 153, 157.
Hemimysis, 5, 6, 163.
  lamornae, 163.
Hemisiriella, 60, 80.
  abbreviata, 80.
  parva, 80.
Heteromysini, 3, 234.
Heteromysis, 5, 179, 199, 234, 235.
  antillensis, 235, 238, 250, 281.
  bermudensis, 10, 235, 237, 250, 281.
  formosa, 5, 6, 235, 236 (fig.), 238 (fig.), 242, 263, 264, 268, 274, 276, 278.
  intermedia, 188.
  mirabilis, 198.
  odontops, 8, 235, 239 (fig.), 241 (fig.), 269, 281.
  spinosa, 235.
  spinosus, 239, 240, 242, 269.

hispida, Amblyops, 7.
Holmesiella, 106.
    affinis, 109.
    anomala, 7, 106, 107 (fig.), 108 (fig.), 267, 274.
Hypererythrops, 118.
    caribbaea, 7, 118, 119 (fig.), 279.

indica, Mysidopsis, 147.
indicus, Gastrosaccus, 90, 93.
inermis, Boreomysis, 8, 46, 58–60.
inermis, Mysidopsis, 138, 142, 147, 245, 265.
    Mysis, 175.
    Petalophthalmus, 46, 47.
    Praunus, 175.
ingens, Gnathophausia, 7, 25, 26.
    Lophogaster, 25.
inornata, Siriella, 65, 66.
integer, Neomysis, 180, 186, 197, 247.
    Praunus, 247.
integrum, Mysidium, 223, 224 (fig.), 250.
intermedia, Eucopia, 32.
    Heteromysis, 188.
    Neomysis, 179, 180, 181, 187, 188, 189 (fig.), 190, 191.
    Synerythrops, 126.
intermedius, Lophogaster, 16, 17, 18 (fig.), 20, 21.
    Paralophogaster, 22, 23.
Inusitatomysis, 159.
    serrata, 7, 160, 161 (fig.), 250.
isaza, Neomysis, 188.

japonica, Neomysis, 179, 180, 194 (fig.).
japonicus, Lophogaster, 16, 18 (fig.), 19–21, 24 (fig.), 250.
johnsoni, Gastrosaccus, 89, 93, 94 (fig.), 95 (fig.), 96 (fig.), 97, 100, 279.

kadiakensis, Neomysis, 8, 179–181, 192, 193 (fig.), 274, 279.
Katerythrops, 118.
    oceanae, 8, 118, 279.
kempii, Mysidopsis, 147.
kruppi, Pseudomma, 244.
kurilensis, Paracanthomysis, 221, 222 (fig.).

lamornae, Hemimysis, 163.
    Mysis, 163.
latitans, Mysis, 164.
Leptomysini, 3, 138, 159.
Leptomysis, 5, 6, 138.
    gracilis, 138.
    mediterranea, 138.
liguriae, Caesaromysides, 8, 10, 137, 244, 265.
Limnomysis, 230.
longicornis, Acanthomysis, 218.
    Mysis, 218.
longirostris, Lophogaster, 7, 21, 267, 279.
longispina, Gnathophausia, 28, 31.
Longithorax, 120.
    capensis, 8, 120 (fig.).
    fuscus, 121.
    similerythrops, 121.
    sp., 120, 279.

Lophogaster, 12, 13, 15, 33, 277, 281.
    affinis, 17.
    americanus, 7, 16, 17, 18 (fig.), 250.
    erythraeus, 17.
    hawaiensis, 17, 242.
    ingens, 25.
    intermedius, 16, 17, 18 (fig.), 20, 21.
    japonicus, 16, 18 (fig.), 19–21, 24 (fig.), 250.
    longirostris, 7, 21, 267, 279.
    rotundatus, 16.
    sp., 17, 18 (fig.), 20, 277.
    spinosus, 7, 16, 21, 274, 279.
    typicus, 15–21, 279.
Lophogastrida, 12.
Lophogastridae, 3, 12.
lucifugus, Scolophthalmus, 8, 43, 243, 267.

Macromysis, 163, 222.
    gracilis, 223, 266.
    magellanica, 246, 265.
macrops, Metamblyops, 7, 116, 117 (fig.), 119 (fig.), 279.
    Paralophogaster, 23.
Macropsis, 216.
macropsis, Acanthomysis, 8, 203, 207, 215, 216 (fig.), 218, 249.
    Neomysis, 215, 279.
maculata, Archaeomysis, 86, 87 (fig.), 88 (fig.), 279.
    Callomysis, 81, 86, 269.
magellanica, Arthromysis, 163, 246.
    Macromysis, 246, 265.
major, Eucopia, 33.
    Mysidopsis, 147.
    Stilomysis, 177, 178 (fig.), 250.
Malacostraca, 11.
maxima, Antarctomysis, 163.
    Mysis, 163.
mecznikowi, Diamysis, 228.
    Euxinomysis, 226.
media, Boreomysis, 52, 54, 55.
    Siriella, 65.
mediterranea, Leptomysis, 138.
megalolepis, Pseudanchialus, 45, 48, 49.
Megalophthalmus, 163.
    fabricianus, 164.
mercedis, Neomysis, 8, 179, 180, 181, 187, 188 (fig.), 269, 279.
meridionalis, Neomysis, 180, 181, 203, 247, 265.
Mesomysis, 163, 164.
    stenolepis, 170.
Mesopodopsis, 5, 6, 175.
    slabberi, 175.
Metamblyops, 116.
    macrops, 7, 116, 117 (fig.), 119 (fig.), 279.
Metamysidopsis, 5, 138, 146, 250.
    elongata, 149, 150 (fig.), 245.
    munda, 147, 148 (fig.), 151.
    pacifica, 149, 151, 245.
Metamysis, 203.
Meterythrops, 113.
    microphthalma, 113, 115 (fig), 250.
    picta, 8, 113.

Meterythrops robusta, 6, 113, 114 (fig.), 116, 271, 277.
mexicanus, Gastrosaccus, 4, 89, 98 99 (fig.), 250.
Michtheimysis, 163, 164.
  mixta, 168, 263, 274, 278.
  stenolepis, 170.
Michthyops, 137.
  parva, 6, 137.
microphthalma, Erythrops, 111.
  Meterythrops, 113, 115 (fig), 250.
microphthalmus, Erythrops, 110.
microps, Boreomysis, 8, 10, 55, 281.
  Doxomysis, 8, 10, 153, 246.
  Erythrops, 6, 111.
  Nematopus, 111.
  Paralophogaster, 23.
mingrelica, Onychomysis, 164.
mirabilis, Heteromysis, 198.
  Neomysis, 179, 180, 181, 194, 198, 199 (fig.) 202.
mixta, Michtheimysis, 168, 263, 274, 278.
  Mysis, 5, 6, 163–165, 168, 169 (fig.), 172–174, 263, 271, 275.
monticelli, Neomysis, 180, 181, 203, 248, 265.
mortenseni, Mysidopsis, 138, 145 (fig.), 250.
munda, Metamysidopsis, 147, 148 (fig.), 151.
  Mysidopsis, 142, 146, 147, 283.
Mysida, 35, 37.
Mysidacea, 12, 37.
Mysidae, 3, 45, 108.
Mysideis grandis, 175, 275, 277.
Mysidellinae, 3, 45.
Mysidetes, 138, 159.
  crassa, 10, 159, 246, 269.
Mysidia, 222.
  columbiae, 223.
  gracilis, 223, 283.
Mysidium, 5, 222.
  colmubiae, 222, 223, 225, 226.
  gracile, 222, 223, 225.
  integrum, 223, 224 (fig.), 250.
Mysidoa, 222.
Mysidopsis, 5, 138, 146, 149.
  acuta, 10, 138, 139, 147, 244, 269.
  angusta, 139, 147.
  bigelowi, 138, 139, 140 (fig.), 147, 279.
  californica, 138, 142, 143 (fig.), 144 (fig.), 147, 245, 279.
  didelphys, 147.
  elongata, 146, 149, 269, 279.
  gibbosa, 139, 147.
  indica, 147.
  inermis, 138, 142, 147, 245, 265.
  kempii, 147.
  major, 147.
  mortenseni, 138, 145 (fig.), 250.
  munda, 142, 146, 147, 283.
  pacifica, 146, 265, 283.
  schultzei, 147.
  similis, 147.
Mysinae, 3, 105, 159.

Mysini, 3, 159, 247.
Mysis, 5, 163, 180.
  americana, 195, 268, 276.
  americanus, 195, 280.
  arctica, 49.
  awatschensis, 190.
  costata, 208, 267, 269.
  diluvianus, 167, 270.
  erythrophthalma, 110.
  fabricii, 165, 263.
  flexuosa, 37.
  flexuosus, 165, 263, 281.
  grandis, 175.
  inermis, 175.
  lamornae, 163.
  latitans, 164.
  longicornis, 218.
  maxima, 163.
  mixta, 5, 6, 163–165, 168, 169 (fig.), 172–174, 263, 271, 275.
  oculata, 4, 5, 9, 163–165, 166 (fig.), 173, 174, 263, 267, 271, 273–278, 281.
  oculatus, 266.
  ornata, 174.
  quadrispinosa, 152.
  rayii, 181, 183, 272.
  relicta, 4, 9, 164, 167, 168 (fig.), 173, 174, 263, 264, 268, 270, 272, 274–277, 280, 281.
  sancta, 90.
  sp., 167, 273, 278, 280.
  spinifera, 90.
  spinulosus, 8, 165, 170, 266, 268, 274.
  spiritus, 174.
  stenolepis, 9, 164, 165, 170, 171 (fig.), 173 (fig.), 263, 264, 268, 271, 274–276, 280.

nakazawi, Neomysis, 179, 198, 199.
nanum, Pseudomma, 137.
Nematopus goesii, 110.
  microps, 111.
Neomysis, 1, 5, 164, 177, 179, 200, 203.
  americana, 180, 181, 195, 196 (fig.), 268, 274, 278, 279.
  andersoni, 198, 200, 202, 276.
  awachensis, 188.
  awatschensis, 180, 187, 188, 190, 191 (fig.).
  columbiae, 204, 279.
  costata, 208, 279.
  czerniawskii, 179–181, 200, 201 (fig.).
  dybowskii, 180.
  franciscana, 181.
  franciscorum, 179, 181, 183–186, 269, 279.
  integer, 180, 186, 197, 247.
  intermedia, 179, 180, 181, 187, 188, 189 (fig.), 190, 191.
  isaza, 188.
  japonica, 179, 180, 194 (fig.).
  kadiakensis, 8, 179, 180, 181, 192, 193 (fig.), 274, 279.
  macropsis, 215, 279.

Neomysis mercedis, 8, 179, 180, 181, 187, 188 (fig.), 269, 279.
meridionalis, 180, 181, 203, 247, 265.
mirabilis, 179, 180, 181, 194, 198, 199 (fig.), 202.
monticelli, 180, 181, 203, 248, 265.
nakazawai, 179, 198, 199.
nigra, 190, 192.
patagona, 180, 181, 202, 247, 265, 269, 282.
pseudomacropsis, 217, 279.
rayi, 181.
rayii, 8, 165, 179, 180, 181, 182 (fig.), 184 (fig.), 185 (fig.), 186 (fig.), 193, 194.
sculpta, 248.
sp., 249.
spinosa, 179, 180.
toion, 181.
nigra, Neomysis, 190, 192.
nobilis, Boreomysis, 7, 47 (fig.), 243.
normani, Gastrosaccus, 83.

obtusata, Boreomysis, 55.
obtusifrons, Anchialina, 102.
occidentalis, Siriella, 66, 70, 279.
oceanae, Katerythrops, 8, 118, 279.
oculata, Mysis, 4, 5, 9, 163–165, 166 (fig.), 173, 174, 263, 267, 271, 273–278, 281.
oculatus, Cancer, 165.
Mysis, 266.
Petalophthalmus, 8, 40, 41 (fig.), 279.
oculospinum, Pseudomma, 7, 135, 136 (fig.), 250.
odontops, Heteromysis, 8, 235, 239 (fig.), 241 (fig.), 269, 281.
ohlinii, Amblyops, 7, 130, 131 (fig.), 250.
Onychomysis, 163, 164.
mingrelica, 164.
orientalis, Promysis, 151, 245, 246.
Orientomysis, 203.
dybowskii, 213, 215.
stelleri, 210.
ornata, Mysis, 174.
Paramysis, 174.
Synmysis, 174.

pacifica, Metamysidopsis, 149, 151, 245.
Mysidopsis, 146, 265, 283.
Siriella, 70, 71 (fig.), 75, 76, 269, 279.
pacificus, Gastrosaccus, 90, 93.
Petalophthalmus, 35, 37, 40, 267.
panamensis, Siriella, 70, 72, 76, 77 (fig.), 250.
Paracanthomysis, 5, 220.
kurilensis, 221, 222 (fig.).
Paralophogaster, 12, 22, 23.
atlanticus, 8, 22, 23, 24 (fig.), 279.
glaber, 22, 24, 25, 279.
intermedius, 22, 23.
macrops, 23.
microps, 23.
sanzoi, 23.

Paramblyops, 132.
rostrata, 6, 132.
Paramysidetes, 138.
Paramysis, 5, 6, 174.
ornata, 174.
parkeri, 175.
spiritus, 174.
Paranchialina, 81.
Parerythrops, 113, 281, 282.
acanthura, 122.
robusta, 113.
parkeri, Paramysis, 175.
Schistomysis, 175.
parva, Gastrosaccus, 90.
Hemisiriella, 80.
Michthyops, 6, 137.
parvum, Pseudomma, 137.
parvus, Gastrosaccus, 93.
patagona, Neomysis, 180, 181, 202, 247, 265, 269, 282.
pedatus, Cancer, 164.
pelagica Doxomysis, 152, 153.
penicillata, Anchialina, 103, 104.
Peracarida, 11, 12.
Petalophthalmidae, 3, 35.
Petalophthalmus, 35, 37, 39, 45, 46.
armiger, 7, 35, 36 (fig.), 38 (fig.), 42, 43, 46, 47, 267.
inermis, 46, 47.
oculatus, 8, 40, 41 (fig.), 279.
pacificus, 35, 37, 40, 267.
philippinensis, Gastrosaccus, 90, 91 (fig.), 250.
Gibberythrops, 122, 123 (fig.), 250.
picta, Meterythrops, 8, 113.
plebeja, Euchaetomera, 112.
Podopsis slabberi, 175.
Pontomysis, 89.
Potamomysis, 226.
Praunus, 5, 6, 175.
flexousus, 37, 175, 247.
inermis, 175.
integer, 247.
Promysis, 5, 151.
atlantica, 10, 152 (fig.), 245.
galatheae, 271.
orientalis, 151, 245, 246.
Proneomysis, 5, 219, 221.
wailesi, 220 (fig.), 221 (fig.), 249, 279.
Pseudanchialina, 81.
Pseudanchialus, 45.
megalolepis, 45, 48, 49.
pseudomacropsis, Acanthomysis, 203, 207, 217, 218 (fig.), 219 (fig.), 249.
Neomysis, 217, 279.
Pseudomma, 132, 244, 281.
sp., 134, 282.
abbreviatum, 128.
affine, 6, 132, 134, 244.
berkeleyi, 7, 135 (fig.), 137, 243, 279.
callopleura, 137.
frigidum, 244.
kruppi, 244.
nanum, 137.

Pseudomma oculospinum, 7, 135, 136 (fig.), 250.
parvum, 137.
roseum, 6, 132, 133 (fig.), 244, 268, 271, 277, 281, 282.
sp., 135, 244, 267, 280.
truncatum, 6, 134 (fig.), 244, 271, 275, 277.
Pseudomysis, 157, 226.
abyssi, 157-159.
dactylops, 157, 158 (fig.), 250.

quadrispinosa, Doxomysis, 152.
Mysis, 152.

rayi, Neomysis, 181.
rayii, Mysis, 181, 183, 272.
Neomysis, 8, 165, 179-182 (fig.), 184 (fig.), 185 (fig.), 186 (fig.), 193, 194.
relicta, Mysis, 4, 9, 164, 167, 168 (fig.), 173, 174, 263, 264, 268, 270, 272, 274-277, 280, 281.
renoculata, Bathymysis, 7, 153, 154 (fig.), 155 (fig.), 250.
Rhopalophthalminae, 3, 45.
robusta, Meterythrops, 6, 113, 114 (fig.), 116, 271, 277.
Parerythrops, 113.
roosevelti, Siriella, 70, 72, 73 (fig.), 74 (fig.), 279.
roseum, Pseudomma, 6, 132, 133 (fig.), 244, 268, 271, 277, 281, 282.
rostrata, Boreomysis, 8, 51, 54, 56, 57 (fig.), 58 (fig.), 59 (fig.).
Paramblyops, 6, 132.
Siriella vulgaris, 63, 64 (fig.), 250.
rotundatus, Lophogaster, 16.

sancta, Mysis, 90.
sanctus, Gastrosaccus, 90, 93.
sanzoi, Paralophogaster, 23.
sarsi, Gnathophausia, 29, 30.
Gnathophausia zoea, 29.
scapularis, Gnathophausia, 31, 274.
Gnathophausia zoae, 8, 31.
Schistomysis parkeri, 175.
schultzei, Mysidopsis, 147.
Scolophthalmus, 35, 43.
lucifugus, 8, 43, 243, 267.
sculpta, Acanthomysis, 202, 203, 208 (fig.), 209 (fig.), 213, 248.
Neomysis, 248.
sculpticauda, Eucopia, 7, 32, 267.
scyphops, Boreomysis, 46, 47.
serrata, Inusitatomysis, 7, 160, 161 (fig.), 250.
sibogae, Boreomysis, 51.
similerythrops, Longithorax, 121.
similis, Mysidopsis, 147.
Siriella, 5, 60, 66.
aequiremis, 78.
affinis, 64, 79.
anomala, 70, 79.

Siriella chierchiae, 66, 67 (fig.), 68 (fig.), 72, 76, 265.
distinguenda, 79.
dubia, 79.
gracilis, 62, 63, 273.
inornata, 65, 66.
media, 65.
occidentalis, 66, 70, 279.
pacifica, 70, 71 (fig.), 75, 76, 269, 279.
panamensis, 70, 72, 76, 77 (fig.), 250.
roosevelti, 70, 72, 73 (fig.), 74 (fig.), 279.
suluensis, 62, 63.
thompsoni, 60.
thompsonii, 7, 9, 10, 60, 271, 273, 279.
vulgaris, 62, 63, 79.
vulgaris rostrata, 63, 64 (fig.), 250.
siriellae, Dajus, 66, 78.
Siriellinae, 3, 60.
siriellus, Dajus, 62.
slabberi, Mesopodopsis, 175.
Podopsis, 175.
spinifer, Gastrosaccus, 90.
spinifera, Mysis, 90.
spinosa, Ceratomysis, 8, 43, 267.
Heteromysis, 235.
Neomysis, 179, 180.
spinosus, Heteromysis, 239, 240, 242, 269.
Lephogaster, 7, 16, 21, 274, 279.
spinulosus, Mysis, 8, 165, 170, 266, 268, 274.
spiritus, Mysis, 174.
Paramysis, 174.
Synmysis, 174.
stelleri, Acanthomysis, 202, 203, 210, 212 (fig.), 213, 249.
Orientomysis, 210.
stenolepis, Mesomysis, 170.
Michtheimysis, 170.
Mysis, 9, 164, 165, 170, 171 (fig.), 173, 263, 264, 268, 271, 274-276, 280.
Stilomysis, 175.
camtschatica, 175.
grandis, 6, 175, 176 (fig.).
major, 177, 178, (fig.), 250.
subpellucida, Boreomysis, 55.
suhmi, Boreomysis, 46, 47.
suluensis, Siriella, 62, 63.
Syncarida, 11.
Synerythrops, 124.
cruciata, 7, 124, 125 (fig.), 250.
intermedia, 126.
Synmysis ornata, 174.
spiritus, 174.

tattersallii, Doxomysis, 10, 152, 153.
Tenagomysis, 247.
tenuis, Euchaetomera, 7-10, 112, 279.
thompsoni, Siriella, 60.

thompsonii, Cynthia, 60.
   Siriella, 7, 9, 10, 60, 271, 273, 279.
toion, Neomysis, 181.
tricornis, Boreomysis, 48, 49.
tridens Boreomysis, 6, 45, 48 (fig.), 279, 281.
truncatum, Pseudomma, 6, 134 (fig.), 244, 271, 275, 277.
typica, Euchaetomera, 7, 8, 112, 273, 279.
   Anchialina, 10, 100, 279.
typicus, Anchialus, 100.
   Lophogaster, 15–21, 279.

unguiculata, Chalaraspis, 13, 34.
   Eucopia, 7, 10, 34, 279, 281.
Uromysis, 151.
   armata, 151.

verrucosa, Boreomysis, 58.
vulgaris, Siriella, 62, 63, 79.

wailesi, Proneomysis, 220 (fig.), 221 (fig.), 249, 279.
willemoesi, Gnathophausia, 30.
willemoesia, Gnathophausia, 29.
willemoesii, Gnathophausia, 29, 264, 267.

yongei, Erythrops, 111.

zimmeri, Anchialina, 103, 104 (fig.), 250.
   Doxomysis, 152, 153.
zoea, Gnathophausia, 7, 27, 29, 31, 178, 267, 268.

U. S. GOVERNMENT PRINTING OFFICE: 1951